Programming, Games and Transportation Networks

PROGRAMMING, GAMES AND TRANSPORTATION NETWORKS

by Claude Berge
Research Director at the Centre National
de la Recherche Scientifique (Paris)

and A. Ghouila-Houri
Associate Professor to the
Faculty of Science at Caen

Translated by Maxine Merrington and C. Ramanujacharyulu

LONDON: METHUEN AND CO LTD
NEW YORK: JOHN WILEY AND SONS INC

First published in France in 1962 *under the title*
Programmes, Jeux et Réseaux de Transport
by Dunod, Paris

First published in Great Britain 1965
Printed in Great Britain by
Spottiswoode, Ballantyne Ltd., London and Colchester

Contents

Preface

Over the last few years, the applications of mathematical programming have extended over an ever widening field, in economics as well as in operational research, in biological and in the social sciences; methods of solution and numerous algorithms have been developed. The aim of this volume is to offer a general theory and to indicate its scope by examples.

Part I (by A. Ghouila-Houri) is concerned with the analytical theory of programming. The framework of 'linear programming' proved too narrow, and from the idea of a linear function there naturally followed the more general idea of a convex function. The reader will find here, first the preliminary ideas of set theory the notation of which makes proofs more intuitive, and secondly, an account of recent advances.

Part II (by C. Berge) aims to demonstrate that a large part of these mathematical programming problems can be solved in a simple and elegant manner using, not analytical methods, but the theory of graphs; these problems will be loosely designated here as 'flow problems'. One, by no means small, advantage of this approach is that one can equally well state each result with real numbers or with integers and thus give the solution of a large number of combinatorial problems, both serious and entertaining.

Translator's note

In translating this book I was fortunate in being able to use as a basis for the first draft the unpublished translation by Mr C. Ramanujacharyulu of the Indian Statistical Institute, Calcutta.

I am much indebted to Mr W. J. Corlett, Mr H. Kestelman and Professor C. A. B. Smith who gave me invaluable advice on technical terms and the mathematical argument while the translation was in progress.

Mr Kestelman and Dr J. Moon assisted greatly by reading and correcting the final manuscript. Mrs Juliet Daniel checked my translation and rephrased clumsy sentences.

I owe warmest thanks to all these experts for their unflagging help in undertaking this arduous task.

MAXINE MERRINGTON
University College London

PART ONE

General Theory of Convex Programming

1. Preliminary ideas; sets, vector spaces

1.1. SETS

A *set* A is a collection of objects, of any kind whatever (points on a plane, numbers, functions, etc....) which are by definition the *elements* (in certain cases, called the *points*) of A; sets are in general denoted by upper-case italics and elements are shown in lower-case italics.

If a is an element of the set A, we write $a \in A$. If A and B are two sets, we say that A is contained in B or that A is a part of B or that A is a *subset* of B or again that B *contains* A, if all the elements of A belong to B, in other words if

$$a \in A \text{ implies } a \in B;$$

one then can write

$$A \subset B \quad \text{(read as } A \textit{ is contained in } B\text{)},$$

or

$$B \supset A \quad \text{(read as } B \textit{ contains } A\text{)}.$$

If both $A \subset B$ and $B \subset A$, the sets A and B have the same elements. One then writes $A = B$.

Let us specify from the start certain universally used conventions of notation, which we shall follow in this book. To be concise, we shall frequently use the following symbols $\Rightarrow$ and $\Leftrightarrow$:

$\Rightarrow$ is read as 'implies',
$\Leftrightarrow$ is read as 'equivalent to';

for example we shall write:

$$A \subset B \Leftrightarrow (a \in A \Rightarrow a \in B)$$

in order to say that the proposition $A \subset B$ is equivalent to the proposition

$$a \in A \text{ implies } a \in B.$$

We shall write $a \notin A$ for 'a does not belong to A', $B \not\supset A$ for 'B does not contain A', $A \neq B$ for 'A is different from B', etc....; $a, b \in A$ for '$a \in A$' and

'$b \in A$', $a,b,c,d \geqslant 0$ for '$a \geqslant 0, b \geqslant 0, c \geqslant 0$ and $d \geqslant 0$, etc....; to express for instance that the n numbers $\alpha_1, \alpha_2, \ldots, \alpha_n$ are positive or zero, we may write either

$$\alpha_1 \geqslant 0, \alpha_2 \geqslant 0, \ldots, \alpha_n \geqslant 0,$$

or making use of the above convention,

$$\alpha_1, \alpha_2, \ldots, \alpha_n \geqslant 0,$$

or again

$$\alpha_i \geqslant 0 \quad \text{for } i = 1,2,\ldots,n.$$

A set can be specified by a complete enumeration of its elements: thus the empty set, denoted by $\varnothing$, is a set which contains no elements; we denote by $\{a_1,a_2,\ldots,a_n\}$ the set formed by the elements $a_1, a_2, \ldots, a_n$. A set can also be specified by a property of its elements; for example we shall speak of the set of real numbers included between 0 and 1: this set is written as

$$\{x | x \in \mathbf{R} \quad \text{and} \quad 0 \leqslant x \leqslant 1\},$$

where **R** indicates the set of all real numbers. Or again, the set of all prime numbers can be written as

$$\{x | x \in \mathbf{N} \text{ and, for every } p \in \mathbf{N} \text{ with } p \neq 1 \text{ and } p \neq x, p \text{ is not a divisor of } x\};$$

or again,

$$\{x | x \in \mathbf{N} \text{ and, for every } p, q \in \mathbf{N} \text{ with } p, q \neq 1, x \neq pq\},$$

where **N** denotes the set of non-negative integers.

Sometimes a set will be described as 'the set of elements of the form...'. For example to designate the set of perfect squares, we can equally well say, 'the set of integers x which satisfy the property: there exists an integer n such that $x = n^2$'; which is written as

$$\{x | x \in \mathbf{N} \text{ and there exists } n \in \mathbf{N} \text{ such that } x = n^2\},$$

or we may say, 'the set of integers of the form n^2, with $n \in \mathbf{N}$', written as

$$\{x | x \in \mathbf{N}, x = n^2; n \in \mathbf{N}\}.$$

In the same way the set of non-negative rational numbers can be written

$$\left\{x | x \in \mathbf{R}, x = \frac{p}{q}; p, q \in \mathbf{N} \quad \text{and} \quad q \neq 0\right\}$$

(read as: the set of real numbers x of the form $x = p/q$, p and q being non-negative integers and q not zero).

IMPORTANT NOTE. It is of the greatest importance for the understanding of the argument to be able to locate those letters in a proposition which in themselves have no individual significance, that is to say the *dummy* letters. Thus, in the proposition $a \in A$ implies $a \in B$, which expresses that A is contained in B, the letter a can be replaced by any other letter (except A or B) without changing in any way the sense of the proposition. Similarly, in the proposition

$$f(x) = 0, \quad \text{for every } x \in \mathbf{R}^n,$$

the letter x is dummy. In the expression

$$\left\{x \middle| x \in \mathbf{R},\ x = \frac{p}{q};\ p, q \in \mathbf{N},\quad q \neq 0\right\},$$

the letters x, p and q are dummy.

DEFINITION. Let X be a set and let A be a subset of X; the set of elements of X which do not belong to A† is called the *complement* of A (relative to X) and is denoted by $\complement_X A$ (or simply $\complement A$ if there is no possibility of confusion):

$$\complement_X A = \{x|x \in X \quad \text{and} \quad x \notin A\}.$$

DEFINITION. A *mapping* f of a set X into a set Y is a correspondence which associates with every element x of X an element on $f(x)$ of Y. f is also said to be a *function defined in X and whose values lie in Y*. In the case where Y is the set $\mathbf{R}$ of real numbers, f is said to be a *numerical* function defined in X.

Let f be a mapping of a set X into a set Y. If A is a subset of X, then the set

$$f(A) = \{y|y \in Y \text{ and there exists } x \in A \text{ such that } y = f(x)\}$$

is called the *image* of A.

If B is a subset of Y, the set

$$f^{-1}(B) = \{x|x \in X \quad \text{and} \quad f(x) \in B\}$$

is called the *inverse image* of B.

f is said to be *bi-uniform* (maps one-one) if, for every $y \in Y$ there exists

† More generally, if A and B are any two sets, $B - A$ denotes the set of elements of B not belonging to A:

$$B - A = \{x|x \in B \quad \text{and} \quad x \notin A\};$$

in the case where A is contained in B, we may obviously write

$$B - A = \complement_B A.$$

exactly one element x of X such that $y = f(x)$. One can then define a mapping f^{-1} of Y into X as

$$x = f^{-1}(y) \Leftrightarrow y = f(x).$$

f^{-1} is called the *inverse* mapping of f; f^{-1} is itself one-one and the inverse mapping of f^{-1} is f.

NOTE. A function may often be represented by using indices. Thus a *series* $a_0, a_1, a_2, \ldots, a_n, \ldots$ of elements of a set A, is simply a mapping of the set $\mathbf{N}$ of positive integers into the set A. More generally, given a set A, we may have a set I called the *index set* and a mapping of I into A which assigns to every index i an element a_i of A. It is then said that there is a *family* of elements of A; this family is generally denoted by $(a_i)_{i \in I}$.

It may often be necessary to introduce sets of sets. In general, whenever we have a set of sets, it is preferable to present it as a family of sets to avoid confusion, and to use indices for notation. Thus instead of stating 'the set of open intervals centred at the origin and of length greater than 2', and denoting it by

$$\{X|X\} = \{x|x \in \mathbf{R} \quad \text{and} \quad |x| < \rho\}; \rho \in \mathbf{R}, \rho > 1\},$$

we prefer to state 'the family of open intervals...', and to denote it by $(I_\rho)_{\rho \in A}$, where

$$I_\rho = \{x|x \in \mathbf{R} \quad \text{and} \quad |x| < \rho\}$$

and

$$A = \{\rho|\rho \in \mathbf{R} \quad \text{and} \quad \rho > 1\}.\dagger$$

DEFINITION. $A \bigcup B$ denotes the *union* of two sets A and B, and is the set of elements which belong to at least one of the two sets:

$$A \bigcup B = \{x|x \in A \quad \text{or} \quad x \in B\}.$$

More generally, the *union of a family*, $(A_i)_{i \in I}$, *of sets* (finite or infinite) is the set of elements which belong to at least one of the sets of that family, that is

$$\bigcup_{i \in I} A_i = \{x|\text{there exists } i \in I \text{ such that } x \in A_i\}.$$

† This provides an excellent exercise on the use of dummy letters: for the family of open intervals centred at the origin and of length greater than 2 can also be denoted by

$$(J_u)_{u \in B},$$

where

$$J_t = \{y|y \in \mathbf{R} \quad \text{and} \quad |y| < t\},$$

$$B = \{y|y \in \mathbf{R} \quad \text{and} \quad y > 1\}.$$

NOTE. Sometimes in the course of the argument it may happen that we define a family of sets $(A_i)_{i \in I}$ without knowing *a priori* if this family is empty or not. If it is found that it is empty, that is to say $I = \emptyset$, then the union is

$$\bigcup_{i \in \emptyset} A_i = \{x \mid \text{there exists } i \in \emptyset \text{ such that } x \in A_i\} = \emptyset.$$

DEFINITION. The *intersection* of two sets A and B, denoted by $A \cap B$, is defined as the set of elements which belong both to A and to B.

$$A \cap B = \{x \mid x \in A \quad \text{and} \quad x \in B\}.$$

DEFINITION. The *intersection of a family* $(A_i)_{i \in I}$ *of subsets of a set* X, is defined as the set of elements of X which belong simultaneously to every set of that family:

$$\bigcap_{i \in I} A_i = \{x \mid x \in X \quad \text{and} \quad x \in A_i \text{ for every } i \in I\}.$$

In the case where $I = \emptyset$, we have

$$\bigcap_{i \in I} A_i = X;$$

this moreover is the only case where X plays a role; in fact, if I is not empty, clearly we have:

$$\bigcap_{i \in I} A_i = \{x \mid x \in A_i \text{ for every } i \in I\}.$$

Two sets A and B are said to be *disjoint* if their intersection is empty. The sets $(A_i)_{i \in I}$ are said to *meet* if their intersection is not empty.

DEFINITION. The *product* (*Cartesian*) of two sets A and B, denoted by $A \times B$, is defined as the set of ordered *pairs* (a,b) with $a \in A$ and $b \in B$.

EXAMPLE. The product

$$\mathbf{R} \times \mathbf{R} = \{(x^1, x^2) \mid x^1, x^2 \in \mathbf{R}\},$$

which can be represented by points on a plane (by means of two co-ordinate axes), is called the *Euclidean plane*.

If one of the two sets is empty their product is empty; if the two sets are equal, we use the notation

$$A^2 = A \times A:$$

thus the Euclidean plane is written $\mathbf{R}^2$. Notice that the two preceding cases are the only cases where the product is commutative. In fact, suppose $A \neq B$, $A \neq \emptyset$ and $B \neq \emptyset$; if, for example, the set A is not contained in the set B, suppose a_0 is a point of A which does not belong to B, and b_0 is a point of B, then

$$(a_0, b_0) \in A \times B \quad \text{and} \quad (a_0, b_0) \notin B \times A,$$

thus

$$A \times B \neq B \times A.$$

The idea of a Cartesian product can be generalized for the case of more than two sets. The product of n sets $A_1, A_2, \ldots, A_n$ is the set $A_1 \times A_2 \times \ldots \times A_n$ of ordered *n-tuples* $(a_1, a_2, \ldots, a_n)$ with $a_1 \in A_1$, $a_2 \in A_2, \ldots, a_n \in A_n$.

For example the product

$$\mathbf{R}^n = \mathbf{R} \times \mathbf{R} \times \ldots \times \mathbf{R} = \{(x^1, x^2, \ldots, x^n) \,|\, x^1, x^2, \ldots, x^n \in \mathbf{R}\}$$

is called the *Euclidean space of n dimensions.*

IMPORTANT NOTE. In general, we shall use the same letter to designate a point of $\mathbf{R}^n$ and its co-ordinates: the latter will have indices either above or below; we shall on each occasion state precisely which convention is used. We shall say, for example, 'let $x = (x^1, x^2, \ldots, x^n)$ be a point of $\mathbf{R}^n$ and let $y = (y_1, y_2, \ldots, y_m)$ be a point of $\mathbf{R}^m$, etc.,...'. However in order to differentiate clearly between the points of $\mathbf{R}^n$ (which are n-tuples of numbers), and their co-ordinates (which are numbers), we shall denote the points of $\mathbf{R}^n$ with bold face type whenever both the points of $\mathbf{R}^n$ and their co-ordinates occur together in this book.

NOTE. Whenever we consider a function defined in a product of sets, we can denote this function by using one or more *arguments*. For example, given a point $\mathbf{a} = (a^1, a^2) \in \mathbf{R}^2$: the mapping f of $\mathbf{R}^2$ into $\mathbf{R}^2$ defined by

$$f(\mathbf{x}) = \mathbf{a} + \mathbf{x},$$

and the mapping f of $\mathbf{R}^2$ into $\mathbf{R}^2$ defined by

$$f(x^1, x^2) = (a^1 + x^1, a^2 + x^2)$$

are the same functions. Similarly the mapping of $\mathbf{R}^n$ into $\mathbf{R}$

$$f(\mathbf{x}) = \|\mathbf{x}\|^2 \qquad \text{(cf. Chapter 2)}$$

can be equally well written as

$$f(x^1, x^2, \ldots, x^n) = (x^1)^2 + (x^2)^2 + \ldots + (x^n)^2;$$

or as

$$f(\mathbf{x}) = (x^1)^2 + (x^2)^2 + \ldots + (x^n)^2,$$

provided no confusion is possible: that is to say if it is obvious that $x^1, x^2, \ldots, x^n$ represent the co-ordinates of the point $\mathbf{x}$.

There are cases where it is necessary to indicate precisely, even if only implicitly, what the arguments represent: for example, if we speak of the mapping f of

$$\mathbf{R}^h \times \mathbf{R}^{n-h} = \mathbf{R}^n$$

into $\mathbf{R}$ defined by

$$f(\mathbf{x}, \mathbf{y}) = \|\mathbf{x}\|^2,$$

we know that the argument $\mathbf{x}$ represents here a point of $\mathbf{R}^h$ and hence we are dealing with the function f defined in $\mathbf{R}^n$ by

$$f(x^1, x^2, \ldots, x^n) = (x^1)^2 + (x^2)^2 + \ldots + (x^h)^2,$$

whereas, if we speak of the mapping f of $\mathbf{R}^n$ into $\mathbf{R}$ defined by

$$f(\mathbf{x}, \mathbf{y}) = \|\mathbf{x}\|^2$$

this has no meaning whatever.

1.2. VECTOR SPACES

A *vector space* is defined as a set X on which two operations 'addition' and 'multiplication by a scalar' are defined, these two operations have certain properties.

Firstly, the operation *addition* assigns to every ordered pair (x, y) of elements of X an element of X denoted by $x+y$, called the *sum* of x and y. This operation possesses the following properties:

(1) $x+(y+z) = (x+y)+z$ (associativity);

(2) there exists an element of X, denoted by $\mathbf{0}$, called *the neutral element* or *zero* (sometimes the *origin*), for which

$$x+\mathbf{0} = \mathbf{0}+x = x \text{ for every } x \in X;$$

(3) to every x of X there corresponds an element $(-x)$ of X, called the *negative* of x satisfying

$$x+(-x) = \mathbf{0};$$

(4) $x+y = y+x$ for any x and y (commutativity).

Secondly, the operation of *multiplication by a scalar* assigns to every ordered pair (λ, x), λ being a real number and x an element of X, an element of X denoted by λx called the *product* of the element x and the *scalar* λ. This operation has the following properties:

(1) $(\lambda\mu)x = \lambda(\mu x)$ (associativity);

(2) $1x = x$

(3) $\lambda(x+y) = \lambda x + \lambda y$ (distributivity with respect to addition of vectors);

(4) $(\lambda+\mu)x = \lambda x + \mu x$ (distributivity with respect to addition of scalars).

Other well-known properties arise from these defining properties. We shall quote a few of these whose proof is self-evident:

(1) $0x = \mathbf{0}$ for every $x \in X$;
(2) $\lambda\mathbf{0} = \mathbf{0}$ for every $\lambda \in \mathbf{R}$;
(3) $(-1)x = (-x)$ for every $x \in X$;
(4) for every $a, b \in X$ the equation $a + x = b$ has a unique solution; this is $b + (-a)$ and is denoted by $b - a$.

EXAMPLE 1. The example of a vector space which occurs most frequently is the set $\mathbf{R}^n$ of n-tuples $(x^1, x^2, \ldots, x^n)$ of real numbers, in which the sum of two points

$$\mathbf{x} = (x^1, x^2, \ldots, x^n) \quad \text{and} \quad \mathbf{y} = (y^1, y^2, \ldots, y^n),$$

is defined as the point

$$\mathbf{x} + \mathbf{y} = (x^1 + y^1, x^2 + y^2, \ldots, x^n + y^n);$$

and the product of a point

$$\mathbf{x} = (x^1, x^2, \ldots, x^n)$$

and a number λ, as the point

$$\lambda\mathbf{x} = (\lambda x^1, \lambda x^2, \ldots, \lambda x^n).$$

An extremely simple particular case arises when $n = 1$: then we have the set of real numbers with ordinary addition and multiplication.

EXAMPLE 2. The set Φ of numerical functions defined on the interval $[0, 1]$ constitutes a vector space, if the sum of two functions f, $g \in \Phi$ is defined as the function which assigns to each point x of this interval the number $f(x) + g(x)$, and the product of a function $f \in \Phi$ and a scalar λ, as the function which assigns the number $\lambda f(x)$, to every point x in this interval.

DEFINITION. Given two subsets A and B in a vector space X, we define as their *sum*, denoted by $A + B$, the set

$$\{x \mid x = a + b;\ a \in A,\ b \in B\}.$$

Similarly there is associated with every subset A and with every real number λ the *product*

$$\lambda A = \{x \mid x = \lambda a;\ a \in A\};$$

in the case where $\lambda = -1$, the product is generally written as $(-A)$ rather than $(-1)A$.†

† The notation $A + (-B)$ should not be confused with the notation $A - B$ (cf. 1.1).

Theorem 1

(1) $A+B = B+A$

(2) $A+(B+C) = (A+B)+C$

(3) $A+\{\mathbf{0}\} = A$

(4) $A+(-A) \supset \{\mathbf{0}\}$

(5) $\lambda(A+B) = \lambda A+\lambda B$

(6) $(\lambda+\mu) A \subset \lambda A+\mu A$

(7) $(\lambda\mu)A = \lambda(\mu A)$

(8) $1A = A$

These formulae are easily proved. They show that, in general, a set $\mathscr{T}(X)$ of subsets of X cannot form a vector space: the inclusion relations (4) and (6) are not equalities, as may be seen in the case where $A = \{a_1, a_2\}$ with $a_1 \neq a_2$; here

$$A+(-A) = \{a_1-a_2, \mathbf{0}, a_2-a_1\} \neq \{\mathbf{0}\}.$$

DEFINITION. Let X and Y be vector spaces and let f be a mapping of X into Y; f is said to be *linear* if

$$f(x+x') = f(x)+f(x') \text{ for every } x, x' \in X$$

and

$$f(\lambda x) = \lambda f(x) \text{ for every } \lambda \in \mathbf{R} \text{ and } x \in X.$$

In the case where f is a numerical linear function, that is to say, where $Y = \mathbf{R}$, f is said to be a *linear form.*

EXAMPLE 1. The mapping π_i of $\mathbf{R}^n$ into $\mathbf{R}$ which associates with every point

$$\mathbf{x} = (x^1, x^2, \ldots, x^n),$$

its co-ordinate of rank i, say x^i, is linear; such a mapping is called a *projection.*

EXAMPLE 2. Let a be a real number; the mapping f_a of $\mathbf{R}$ into $\mathbf{R}$ defined by $f_a(x) = ax$ is linear.

Theorem 2. *If f_1 is a linear mapping of X into Y and f_2 is a linear mapping of Y into Z, the composite function $f = f_2 \circ f_1$ defined by $f(x) = f_2(f_1(x))$ is linear.*

Theorem 3. *If f is a one-one linear mapping of X onto Y, then the inverse mapping f^{-1} is also linear.*

Theorem 4. *If f_1 and f_2 are two linear mappings of X into Y and if λ_1 and λ_2 are two real numbers, the mapping*

$$f = \lambda_1 f_1 + \lambda_2 f_2$$

defined by

$$f(x) = \lambda_1 f_1(x) + \lambda_2 f_2(x)$$

is linear.

These three theorems can be easily proved.

DEFINITION. In a vector space X, a set E is a *vector subspace* if

$$x, y \in E \Rightarrow x+y \in E$$

and

$$x \in E, \lambda \in \mathbf{R} \Rightarrow \lambda x \in E.$$

Notice that these conditions are equivalent to the following condition:

$$\begin{cases} x, y \in E \\ \lambda, \mu \in \mathbf{R} \end{cases} \Rightarrow \lambda x + \mu y \in E.$$

EXAMPLE 1. The sets $\varnothing$, $\{\mathbf{0}\}$ and X are vector subspaces of X. Further we see that every non-empty vector subspace contains the point $\mathbf{0}$.

EXAMPLE 2. The set of mappings of a vector space X into another vector space Y, is itself a vector space if we define the sum $[f+g]$ of two mappings f and g by

$$[f+g](x) = f(x) + g(x)$$

and the product $[\lambda f]$ of a mapping f by a real number λ by

$$[\lambda f](x) = \lambda . f(x).$$

We see then that the set of linear mappings of X into Y is, by Theorem 4, a vector subspace of this vector space.

DEFINITION. Two vector subspaces E_1 and E_2 are said to be *supplementary* if

$$E_1 + E_2 = X \quad \text{and} \quad E_1 \cap E_2 = \{\mathbf{0}\}.$$

If E_1 and E_2 are two supplementary subspaces, every point x of X can be written as $x = x_1 + x_2$ with $x_1 \in E_1$ and $x_2 \in E_2$; moreover this decomposition is unique, for,

$$\begin{cases} x = x_1 + x_2 = y_1 + y_2 \\ x_1, y_1 \in E_1 \quad \text{and} \quad x_2, y_2 \in E_2 \end{cases} \Rightarrow \begin{cases} x_1 - y_1 = y_2 - x_2 \\ x_1 - y_1 \in E_1 \quad \text{and} \quad x_2 - y_2 \in E_2 \end{cases}$$

$$\Rightarrow x_1 - y_1 = y_2 - x_2 = \mathbf{0} \quad \Rightarrow \begin{cases} x_1 = y_1 \\ x_2 = y_2. \end{cases}$$

DEFINITION. A set of the form

$$D_a = \{x | x = \lambda a; \lambda \in \mathbf{R}\} \quad \text{with } a \neq \mathbf{0}$$

is called a *straight line passing through* $\mathbf{0}$. A straight line passing through $\mathbf{0}$ is a vector subspace.

DEFINITION. A vector subspace which is supplementary to a line D_a (through the origin) is called a *plane passing through* $\mathbf{0}$.

Theorem 5. *If f is a linear form, not identically zero, the set $E_f = \{x/f(x) = 0\}$ is a plane passing through* $\mathbf{0}$; *conversely every plane passing through* $\mathbf{0}$ *is a set of this form.*

It can easily be verified that E_f is a vector subspace. On the other hand, if a is a point satisfying $f(a) \neq 0$, the straight line D_a satisfies

$$D_a \cap E_f = \{\mathbf{0}\},$$

since

$$f(\lambda a) = 0 \Rightarrow \lambda f(a) = 0 \Rightarrow \lambda = 0,$$

and also $D_a + E_f = X$, for if $x \in X$ and if we write

$$\lambda = \frac{f(x)}{f(a)},$$

then

$$f(x - \lambda a) = 0,$$

hence

$$x - \lambda a \in E_f.$$

Conversely, let P be a plane passing through $\mathbf{0}$ and let D_a be a straight line supplementary to P. Every point x of X can be written in the unique form $x = \lambda a + b$ with $b \in P$: the number λ defined by this formula is a numerical function of x, which is easily verified as being linear; let f be this function: it is not identically zero, since $f(a) = 1$ and

$$P = \{x | f(x) = 0\}.$$

Theorem 6. *If f is a linear mapping of a vector space X into a vector space Y, and if E and F are two vector subspaces in X and Y respectively, then $f(E)$ is a vector subspace in Y and $f^{-1}(F)$ is a vector subspace in X.*

For, if

$$y_1 = f(x_1) \quad \text{and} \quad y_2 = f(x_2) \quad \text{with } x_1, x_2 \in E$$

and if λ_1 and λ_2 are two real numbers, then

$$\lambda_1 y_1 + \lambda_2 y_2 = f(\lambda_1 x_1 + \lambda_2 x_2) \quad \text{with } \lambda_1 x_1 + \lambda_2 x_2 \in E.$$

Similarly if $f(x_1) \in F$ and $f(x_2) \in F$, then also

$$f(\lambda_1 x_1 + \lambda_2 x_2) = \lambda_1 f(x_1) + \lambda_2 f(x_2) \in F$$

for every $\lambda_1, \lambda_2 \in \mathbf{R}$.

Theorem 7. *If $(E_i)_{i \in I}$ is a family of vector subspaces in a vector space X, the intersection*

$$\bigcap_{i \in I} E_i$$

is also a vector subspace.

This follows immediately from the definition.

DEFINITION. If A is a set in a vector space X, the intersection $s[A]$ of all vector subspaces containing A is called the *linear hull* of A. This intersection $s[A]$ is itself, according to the preceding theorem, a vector subspace containing A.

Theorem 8. *If X is a vector space and if A is a set in X, then,*

$$s[A] = \{x | x = \lambda_1 a_1 + \lambda_2 a_2 + \ldots + \lambda_n a_n; \\ n \in \mathbf{N}, \lambda_1, \lambda_2, \ldots, \lambda_n \in \mathbf{R}, a_1, a_2, \ldots, a_n \in A\};$$

in other words, the vector hull of a set A is equal to the set of points of X which can be expressed as a linear combination of points of A.

For, the set defined in the right-hand side of the equation is a vector subspace containing A and it is contained in every vector subspace containing A.

It is said that $s[A]$ is the vector subspace *generated* (spanned) by A.

1.3. DIMENSION OF A VECTOR SPACE

DEFINITION. The points $x_1, x_2, \ldots, x_n$ belonging to a vector space X are said to be *linearly independent* if

$$\lambda_1 x_1 + \lambda_2 x_2 + \ldots + \lambda_n x_n = \mathbf{0} \Rightarrow \lambda_1 = \lambda_2 = \ldots = \lambda_n = 0;$$

otherwise they are said to be *linearly dependent*.

DEFINITION. Points $e_1, e_2, \ldots, e_n$ belonging to a vector subspace E, are said to form a *basis* of E, if they are linearly independent and if the vector hull of $\{e_1, e_2, \ldots, e_n\}$ is E.

Theorem 1. *In order that the points $e_1, e_2, \ldots, e_n$ belonging to a vector subspace E may form a basis of E, it is necessary and sufficient that every point x of E*

can be expressed uniquely in the form $x = \lambda_1 e_1 + \lambda_2 e_2 + \ldots + \lambda_n e_n$ *with* $\lambda_1, \lambda_2, \ldots, \lambda_n \in \mathbf{R}$.

If $e_1, e_2, \ldots, e_n$ form a basis of E, every point x of E can be expressed in this form, according to Theorem 8 of the preceding section. On the other hand if, at the same time,
$x = \lambda_1 e_1 + \lambda_2 e_2 + \ldots + \lambda_n e_n$ and $x = \lambda'_1 e_1 + \lambda'_2 e_2 + \ldots + \lambda'_n e_n$

then $$(\lambda_1 - \lambda'_1)\, e_1 + (\lambda_2 - \lambda'_2)\, e_2 + \ldots + (\lambda_n - \lambda'_n)\, e_n = \mathbf{0};$$
hence
$$\lambda_1 - \lambda'_1 = \lambda_2 - \lambda'_2 = \ldots = \lambda_n - \lambda'_n = 0.$$

Conversely, if every point x of E can be expressed in the unique form indicated above, the points $e_1, e_2, \ldots, e_n$ span E and they are linearly independent since $\mathbf{0}$ can be expressed only as
$$\mathbf{0} = 0e_1 + 0e_2 + \ldots + 0e_n.$$

Theorem 2. *Let* $e_1, e_2, \ldots, e_n$ *be linearly independent points belonging to a vector subspace* E; *then for these points to form a basis of* E, *it is necessary and sufficient that every set of points* $x_1, x_2, \ldots, x_{n+1}$ *in* E *be linearly dependent.*

Suppose that any $n+1$ points of E are necessarily linearly dependent and let x be any point of E. The points $x, e_1, e_2, \ldots, e_n$ are linearly dependent, while the points $e_1, e_2, \ldots, e_n$ are not, so that we have a relation of the form
$$\mu x + \mu_1 e_1 + \mu_2 e_2 + \ldots + \mu_n e_n = \mathbf{0},$$
with $\mu \neq 0$; hence writing $\lambda_i = -\mu_i/\mu$ for $i = 1, 2, \ldots, n$
$$x = \lambda_1 e_1 + \lambda_2 e_2 + \ldots + \lambda_n e_n.$$

Conversely, suppose that $e_1, e_2, \ldots, e_n$ form a basis of E, and that there exist in E, $n+1$ linearly independent points, $a_1, a_2, \ldots, a_{n+1}$: we obtain a contradiction. In fact, a_1 can be expressed in the form
$$a_1 = \lambda_1 e_1 + \lambda_2 e_2 + \ldots + \lambda_n e_n,$$
and one of the numbers $\lambda_1, \lambda_2, \ldots, \lambda_n$, say λ_1 is not zero, since it is impossible to have $1.a_1 = \mathbf{0}$. We can thus write
$$e_1 = \frac{1}{\lambda_1} a_1 - \frac{\lambda_2}{\lambda_1} e_2 - \ldots - \frac{\lambda_n}{\lambda_1} e_n,$$
so that a_2 can be expressed as
$$a_2 = \lambda'_1 a_1 + \lambda'_2 e_2 + \ldots + \lambda'_n e_n,$$
when one of the numbers $\lambda'_2, \lambda'_3, \ldots, \lambda'_n$, say λ'_2, is different from zero, since we could not have
$$1.a_2 - \lambda'_1 a_1 = \mathbf{0}.$$

Repeating this operation with a_3, a_4, etc., we finally obtain

$$a_{n+1} = \mu_1 a_1 + \mu_2 a_2 + \ldots + \ldots + \mu_n a_n$$

which contradicts the hypotheses.

Corollary. *If* $e_1, e_2, \ldots, e_n$ *and* $e'_1, e'_2, \ldots, e'_m$ *are two bases of* E, *then* $m = n$.

Since the points $e'_1, e'_2, \ldots, e'_m$ are linearly independent, $m \leqslant n$; but similarly $n \leqslant m$, hence $m = n$.

DEFINITION. A vector subspace E is said to have *finite dimension* if it has at least one basis. Then the *dimension* of E, denoted by $\dim E$, is the number of elements in any basis of E (cf. preceding corollary). In the case where $E = \{\mathbf{0}\}$, we write $\dim E = 0$.

EXAMPLE. The space $\mathbf{R}^n$ is of dimension n. For, the points

$$\boldsymbol{\delta}_1 = (1, 0, 0, \ldots, 0), \quad \boldsymbol{\delta}_2 = (0, 1, 0, \ldots, 0), \quad \ldots, \quad \boldsymbol{\delta}_n = (0, 0, \ldots, 1)$$

are linearly independent since

$$\lambda_1 \boldsymbol{\delta}_1 + \lambda_2 \boldsymbol{\delta}_2 + \ldots + \lambda_n \boldsymbol{\delta}_n = \mathbf{0} \Leftrightarrow (\lambda_1, \lambda_2, \ldots, \lambda_n) = \mathbf{0}$$
$$\Leftrightarrow \lambda_1 = \lambda_2 = \ldots = \lambda_n = 0,$$

and they span the whole space.

Theorem 3. *If E is a vector subspace of finite dimension n and E' is a non-empty vector subspace contained in E, then E' is of finite dimension and $\dim E' \leqslant n$.*

Let m be the smallest positive integer such that any $m+1$ points of E' are linearly dependent: then $m \leqslant n$. If $m = 0$, then $E' = \{\mathbf{0}\}$ and $\dim E' = 0 = m$; if $m \neq 0$, there exist linearly independent points $e_1, e_2, \ldots, e_m$ in E', which form a basis of E' (cf. Theorem 2), so that here again $\dim E' = m$.

Theorem 4. *If X is a vector space of dimension n and if E_1 and E_2 are two supplementary vector subspaces in X, then $\dim E_1 + \dim E_2 = n$.*

If $e_1, e_2, \ldots, e_p$ form a basis of E_1 and if $e'_1, e'_2, \ldots, e'_q$ form a basis of E_2, then every point x of X can be expressed uniquely in the form $x = x_1 + x_2$ with $x_1 \in E_1$ and $x_2 \in E_2$. As x_1 and x_2 can themselves be expressed uniquely in the form

$$x_1 = \lambda_1 e_1 + \lambda_2 e_2 + \ldots + \lambda_p e_p$$
$$x_2 = \mu_1 e'_1 + \mu_2 e'_2 + \ldots + \mu_q e'_q,$$

it can be seen that $e_1, e_2, \ldots, e_p, e'_1, e'_2, \ldots, e'_q$ form a basis of X.

Corollary. *If X has dimension n, every plane passing through the origin has dimension $n-1$.*

1.4. LINEAR MANIFOLDS. CONES

DEFINITION. Let X be a vector space; the set A in X is said to be a *linear manifold* if it is of the form $A = E+\{x_0\}$, where x_0 is a point of X and E a vector subspace of X. A is said to be a *straight line* if E is a straight line passing through the origin, and A is a *plane* if E is a plane passing through the origin.

NOTE. If a linear manifold A can be written as $A = E_1+\{x_1\}$ and $A = E_2+\{x_2\}$ simultaneously, we can show that $E_1 = E_2$. For we have

$$x_1 = \mathbf{0}+x_1 \in A = E_2+\{x_2\}$$

hence

$$x_1-x_2 \in E_2;$$

therefore

$$E_1 = E_2+\{x_1-x_2\} \subset E_2+E_2 = E_2.$$

Similarly $E_2 \subset E_1$, hence finally $E_1 = E_2$. The subspace $E_1 = E_2$ is called the *subspace parallel to* A. If two linear manifolds A and B have the same parallel subspace, then they are said to be *parallel.*

Theorem 1. *Let A be a linear manifold parallel to a subspace E. In order that $E+\{a\}$ may be equal to A, it is necessary and sufficient that a belong to A.*

We have

$$A = E+\{a\} \Rightarrow a = \mathbf{0}+a \in A.$$

Conversely, if $a \in A$ and if we write $A = E+\{x_0\}$ we have $a-x_0 \in E$, hence

$$A = E+\{x_0\} = E+\{a\}+\{x_0-a\} = E+\{a\}.$$

Corollary. *Two parallel manifolds are either identical or disjoint.*

Let E be the vector subspace which is parallel to them, if they have a common point a they are both equal to $E+\{a\}$.

Theorem 2. *Every plane is of the form*

$$E_f^\alpha = \{x \mid f(x) = \alpha\},$$

where α is a real number and f a linear form not identically zero; conversely, every set of this form is a plane.

Every plane is of the form $E_f+\{x_0\}$, and we get

$$x \in E_f+\{x_0\} \Leftrightarrow f(x-x_0) = 0 \Leftrightarrow f(x) = \alpha,$$

where

$$\alpha = f(x_0).$$

Conversely, if α is a real number and f a linear form, not identically zero, take a point a such that $f(a) \neq 0$ and write

$$x_0 = \frac{\alpha}{f(a)}a.$$

Then

$$f(x) = \alpha \Leftrightarrow f(x-x_0) = 0 \Leftrightarrow x \in E_f+\{x_0\}.$$

Theorem 3. *Let f be linear mapping of the vector space X into a vector space Y. If A is a linear manifold of X, $f(A)$ is a linear manifold of Y.*

In fact,

$$A = E+\{x_0\} \Rightarrow f(A) = f(E)+\{f(x_0)\},$$

and we know that if E is a vector subspace of X, $f(E)$ is a vector subspace of Y.

DEFINITION. A numerical function defined in a vector space X, is said to be *linear affine* if $f(x)-f(\mathbf{0})$ is linear.

Corollary. *If a linear affine function $f(x)$ defined in a vector space X, is bounded above (or below) in X, then it is constant in X.*

For, by the preceding theorem, the set $f(X)-\{f(\mathbf{0})\}$ is a linear manifold of $\mathbf{R}$, since the function $f(x)-f(\mathbf{0})$ is linear; hence $f(X)$ is a linear manifold. Now in $\mathbf{R}$, the only two non-empty vector subspaces are $\mathbf{R}$ and $\{\mathbf{0}\}$. Since the subspace parallel to $f(X)$ cannot be $\mathbf{R}$, we see that $f(X)$ reduces to a point of $\mathbf{R}$, in other words $f(x)$ is constant in X.

We shall frequently use this corollary later.

Theorem 4. *Every straight line is of the form*

$$D(a,b) = \{x|x = \lambda a+\mu b;\ \lambda, \mu \in \mathbf{R},\ \lambda+\mu = 1\}, \quad \text{with } a \neq b,$$

and conversely every set of this form is a straight line.

If D_a is a straight line passing through $\mathbf{0}$, then

$$x \in D_a+\{x_0\} \Leftrightarrow x = x_0+\mu a \quad \text{with } \mu \in \mathbf{R}$$

$$\Leftrightarrow x = (1-\mu)x_0+\mu(x_0+a) \quad \text{with } \mu \in \mathbf{R},$$

hence

$$D_a+\{x_0\} = D(x_0, x_0+a),$$

which proves the theorem.

Theorem 5. *A set A is a linear manifold if and only if*

$$\begin{cases} x, x' \in A \\ \lambda, \lambda' \in \mathbf{R} \\ \lambda+\lambda' = 1 \end{cases} \Rightarrow \lambda x+\lambda' x' \in A,$$

in other words, if $x, x' \in A$ and $x \neq x' \Rightarrow D(x,x') \subset A$.

Suppose the above condition to be satisfied. Then if $A = \varnothing$, A is clearly a linear manifold. If $A \neq \varnothing$, let x_0 be an element of A: let us show that

$$E = A-\{x_0\}$$

is a vector subspace.

$$\begin{cases} x \in E \\ \lambda \in \mathbf{R} \end{cases} \Rightarrow \begin{cases} x+x_0 \in A \\ \lambda \in \mathbf{R} \end{cases} \Rightarrow \lambda(x+x_0)+(1-\lambda)\, x_0 \in A$$

$$\Rightarrow \lambda x \in E;$$

and

$$\begin{cases} x \in E \\ x' \in E \end{cases} \Rightarrow \begin{cases} x+x_0 \in A \\ x'+x_0 \in A \end{cases} \Rightarrow \frac{x+x_0}{2}+\frac{x'+x_0}{2} \in A$$

$$\Rightarrow \frac{x+x'}{2} \in E$$

$$\Rightarrow x+x' \in E.$$

Conversely, if $A = E+\{x_0\}$, where E is a vector subspace, then

$$\begin{cases} x, x' \in A \\ \lambda, \lambda' \in \mathbf{R} \\ \lambda+\lambda' = 1 \end{cases} \Rightarrow \begin{cases} x-x_0, x'-x_0 \in E \\ \lambda, \lambda' \in \mathbf{R} \\ \lambda+\lambda' = 1 \end{cases}$$

$$\Rightarrow \begin{cases} \lambda(x-x_0)+\lambda'(x'-x_0) \in E \\ \lambda+\lambda' = 1 \end{cases}$$

$$\Rightarrow \lambda x+\lambda' x' \in A.$$

Corollary 1. *If A and B are two linear manifolds, then $A+B$ is a linear manifold.*

Corollary 2. *If $(A_i)_{i \in I}$ is a family of linear manifolds the intersection*

$$\bigcap_{i \in I} A_i$$

is a linear manifold.

DEFINITION. The intersection $l[A]$ of linear manifolds containing a set A is called the *linear hull* of the set A. $l[A]$ is a linear manifold containing A. The *dimension* of A is the dimension of the vector subspace parallel to $l[A]$.

DEFINITION. A set of the form

$$D_a^+ = \{x | x = \lambda a;\, \lambda \geqslant 0\}, \quad \text{with } a \neq 0$$

is called a *half-line issuing from the origin*.

A set H which satisfies

$$\begin{cases} x \in H \\ \lambda \geqslant 0 \end{cases} \Rightarrow \lambda x \in H$$

is called a *cone* (*issuing from the origin*), in other words, it satisfies

$$x \in H \Rightarrow D_x^+ \subset H.$$

EXAMPLE. If f is a linear form, the set

$$H_f = \{x | f(x) \leqslant 0\}$$

is a cone.

1.5. CONVEX SETS

DEFINITION. A set C contained in a vector space X is said to be *convex* if

$$\begin{cases} x, x' \in C \\ \lambda, \lambda' \geqslant 0 \\ \lambda + \lambda' = 1 \end{cases} \Rightarrow \lambda x + \lambda' x' \in C.$$

Every linear manifold is a convex set.

EXAMPLE 1. If f is a linear form, not identically zero, and if α is a real number, then the following sets are convex:

the plane $\quad E_f^\alpha = \{x | f(x) = \alpha\}$,

the *closed half-space* $\quad H_f^\alpha = \{x | f(x) \leqslant \alpha\}$,

the *open half-space* $\quad G_f^\alpha = \{x | f(x) < \alpha\}$.

EXAMPLE 2. The following sets are called *linear intervals*:

$$\text{the } \textit{line segment}: \quad [a,b] = \{\lambda a+\mu b \mid \lambda, \mu \geqslant 0, \quad \lambda+\mu = 1\},$$

$$[a,b[\; = \{\lambda a+\mu b \mid \lambda > 0, \mu \geqslant 0, \quad \lambda+\mu = 1\},$$

$$]a,b] = \{\lambda a+\mu b \mid \lambda \geqslant 0, \mu > 0, \quad \lambda+\mu = 1\},$$

$$]a,b[\; = \{\lambda a+\mu b \mid \lambda, \mu > 0, \quad \lambda+\mu = 1\}.$$

These sets are convex. On the other hand, we may notice that, for a set C to be convex, it is necessary and sufficient that every line segment $[x,x']$ joining two points x, x' of C be contained in C.

EXAMPLE 3. In what follows, we shall denote by $\mathbf{P}_n$ the set of elements $(p^1, p^2, \ldots, p^n)$ of $\mathbf{R}^n$ which satisfy

$$p^1, p^2, \ldots, p^n \geqslant 0 \quad \text{and} \quad p^1+p^2+\ldots+p^n = 1.$$

This is a convex set.

DEFINITION. A point a is said to be a *convex linear combination* of points $a_1, a_2, \ldots, a_n$ if it can be expressed in the form

$$a = p^1 a_1+p^2 a_2+\ldots+p^n a_n, \quad \text{with } (p^1, p^2, \ldots, p^n) \in \mathbf{P}_n.$$

Theorem 1. *For a set C to be convex, it is necessary and sufficient that every convex linear combination of points of C belong to C.*

If, for every n, the property

$$\text{(1)} \qquad \begin{cases} x_1, x_2, \ldots, x_n \in C \\ (p^1, p^2, \ldots, p^n) \in \mathbf{P}_n \end{cases} \Rightarrow p^1 x_1+p^2 x_2+\ldots+p^n x_n \in C,$$

then, in particular, for $n = 2$

$$\begin{cases} x_1, x_2 \in C \\ p^1, p^2 \geqslant 0 \\ p^1+p^2 = 1 \end{cases} \Rightarrow p^1 x_1+p^2 x_2 \in C.$$

Conversely, suppose that C is convex: the property (1) is then true for $n = 2$. We assume that it is true for $n = k$ and show that it is true for $n = k+1$.

Given

$$x_1, x_2, \ldots, x_{k+1} \in C \quad \text{and} \quad (p^1, p^2, \ldots, p^{k+1}) \in \mathbf{P}_{k+1};$$

if $p^{k+1} = 0$, then

$$\sum_{i=1}^{k+1} p^i x_i = \sum_{i=1}^{k} p\, x_i \in C;$$

if $p^{k+1} \neq 0$, we can write

$$\sum_{i=1}^{k+1} p^i x_i = \left[\sum_{i=1}^{k} p^i\right]\left[\frac{p^1}{\sum_{i=1}^{k} p^i} x_1 + \frac{p^2}{\sum_{i=1}^{k} p^i} x_2 + \ldots + \frac{p^k}{\sum_{i=1}^{k} p^i} x_k\right] + p^{k+1} x_{k+1} \in C.$$

Theorem 2. *If f is a linear mapping of a vector space X into a vector space Y, and if C is a convex set in X, then $f(C)$ is a convex set in Y.*

For

$$\left\{\begin{array}{l} y_1 = f(x_1), y_2 = f(x_2) \\ x_1, x_2 \in C \\ (p^1, p^2) \in \mathbf{P}_2 \end{array}\right. \Rightarrow p^1 y_1 + p^2 y_2 = f(p^1 x_1 + p^2 x_2) \in f(C).$$

Theorem 3. *The sum of any two convex sets is a convex set.*

Let A and B be two convex sets. Then

$$\left\{\begin{array}{ll} x_1 = a_1 + b_1 & \text{with } a_1 \in A,\, b_1 \in B \\ x_2 = a_2 + b_2 & \text{with } a_2 \in A,\, b_2 \in B \Rightarrow \\ (p^1, p^2) \in \mathbf{P}_2 & \end{array}\right.$$

$$\Rightarrow p^1 x_1 + p^2 x_2 = (p^1 a_1 + p^2 a_2) + (p^1 b_1 + p^2 b_2),$$

$$\text{with } p^1 a_1 + p^2 a_2 \in A,\ p^1 b_1 + p^2 b_2 \in B.$$

Theorem 4. *If $(A_i)_{i \in I}$ is a family of convex sets, their intersection $\bigcap_{i \in I} A_i$ is a convex set.*

Let x_1 and x_2 be two points in such an intersection and let

$$(p^1, p^2) \in \mathbf{P}_2.$$

Then, for every $i \in I$, $x_1 \in A_i$ and $x_2 \in A_i$, it follows that

$$p^1 x_1 + p^2 x_2 \in A_i.$$

DEFINITION. Let A be a set in the vector space X, and consider the family of convex sets which contain A: the intersection of sets of this family is a convex set which contains A and is called the *convex hull* of A. This set is denoted by $[A]$.

Theorem 5. *The convex hull of a set A is equal to the set of convex linear combinations of A.*†

It is easy to verify that the set is convex, that it contains A and that it is contained in every convex set containing A.

DEFINITION. A plane E_f^α is called a *supporting plane* of a set A if

$$x \in A \Rightarrow f(x) \geqslant \alpha$$

and if there exists at least one element x of A with $f(x) = \alpha$.

Corollary. *If E_f^α is a supporting plane of the set A then*

$$E_f^\alpha \cap [A] = [E_f^\alpha \cap A].$$

If a point x belongs to $[E_f^\alpha \cap A]$, it belongs also to $[A]$ and to E_f^α, which are two convex sets containing $E_f^\alpha \cap A$; hence it belongs to $E_f^\alpha \cap [A]$. Conversely, any point $x \in [A]$ satisfying $f(x) = \alpha$ can be expressed in the form

$$x = p^1 a_1 + p^2 a_2 + \ldots + p^n a_n \quad \text{with } a_1, a_2, \ldots, a_n \in A,$$

and we can always assume $p^1, p^2, \ldots, p^n > 0$; then necessarily

$$f(a_1) = f(a_2) = \ldots = f(a_n) = \alpha,$$

hence

$$a_1, a_2, \ldots, a_n \in E_f^\alpha \cap A,$$

and consequently

$$x \in [E_f^\alpha \cap A].$$

Theorem 6. *If A is a set of dimension n, every point of $[A]$ can be expressed in the form of a convex linear combination of at most $n+1$ points of A.*

We have to show that every point of the form

$$x = p^1 a_1 + p^2 a_2 + \ldots + p^m a_m,$$

with

$$a_1, a_2, \ldots, a_m \in A \quad \text{and} \quad (p^1, p^2, \ldots, p^m) \in \mathbf{P}_m,$$

can be expressed in the form

$$x = q^1 a_1' + q^2 a_2' + \ldots + q^r a_r,$$

with

$$r \leqslant n+1, a_1', a_2', \ldots, a_r' \in A \quad \text{and} \quad (q^1, q^2, \ldots, q^r) \in \mathbf{P}_r.$$

† In other words, we can write
$[A] = \{x | x = p^1 a_1 + p^2 a_2 + \ldots + p^n a_n;\ n \in \mathbf{N}, (p^1, p^2, \ldots p^n) \in \mathbf{P}_n, a_1, a_2, \ldots, a_n \in A\}$.

This is clearly true for $m \leqslant n+1$; we assume that it is true for $m = k$, and show that it remains true for $m = k+1$; we may assume that $k > n$. The points

$$a_1 - a_{k+1}, a_2 - a_{k+1}, \ldots, a_k - a_{k+1}$$

are all contained in the same subspace of dimension $n < k$, hence there exist numbers $\lambda_1, \lambda_2, \ldots, \lambda_k$ not all zero such that

$$\lambda_1(a_1 - a_{k+1}) + \lambda_2(a_2 - a_{k+1}) + \ldots + \lambda_k(a_k - a_{k+1}) = \mathbf{0};$$

thus, writing

$$\lambda_{k+1} = -(\lambda_1 + \lambda_2 + \ldots + \lambda_k),$$

$$\sum_{i=1}^{k+1} \lambda_i a_i = \mathbf{0} \quad \text{and} \quad \sum_{i=1}^{k+1} \lambda_i = 0.$$

Let μ be any number; if we write

$$q^i = p^i - \mu\lambda_i \quad \text{for } i = 1, 2, \ldots, k+1,$$

we obtain

$$x = x - \mathbf{0} = \sum_{i=1}^{k+1} p^i a_i - \mu \sum_{i=1}^{k+1} \lambda_i a_i = \sum_{i=1}^{k+1} q^i a_i,$$

and

$$\sum_{i=1}^{k+1} q^i = \sum_{i=1}^{k+1} p^i - \mu \sum_{i=1}^{k+1} \lambda_i = 1;$$

now, we can choose μ, so that $q^1, q^2, \ldots, q^{k+1} \geqslant 0$ and so that at least one of the numbers $q^1, q^2, \ldots, q^{k+1}$ is zero. In view of the induction hypothesis we see finally that x can be expressed as a convex linear combination of at most $n+1$ points of A.

DEFINITION. Let C be a convex set, a a point $\in C$ and D a straight line through a. We say that a is an *internal point of* C *with respect to* D if there exist two points $a_1, a_2 \in D$ such that

$$a_1, a_2 \neq a \quad \text{and} \quad a \in [a_1, a_2] \subset C.$$

We call a an *internal point* of C (without restriction) if it is an internal point of C with respect to every line D through a. Also a is called an *extreme point* or *vertex* of C if it is not an internal point with respect to any line through a.

Theorem 7. *For a point a, belonging to a convex set C to be an extreme point, it is necessary and sufficient that the set $C - \{a\}$ is convex.*

Firstly, if a is not an extreme point, there exist two distinct points a_1, a_2 different from a such that

$$a \in [a_1, a_2] \subset C.$$

Then

$$a_1, a_2 \in C - \{a\} \quad \text{and} \quad [a_1, a_2] \not\subset C - \{a\},$$

which shows that $C - \{a\}$ is not convex.

Conversely if $C - \{a\}$ is not convex, there exist two points

$$a_1, a_2 \in C - \{a\}$$

such that

$$[a_1, a_2] \not\subset C - \{a\}.$$

Now

$$[a_1, a_2] \subset C,$$

hence

$$a \in [a_1, a_2].$$

This shows that a is not an extreme point of C.

1.6. CONVEX FUNCTIONS

DEFINITION. Let C be a convex set and f a numerical function defined in C; f is said to be *convex* in C if

$$\begin{cases} x_1, x_2 \in C \\ (p^1, p^2) \in \mathbf{P}_2 \end{cases} \Rightarrow f(p^1 x_1 + p^2 x_2) \leqslant p^1 f(x_1) + p^2 f(x_2).$$

f is said to be *concave* if $(-f)$ is convex.

EXAMPLE 1. If f is a linear affine function defined in $\mathbf{R}^n$, then

$$\begin{cases} x_1, x_2 \in \mathbf{R}^n \\ (p^1, p^2) \in \mathbf{P}_2 \end{cases} \Rightarrow f(p^1 x_1 + p^2 x_2) = p^1 f(x_1) + p^2 f(x_2).$$

It can be seen that f is both convex and concave in $\mathbf{R}^n$.

EXAMPLE 2. In the following chapter, we shall define the norm of a point $x = (x^1, x^2, \ldots, x^n)$ of $\mathbf{R}^n$ as the number

$$\|x\| = \sqrt{\{(x^1)^2 + (x^2)^2 + \ldots + (x^n)^2\}}$$

it will be seen that the norm possesses the following properties:

$$\|\lambda x\| = |\lambda| . \|x\|,$$

$$\|x_1 + x_2\| \leqslant \|x_1\| + \|x_2\|.$$

It follows that $\|x\|$ is a convex function of x. Indeed for any x_1, $x_2 \in \mathbf{R}^n$ and $(p^1, p^2) \in \mathbf{P}_2$,

$$\|p^1 x_1 + p^2 x_2\| \leqslant \|p^1 x_1\| + \|p^2 x_2\| = p^1\|x_1\| + p^2\|x_2\|.$$

Theorem 1. *Every positive linear combination of convex functions in C is convex in C.*

Let $f_1, f_2, \ldots, f_m$ be convex functions in C and let

$$f = y^1 f_1 + y^2 f_2 + \ldots + y^m f_m \quad \text{with } y^1, y^2, \ldots, y^m \geqslant 0.$$

Then, for any x_1, $x_2 \in C$ and $(p^1, p^2) \in \mathbf{P}_2$,

$$\sum_{i=1}^{m} y^i f_i(p^1 x_1 + p^2 x_2) \leqslant p^1 \sum_{i=1}^{m} y^i f_i(x_1) + p^2 \sum_{i=1}^{m} y^i f_i(x_2).$$

Theorem 2. *For a numerical function f defined in a convex set C to be convex, it is necessary and sufficient that for any points c, $c' \in C$, the function*

$$\varphi(\lambda) = f(\lambda c + (1-\lambda)\, c')$$

be convex in the segment $[0,1]$.

Let c, $c' \in C$; if $\varphi(\lambda)$ is convex in $[0,1]$ and if $(p, p') \in \mathbf{P}_2$, then

$$f(pc + p'c') = \varphi(p) = \varphi(p \times 1 + p' \times 0) \leqslant p\varphi(1) + p'\varphi(0) = pf(c) + p'f(c').$$

Conversely, if f is convex in C and if c, $c' \in C$, let

$$\lambda_1, \lambda_2 \in [0,1] \quad \text{and} \quad (p^1, p^2) \in \mathbf{P}_2.$$

Then

$$\begin{aligned} \varphi(p^1\lambda_1 + p^2\lambda_2) &= f[(p^1\lambda_1 + p^2\lambda_2)\, c + (1 - p^1\lambda_1 - p^2\lambda_2)\, c'] \\ &= f[p^1(\lambda_1 c + (1-\lambda_1)\, c') + p^2(\lambda_2 c + (1-\lambda_2)\, c')] \\ &\leqslant p^1\varphi(\lambda_1) + p^2\varphi(\lambda_2). \end{aligned}$$

We shall now establish a relationship between convex sets and convex functions. For this, we shall first define the *product of two vector spaces* A and B: this is a vector space formed by the set $A \times B$ of ordered pairs (a, b) with $a \in A$ and $b \in B$, in which addition is defined by

$$(a, b) + (a', b') = (a + a', b + b'),$$

and scalar multiplication is defined by

$$\lambda(a, b) = (\lambda a, \lambda b).$$

For example, the vector space $\mathbf{R}^n$ is the product of n vector spaces each equal to $\mathbf{R}$.

Theorem 3. *For a function f, defined in a convex set C, contained in a vector space X, to be convex in C, it is necessary and sufficient that in $X \times \mathbf{R}$ the set*

$$\overline{T}_f = \{(x, z) \,|\, x \in C, z \in \mathbf{R} \quad \text{and} \quad f(x) \leqslant z\}$$

be convex.

If $\overline{T}_f$ is convex, and if x and x' are two points of C, then for any $(p,p') \in \mathbf{P}_2$,

$$p(x,f(x)) + p'(x',f(x')) \in \overline{T}_f;$$

that is to say

$$(px + p'x', pf(x) + p'f(x')) \in \overline{T}_f,$$

hence

$$f(px + p'x') \leqslant pf(x) + p'f(x').$$

Conversely, if f is a convex function and if (x,z) and (x',z') are two points of $\overline{T}_f$, then, for every $(p,p') \in \mathbf{P}_2$,

$$f(px + p'x') \leqslant pf(x) + p'f(x') \leqslant pz + p'z',$$

hence

$$p(x,z) + p'(x',z') \in \overline{T}_f.$$

Corollary 1. *In C, for a numerical function f to be convex it is necessary and sufficient that for every*

$$x_1, x_2, \ldots, x_m \in C \quad \textit{and} \quad (p^1, p^2, \ldots, p^m) \in \mathbf{P}_m,$$

$$f(p^1 x_1 + p^2 x_2 + \ldots + p^m x_m) \leqslant p^1 f(x_1) + p^2 f(x_2) + \ldots + p^m f(x_m).$$

Corollary 2. *If $(f_i)_{i \in I}$ is a family of convex functions in C, and if for every $x \in C$ the set $\{f_i(x) | i \in I\}$ is bounded above, then the function*

$$f(x) = \sup_{i \in I} f_i(x)$$

is a convex function in C.

In fact

$$\overline{T}_f = \bigcap_{i \in I} \overline{T}_f$$

is convex.

2. Preliminary ideas; topological properties of the space $\mathbf{R}^n$

2.1. SCALAR PRODUCT. NORM

DEFINITION. If

$$\mathbf{a} = (a^1, a^2, \ldots, a^n) \quad \text{and} \quad \mathbf{x} = (x^1, x^2, \ldots, x^n)$$

are two points of $\mathbf{R}^n$, we write

$$\langle \mathbf{a}, \mathbf{x} \rangle = a^1 x^1 + a^2 x^2 + \ldots + a^n x^n.$$

The number $\langle \mathbf{a}, \mathbf{x} \rangle$ is called the *scalar product* of the points $\mathbf{a}$ and $\mathbf{x}$.

We have

$$(1) \qquad \langle \mathbf{a}, \mathbf{x} \rangle = \langle \mathbf{x}, \mathbf{a} \rangle,$$

$$(2) \qquad \langle \mathbf{a}, \lambda\mathbf{x} \rangle = \lambda \langle \mathbf{a}, \mathbf{x} \rangle,$$

$$(3) \qquad \langle \mathbf{a}, \mathbf{x}_1 + \mathbf{x}_2 \rangle = \langle \mathbf{a}, \mathbf{x}_1 \rangle + \langle \mathbf{a}, \mathbf{x}_2 \rangle.$$

NOTE. To every point $\mathbf{a}$ of $\mathbf{R}^n$ we can assign the numerical function f_a defined in $\mathbf{R}^n$ by

$$f_a(\mathbf{x}) = \langle \mathbf{a}, \mathbf{x} \rangle:$$

this is a linear function. Conversely, let f be a linear form defined in $\mathbf{R}^n$, then we have

$$f(\mathbf{x}) = x^1 f(\boldsymbol{\delta}_1) + x^2 f(\boldsymbol{\delta}_2) + \ldots + x^n f(\boldsymbol{\delta}_n),$$

remembering that we have defined the points $\boldsymbol{\delta}_1, \boldsymbol{\delta}_2, \ldots, \boldsymbol{\delta}_n$ by writing

$$\boldsymbol{\delta}_i = (\delta_i^1, \delta_i^2 \ldots, \delta_i^n) \quad \text{for } i = 1, 2, \ldots, n,$$

with

$$\delta_i^j = \begin{cases} +1 & \text{if } i = j, \\ 0 & \text{if } i \neq j. \end{cases}$$

Suppose

$$a = (f(\boldsymbol{\delta}_1), f(\boldsymbol{\delta}_2), \ldots, f(\boldsymbol{\delta}_n));$$

then

$$f(\mathbf{x}) = \langle \mathbf{a}, \mathbf{x} \rangle.$$

DEFINITION. If $\mathbf{x} = (x^1, x^2, \ldots, x^n)$ is a point in $\mathbf{R}^n$, the number

$$\langle \mathbf{x}, \mathbf{x} \rangle = (x^1)^2 + (x^2)^2 + \ldots + (x^n)^2$$

is non-negative. The number $\sqrt{\langle \mathbf{x}, \mathbf{x} \rangle}$ is called the *norm* of $\mathbf{x}$; and is denoted by $\|\mathbf{x}\|$.

Lemma. *We have*

$$|\langle \mathbf{x}, \mathbf{y} \rangle| \leqslant \|\mathbf{x}\| \cdot \|\mathbf{y}\| \quad \textit{(Cauchy–Schwartz inequality)}.$$

This is obvious if $\mathbf{x} = \mathbf{0}$; suppose $\mathbf{x} \neq \mathbf{0}$, then $\|\mathbf{x}\| \neq 0$. The expression

$$\|\lambda\mathbf{x} + \mathbf{y}\|^2 = \langle \lambda\mathbf{x} + \mathbf{y}, \lambda\mathbf{x} + \mathbf{y} \rangle = \lambda^2\|\mathbf{x}\|^2 + 2\lambda\langle \mathbf{x}, \mathbf{y} \rangle + \|\mathbf{y}\|^2$$

is a quadratic in λ, which can never be negative, hence

$$|\langle \mathbf{x}, \mathbf{y} \rangle|^2 - \|\mathbf{x}\|^2\|\mathbf{y}\|^2 \leqslant 0.$$

Theorem. *The norm possesses the following properties*

$$\|\mathbf{x}\| \geqslant 0,$$

$$\|\mathbf{x}\| = 0 \Leftrightarrow \mathbf{x} = \mathbf{0},$$

$$\|\lambda\mathbf{x}\| = |\lambda| \, \|\mathbf{x}\|,$$

$$\|\mathbf{x} + \mathbf{y}\| \leqslant \|\mathbf{x}\| + \|\mathbf{y}\| \quad \textit{(triangular inequality)}.$$

The first three properties are obvious. Furthermore

$$\begin{aligned} \|\mathbf{x} + \mathbf{y}\|^2 &= \langle \mathbf{x} + \mathbf{y}, \mathbf{x} + \mathbf{y} \rangle = \|\mathbf{x}\|^2 + 2\langle \mathbf{x}, \mathbf{y} \rangle + \|\mathbf{y}\|^2 \\ &\leqslant \|\mathbf{x}\|^2 + 2\|\mathbf{x}\| \cdot \|\mathbf{y}\| + \|\mathbf{y}\|^2 \\ &= [\|\mathbf{x}\| + \|\mathbf{y}\|]^2. \end{aligned}$$

DEFINITION. The number

$$d(\mathbf{x}, \mathbf{y}) = \|\mathbf{x} - \mathbf{y}\|$$

is called the *distance* between two points $\mathbf{x}$ and $\mathbf{y}$ in $\mathbf{R}^n$.

Corollary. *The distance has the following properties*:

$$d(\mathbf{x}, \mathbf{y}) \geqslant 0,$$

$$d(\mathbf{x}, \mathbf{y}) = 0 \Leftrightarrow \mathbf{x} = \mathbf{y},$$

$$d(\mathbf{x}, \mathbf{y}) = d(\mathbf{y}, \mathbf{x}),$$

$$d(\mathbf{x}, \mathbf{z}) \leqslant d(\mathbf{x}, \mathbf{y}) + d(\mathbf{y}, \mathbf{z}) \quad \textit{(triangular inequality)}.$$

The first three properties are obvious. For the fourth one, we can write

$$d(\mathbf{x},\mathbf{z}) = \|\mathbf{z}-\mathbf{x}\| = \|(\mathbf{z}-\mathbf{y})+(\mathbf{y}-\mathbf{x})\| \leqslant \|\mathbf{z}-\mathbf{y}\|+\|\mathbf{y}-\mathbf{x}\|$$
$$= d(\mathbf{x},\mathbf{y})+d(\mathbf{y},\mathbf{z}).$$

DEFINITION. Given a point $\mathbf{x}_0 \in \mathbf{R}^n$ and a number $\lambda > 0$; the set

$$B_\lambda(\mathbf{x}_0) = \{\mathbf{x} | \mathbf{x} \in \mathbf{R}^n \quad \text{and} \quad d(\mathbf{x}_0,\mathbf{x}) < \lambda\}$$

is called an *open ball with centre* $\mathbf{x}_0$ *and radius* λ. The set

$$S_\lambda(\mathbf{x}_0) = \{\mathbf{x} | \mathbf{x} \in \mathbf{R}^n \quad \text{and} \quad d(\mathbf{x}_0,\mathbf{x}) = \lambda\}$$

is called a *sphere with centre* $\mathbf{x}_0$ *and radius* λ.

2.2. OPEN AND CLOSED SETS

DEFINITION. A point a is said to be *interior* to a set $A \subset \mathbf{R}^n$, if there exists a number $\epsilon > 0$, such that $B_\epsilon(a) \subset A$. A point a is called a *point of closure* of the set A, if for every given number $\epsilon > 0$,

$$B_\epsilon(a) \cap A \neq \emptyset.$$

For a point a to be a point of closure of a set A, it is necessary and sufficient that it is not interior to its complement $\complement A$.

The *closure* of a set A is the set $\bar{A}$ of points of closure of A. Clearly $A \subset \bar{A}$; a set equal to its closure is called *closed*.

The *interior* of a set A, is the set $\mathring{A}$ of interior points of A. Thus $\mathring{A} \subset A$. A set equal to its interior is called *open*.

Obviously

$$A \subset B \Rightarrow \mathring{A} \subset \mathring{B} \quad \text{and} \quad \bar{A} \subset \bar{B}.$$

EXAMPLE 1. In $\mathbf{R}$, the distance between two points x and y is

$$d(x,y) = \sqrt{\{(x-y)^2\}} = |x-y|.$$

Consider the set

$$A = \left\{1, \tfrac{1}{2}, \ldots, \frac{1}{n}, \ldots\right\}.$$

It is easily seen that 0 is a point of closure of A.

EXAMPLE 2. Let a be any point of $\mathbf{R}^n$: the set $\{a\}$ is closed. For suppose x is a point $\neq a$, and suppose $\lambda = d(x,a)$, then

$$B_\lambda(x) \cap \{a\} = \emptyset.$$

EXAMPLE 3. In $\mathbf{R}^n$, every open ball $B_\lambda(a)$ is an open set. For, consider a point $x \in B_\lambda(a)$ and suppose that

$$\rho = d(a,x) < \lambda.$$

Then

$$d(x,y) < \lambda - \rho \Rightarrow d(a,y) \leqslant d(a,x) + d(x,y) < \lambda;$$

hence

$$B_{\lambda-\rho}(x) \subset B_\lambda(a).$$

EXAMPLE 4. In $\mathbf{R}^n$, the closure of an open ball $B_\lambda(a)$ is a *closed ball*

$$\overline{B_\lambda(a)} = \{x \mid d(a,x) \leqslant \lambda\};$$

conversely, the interior of a closed ball $\overline{B_\lambda(a)}$ is an open ball $B_\lambda(a)$.

For, let x be a point such that $d(a,x) > \lambda$; writing

$$\epsilon = d(a,x) - \lambda,$$

we have

$$B_\epsilon(x) \cap B_\lambda(a) = \varnothing.$$

This shows that x is not a point of closure of $B_\lambda(a)$.

Consider now a point x such that $d(a,x) = \lambda$ and let ϵ be a number > 0; let us put

$$\alpha = \begin{cases} 1 & \text{if } \epsilon \geqslant \lambda \\ \dfrac{\epsilon}{\lambda} & \text{if } \epsilon < \lambda; \end{cases}$$

the point

$$x + \frac{\alpha}{2}(a-x)$$

belongs to both the sets $B_\epsilon(x)$ and $B_\lambda(a)$. The closure of $B_\lambda(a)$ is then $\overline{B_\lambda(a)}$, since we have seen that

$$d(a,x) > \lambda \Rightarrow x \text{ is not a point of closure of } B_\lambda(a),$$

and

$$d(a,x) = \lambda \Rightarrow x \text{ is a point of closure of } B_\lambda(a);$$

on the other hand, the point

$$x - \frac{\alpha}{2}(a-x)$$

belongs to $B_\epsilon(x)$ and does not belong to $\overline{B_\lambda(a)}$: thus we see that the only interior points of $\overline{B_\lambda(a)}$ are the points of $B_\lambda(a)$.

NOTE 1. In $\mathbf{R}$, the balls $B_\lambda(a)$ and $\overline{B_\lambda(a)}$ are simply the intervals $]a-\lambda, a+\lambda[$ and $[a-\lambda, a+\lambda]$. Conversely we can also write the intervals $]a,b[$ and $[a,b]$ as

$$B_{(a-b)/2}\left(\frac{a+b}{2}\right) \quad \text{and} \quad \overline{B_{(a-b)/2}\left(\frac{a+b}{2}\right)}.$$

NOTE 2. Example 4 should not necessarily suggest that, for every set A, $\overline{\mathring{A}} = A$.

For instance, consider in $\mathbf{R}$, the set

$$A = \{x | 0 < |x| \leqslant 1\};$$

then

$$\overline{A} = \{x | |x| \leqslant 1\},$$

and

$$\overline{\mathring{A}} = \{x | |x| < 1\}.$$

Theorem 1. *Let A be any set, then*

$$\complement \overline{A} = \mathring{\complement} A.$$

For, in order that a point x may be a point of closure in the set A, it is necessary and sufficient that it should not belong to the interior of $\complement A$.

Corollary. *The complement of an open set is a closed set, and vice versa.*

For, we have

$$A \text{ is closed} \Leftrightarrow A = \overline{A} \Leftrightarrow \complement A = \complement \overline{A} = \mathring{\complement} A$$

$$\Leftrightarrow \complement A \text{ is open.}$$

Theorem 2. *The interior of every set is open.*

Let A be any set of $\mathbf{R}^n$ and x be a point of $\mathring{A}$. It will be shown that x is interior to $\mathring{A}$. There exists a number $\epsilon > 0$, such that $B_\epsilon(x) \subset A$; if y is any point of $B_\epsilon(x)$, then

$$d(y,z) < \epsilon' \Rightarrow d(x,z) \leqslant d(x,y) + d(y,z) < \epsilon,$$

where $\epsilon' = \epsilon - d(x,y)$. Hence

$$B_{\epsilon'}(y) \subset B_\epsilon(x) \subset A,$$

which shows that y is interior to A. Also

$$B_\epsilon(x) \subset \mathring{A},$$

showing clearly that x is interior to $\mathring{A}$.

Corollary. *The closure of every set is a closed set.*

For, if A is any set in $\mathbf{R}^n$, the set $\complement \bar{A} = \mathring{\complement A}$ is an open set.

EXAMPLE. Every closed ball $\overline{B_\lambda(a)}$ is closed, since it is the closure of $B_\lambda(a)$.

NOTE. The closure $\bar{A}$ of a set A is contained in every closed set containing A. For, if B is a closed set containing A, then

$$\bar{A} \subset \bar{B} = B.$$

It is for this reason that we sometimes say that the closure of a set A is the smallest closed set containing A. Similarly, we say the interior of a set A is the largest open set contained in A.

Theorem 3. *The family of open sets in* $\mathbf{R}^n$, *has the following properties:*

(1) *Every union of open sets is open,*
(2) *Every finite intersection of open sets is open,*
(3) *The sets* $\varnothing$ *and* $\mathbf{R}^n$ *are open.*†

Firstly, let

$$G = \bigcup_{i \in I} G_i$$

be a union of open sets. If a is any point of G, there exists at least one open set G_i such that $a \in G_i$; a is interior to G_i, hence to G.

Secondly, let

$$G = \bigcap_{i=1}^{m} G_i$$

be a finite intersection of open sets and let a be any point of G. There exist numbers $\epsilon_1, \epsilon_2, \ldots, \epsilon_m > 0$ such that

$$B_{\epsilon_i}(a) \subset G_i \quad \text{for } i = 1, 2, \ldots, m.$$

† In general, given a set E, if a family $\mathscr{T}$ of subsets of E is defined, called open sets of E, that has the properties (1) and (2), and such that $\varnothing \in \mathscr{T}$ and $E \in \mathscr{T}$, then they are said to define a *topology* on E, the subsets of E whose complements are open are called *closed*. A set E on which a topology is defined is called a *topological space*.

General topology is a branch of mathematics whose object is the study of different categories of topological spaces. For example a topological space E is said to be *separable*, if for any x and $y \in E$ with $x \neq y$ there exist two open sets U and V satisfying

$$x \in U, y \in V \quad \text{and} \quad U \cap V = \varnothing;$$

It is obvious that $\mathbf{R}^n$ is a separable space, for if x and y are two distinct points in $\mathbf{R}^n$, and if we write $d(x,y) = 2\rho$ then

$$x \in B_\rho(x),\ y \in B_\rho(y) \quad \text{and} \quad B_\rho(x) \cap B_\rho(y) = \varnothing.$$

Let ϵ be the smallest of these numbers, then

$$B_\epsilon(a) \subset B_{\epsilon_i}(a) \subset G_i \quad \text{for } i = 1, 2, \ldots, m,$$

hence

$$B_\epsilon(a) \subset G.$$

Finally, it is clear that the interior of an empty set is empty and that every point of $\mathbf{R}^n$ is interior to $\mathbf{R}^n$.

Corollary. *The family of closed sets in* $\mathbf{R}^n$ *has the following properties.*

(1) *Every intersection of closed sets is closed,*
(2) *Every finite union of closed sets is closed,*
(3) *The sets* $\emptyset$ *and* $\mathbf{R}^n$ *are closed.*

NOTE. The intersection of an infinite family of open sets is not always open. Consider, for instance in $\mathbf{R}$, the open sets $G_1, G_2, \ldots, G_n, \ldots$ defined by

$$G_n = \left]-\frac{1}{n}, +1\right[.$$

Their intersection

$$G = \bigcap_{n=1}^{\infty} G_n = [0, 1[$$

is not an open set, since it does not include 0 as an interior point.

DEFINITION. Let A and B be two sets such that $B \subset A \subset \mathbf{R}^n$. B is said to be *open (closed) relative to A* if B is equal to the intersection with A of an open (closed) set of $\mathbf{R}^n$.

EXAMPLE. Given in $\mathbf{R}$, the set

$$A = \{x | 0 \leqslant x \leqslant 1 \quad \text{or} \quad 1 < x \leqslant 2\}.$$

The set $[0, \frac{1}{2}[$ is open relative to A, since

$$[0, \tfrac{1}{2}[= A \cap]-1, +\tfrac{1}{2}[.$$

Similarly, the set

$$[0, \tfrac{1}{2}] = A \cap [-1, +\tfrac{1}{2}]$$

is closed. However the set $[0, 1[$ is both open and closed, since we can write

$$[0, 1[=]-1, +1[\cap A = [-1, +1] \cap A.$$

It is clear that Theorem 3 and its corollary remain true even if we replace $\mathbf{R}^n$ by A, open and closed by open relative to A and closed relative to A,† respectively.

If B is an open set (closed) contained in A, it is open (closed) relative to A: for $B = B \cap A$. But, in general, the converse is not true: we can see this easily, if we note that any set A of $\mathbf{R}^n$ is open and closed relative to itself, since we can write $A = A \cap \mathbf{R}^n$. However, if A is open, any set open relative to A is open, as the intersection of the two open sets is open. Similarly if A is closed, any set closed relative to A is closed.

2.3. LIMITS. CONTINUOUS FUNCTIONS

DEFINITION. Suppose a set $A \subset \mathbf{R}^n$, and let f be a mapping of A into $\mathbf{R}^m$; let x_0 be a point $x_0 \in \bar{A}$ with $x_0 \notin A$. It is said that $f(x)$ *tends to a limit* l *when* x *tends to* x_0, *in* A if, for any number $\epsilon > 0$, there is a number $\eta > 0$ such that

$$x \in A \quad \text{and} \quad d(x_0, x) < \eta \Rightarrow d(l, f(x)) < \epsilon.$$

We will denote this by

$$l = \lim_{\substack{x \in A \\ x \to x_0}} f(x).$$

EXAMPLE 1. Let

$$A = \{x \mid x \neq 0\}$$

be a set in $\mathbf{R}$. Then $0 \in \bar{A}$ and $0 \notin A$; the function

$$\frac{\sin x}{x},$$

defined in A tends to 1 when x tends to 0 in the set A.

EXAMPLE 2. The function

$$\frac{|\sin x|}{x}$$

tends to 1 when x tends to 0 taking only positive values.

† In other words, the sets open relative to A define a topology on A. More generally, if E is a topological space and if A is a subset of E, the intersections of open sets in E with A are called open sets relative to A: then it is evident that the open sets relative to A define a topology on A, which is called a topology *induced* on A by the topology of E. If E is separable then A (with the induced topology) is separable (cf. note, page 33).

EXAMPLE 3. The function

$$\sin \frac{1}{x},$$

where $x \neq 0$, does not tend to any limit as x tends to 0.

It should be noted that there cannot be more than one limit. For if l_1 and l_2 are two distinct limits and if we write $d(l_1, l_2) = 2\epsilon$, we know that there exist two numbers η_1, $\eta_2 > 0$ such that

$$x \in A \quad \text{and} \quad d(x_0, x) < \eta_1 \Rightarrow d(l_1, f(x)) < \epsilon$$

and

$$x \in A \quad \text{and} \quad d(x_0, x) < \eta_2 \Rightarrow d(l_2, f(x)) < \epsilon.$$

Let $\eta > 0$ be a number such that $\eta \leqslant \eta_1$ and $\eta \leqslant \eta_2$: as $x_0 \in \bar{A}$, there exists at least one point $x_1 \in A$ such that $d(x_0, x_1) < \eta$; then

$$d(l_1, l_2) \leqslant d(l_1, f(x_1)) + d(f(x_1), l_2) < 2\epsilon,$$

which is impossible.

DEFINITION. Let $x_1, x_2, \ldots, x_p, \ldots$ be a sequence of points of $\mathbf{R}^n$. The sequence is said to *tend to a limit* x_0, if for every given number $\epsilon > 0$, there exists an integer p_0 such that

$$p \geqslant p_0 \Rightarrow d(x_0, x_p) < \epsilon.$$

We denote this by

$$x_0 = \lim_{p \to \infty} (x_p).$$

A point a is said to be a *limit point* of the sequence if, for every given number $\epsilon > 0$ and every integer p, there exists an integer $p' \geqslant p$ such that

$$d(a, x_{p'}) < \epsilon.$$

It should be noted that if a is a limit point of the sequence, there exists a subsequence which tends to a: for, let p_1 be an integer such that

$$d(a, x_{p_1}) < 1,$$

let $p_2 \geqslant p_1 + 1$ be an integer such that

$$d(a, x_{p_2}) < \tfrac{1}{2},$$

let $p_3 \geqslant p_2 + 1$ be an integer such that

$$d(a, x_{p_3}) < \tfrac{1}{3},$$

etc.... then it is obvious that the subsequence $x_{p_1}, x_{p_2}, x_{p_3}, \ldots$ tends to a. Conversely, if there exists a subsequence which tends to a it is obvious that a is a limit point of the sequence, in particular if a is the limit of the sequence, then a is also a limit point. Finally, notice that if the sequence tends to a limit x_0, there cannot be a limit point other than x_0 (nor, *a fortiori*, another limit); for given a point $a \neq x_0$ and a number $\rho > 0$ with $\rho < d(x_0, a)$, then there exists an integer p_0 such that

$$p \geqslant p_0 \Rightarrow d(x_0, x_p) < \rho \Rightarrow d(a, x_p) \geqslant d(x_0, a) - \rho,$$

which shows that a is not a limit point.

EXAMPLE 1. The sequence defined in $\mathbf{R}$ by

$$a_{2p} = -1 + \frac{1}{p} \quad \text{and} \quad a_{2p+1} = 1 - \frac{1}{p}$$

has -1 and $+1$ as limit points.

EXAMPLE 2. The sequence defined in $\mathbf{R}$ by

$$a_n = \sin n$$

has all numbers between -1 and $+1$ as limit points.

DEFINITION. Suppose a set $A \subset \mathbf{R}^n$ and let f be a mapping of A into $\mathbf{R}^m$. f is said to be *continuous* (*with respect to* A) *at a point* $x_0 \in A$ if, for any number $\epsilon > 0$, there exists a number $\eta > 0$ such that

$$x \in A \quad \text{and} \quad d(x_0, x) < \eta \Rightarrow d(f(x_0), f(x)) < \epsilon.$$

It should be noticed that if f is defined on the set $B \supset A$, and if f is continuous at x_0 with respect to B, then f is continuous at x_0 with respect to A. For,

$$x_0 \in B \quad \text{and} \quad d(x_0, x) < \eta \Rightarrow d(f(x_0), f(x)) < \epsilon;$$

hence, *a fortiori*,

$$x \in A \quad \text{and} \quad d(x_0, x) < \eta \Rightarrow d(f(x_0), f(x)) < \epsilon.$$

f is said to be *continuous in* A (*with respect to* A) if it is continuous at every point of A.

EXAMPLE 1. Every constant function is continuous.

EXAMPLE 2. Every linear form defined in $\mathbf{R}^n$ is continuous. For, let

$$f(x) = \langle a, x \rangle$$

be a linear form; if $a = \mathbf{0}$, $f(x)$, being constant, iscontinuous. Suppose that $a \neq 0$, and let $\epsilon > \mathbf{0}$ be given: then writing

$$\eta = \frac{\epsilon}{\|a\|},$$

we have

$$\|x - x_0\| < \eta \Rightarrow |f(x) - f(x_0)| = |\langle a, x - x_0 \rangle| \leqslant \|a\| \, \|x - x_0\| < \epsilon.$$

EXAMPLE 3. The norm is a continuous mapping of $\mathbf{R}^n$ into $\mathbf{R}$. Because of the triangular inequality

$$\|x - x_0\| < \epsilon \Rightarrow \big| \|x\| - \|x_0\| \big| < \epsilon.$$

EXAMPLE 4. The mapping $\sigma(x, y)$ of $\mathbf{R}^n \times \mathbf{R}^n = \mathbf{R}^{2n}$ into $\mathbf{R}^n$ defined by

$$\sigma(x, y) = x + y$$

is continuous. In fact

$$\sqrt{(\|x - x_0\|^2 + \|y - y_0\|^2)} < \frac{\epsilon}{2} \Rightarrow \begin{cases} \|x - x_0\| < \dfrac{\epsilon}{2} \\ \|y - y_0\| < \dfrac{\epsilon}{2} \end{cases}$$

$$\Rightarrow \|(x + y) - (x_0 + y_0)\| = \|(x - x_0) + (y - y_0)\| \leqslant \|x - x_0\| + \|y - y_0\| < \epsilon.$$

EXAMPLE 5. The mapping $\tau(\lambda, x)$ of $\mathbf{R} \times \mathbf{R}^n = \mathbf{R}^{n+1}$ into $\mathbf{R}^n$ defined by

$$\tau(\lambda, x) = \lambda x$$

is continuous. For

$$\|\lambda x - \lambda_0 x_0\| = \|(\lambda_0 + (\lambda - \lambda_0))(x_0 + (x - x_0)) - \lambda_0 x_0\| \leqslant |\lambda_0| \, \|x - x_0\| + |\lambda - \lambda_0| \, \|x_0\| + |\lambda - \lambda_0| \, . \, \|x - x_0\|.$$

For any positive number ϵ, choose a positive number η so that

$$|\lambda_0| \, \eta \leqslant \epsilon/3, \eta \|x_0\| \leqslant \epsilon/3, \quad \text{and} \quad \eta^2 \leqslant \epsilon/3;$$

then

$$\sqrt{\{(\lambda - \lambda_0)^2 + \|x - x_0\|^2\}} < \eta \Rightarrow \begin{cases} |\lambda - \lambda_0| < \eta \\ \|x - x_0\| < \eta \end{cases}$$

$$\Rightarrow \|\lambda x - \lambda_0 x_0\| < |\lambda_0| \, \eta + \eta \|x_0\| + \eta^2 \leqslant \epsilon.$$

EXAMPLE 6. Every convex function f defined in a convex set $C \subset \mathbf{R}^n$ is continuous in the interior of C (in particular, if f is convex in $\mathbf{R}^n$, f is continuous in $\mathbf{R}^n$). Let $\mathbf{x}_0$ be an interior point of C and $\rho > 0$ such that

$$d(\mathbf{x}_0, \mathbf{x}) < \rho \Rightarrow \mathbf{x} \in C.$$

For any positive number ϵ, choose a number η so that $0 \leqslant \eta < \rho$, then

$$f(\mathbf{x}_0+\eta\boldsymbol{\delta}_i) \leqslant \left(1-\frac{\eta}{\rho}\right)f(\mathbf{x}_0)+\frac{\eta}{\rho}f(\mathbf{x}_0+\rho\boldsymbol{\delta}_i) \quad \text{for } i = 1, 2, \ldots, n,$$

that is to say

$$f(\mathbf{x}_0+\eta\boldsymbol{\delta}_i)-f(\mathbf{x}_0) \leqslant \frac{\eta}{\rho}[f(\mathbf{x}_0+\rho\boldsymbol{\delta}_i)-f(\mathbf{x}_0)] \quad \text{for } i = 1, 2, \ldots, n,$$

and similarly

$$f(\mathbf{x}_0-\eta\boldsymbol{\delta}_i)-f(\mathbf{x}_0) \leqslant \frac{\eta}{\rho}[f(\mathbf{x}_0-\rho\boldsymbol{\delta}_i)-f(\mathbf{x}_0)] \quad \text{for } i = 1, 2, \ldots, n.$$

These two series of inequalities show that it is possible to find a number η_0 with $0 < \eta_0 < \rho$ such that

$$|\eta| < \eta_0 \Rightarrow f(\mathbf{x}_0+\eta\boldsymbol{\delta}_i)-f(\mathbf{x}_0) < \epsilon \quad \text{for } i = 1, 2, \ldots, n.$$

Now for every point $\mathbf{u} = (u^1, u^2, \ldots, u^n) \in \mathbf{R}^n$, we have

$$\begin{aligned} f(\mathbf{x}_0+\mathbf{u})-f(\mathbf{x}_0) &= f\left(\mathbf{x}_0+\frac{\sum nu^i\boldsymbol{\delta}_i}{n}\right)-f(\mathbf{x}_0) \\ &\leqslant \frac{1}{n}\sum_{i=1}^{n}[f(\mathbf{x}_0+nu^i\boldsymbol{\delta}_i)-f(\mathbf{x}_0)]; \end{aligned}$$

hence

$$\begin{aligned} \|\mathbf{u}\| < \eta_0/n \Rightarrow |nu^i| < \eta_0 \quad &\text{for } i = 1, 2, \ldots, n \\ \Rightarrow f(\mathbf{x}_0+\mathbf{u})-f(\mathbf{x}_0) < \epsilon.& \end{aligned}$$

On the other hand, we have

$$f(\mathbf{x}_0) \leqslant \tfrac{1}{2}f(\mathbf{x}_0+\mathbf{u})+\tfrac{1}{2}f(\mathbf{x}_0-\mathbf{u}),$$

hence

$$\begin{aligned} \|\mathbf{u}\| < \eta_0/n \Rightarrow \|-\mathbf{u}\| \leqslant \eta_0/n &\Rightarrow f(\mathbf{x}_0-\mathbf{u})-f(\mathbf{x}_0) < \epsilon \\ &\Rightarrow f(\mathbf{x}_0)-f(\mathbf{x}_0-\mathbf{u}) < \epsilon. \end{aligned}$$

Finally

$$\|\mathbf{u}\| < \eta_0/n \Rightarrow |f(\mathbf{x}_0+\mathbf{u})-f(\mathbf{x}_0)| < \epsilon.$$

Thus we see that f is continuous at the point $\mathbf{x}_0$.

As an example, consider a function f defined in the interval $[0,1] \subset \mathbf{R}$ and satisfying

$$f(x) = 0 \quad \text{for } 0 < x < 1, f(0) \geqslant 0 \quad \text{and} \quad f(1) \geqslant 0;$$

f is convex in $[0,1]$ and it is continuous at every point x satisfying $0 < x < 1$; it is continuous at the point 0 (or at the point 1) only if $f(0)$ (or $f(1)$) is zero.

NOTE. If a mapping $f(x,y)$ of $\mathbf{R}^p \times \mathbf{R}^q = \mathbf{R}^{p+q}$ into $\mathbf{R}^m$ is continuous, then every mapping f_{y_0} of $\mathbf{R}^p$ into $\mathbf{R}^m$ defined by

$$f_{y_0}(x) = f(x, y_0)$$

is continuous. For then

$$\|x - x_0\| = \|(x, y_0) - (x_0, y_0)\|.$$

Similarly every mapping f_{x_0} of $\mathbf{R}^q$ into $\mathbf{R}^m$ defined by

$$f_x(y) = f(x_0, y)$$

is continuous. In other words, every function continuous with respect to a pair of two variables is separately continuous with respect to each of the two variables. But the converse of this proposition is not true. For instance consider in $\mathbf{R}^2$ the numerical function $f(x^1, x^2)$ defined by

$$f(x^1, x^2) = \begin{cases} \dfrac{x^1 x^2}{(x^1)^2 + (x^2)^2} & \text{if } x^1 \neq 0 \text{ or } x^2 \neq 0 \\ 0 & \text{if } x^1 = x^2 = 0. \end{cases}$$

This function is separately continuous with respect to the two variables x^1 and x^2, but it is not continuous at the point $\mathbf{0} = (0,0)$.

Theorem on composite functions. *Given a set* $A \subset \mathbf{R}^m$; *if* $f_1, f_2, \ldots, f_k$ *are continuous mappings of* A *into*

$$\mathbf{R}^{n_1}, \mathbf{R}^{n_2}, \ldots, \mathbf{R}^{n_k}, \textit{ respectively}$$

and if φ *is a continuous mapping of*

$$f_1(A) \times f_2(A) \times \ldots \times f_k(A) \subset \mathbf{R}^{n_1+n_2+\ldots+n_k}$$

into $\mathbf{R}^n$, *then the mapping* f *of* A *into* $\mathbf{R}^n$ *defined by*

$$f(x) = \varphi(f_1(x), f_2(x), \ldots, f_k(x))$$

is continuous.

Let x_0 be a point of A and let ϵ be a number > 0; there exists a number $\eta > 0$ such that

$$\sqrt{\{\|y_1 - f_1(x_0)\|^2 + \|y_2 - f_2(x_0)\|^2 + \ldots + \|y_k - f_k(x_0)\|^2\}} < \eta$$
$$\Rightarrow \|\varphi(y_1, y_2, \ldots, y_k) - \varphi(f_1(x_0), f_2(x_0), \ldots, f_k(x_0))\| < \epsilon.$$

There exist numbers $\eta_1, \eta_2, \ldots, \eta_k > 0$ such that

$$\|x - x_0\| < \eta_i \Rightarrow \|f_i(x) - f_i(x_0)\| < \eta/\sqrt{k} \quad \text{for } i = 1, 2, \ldots, k.$$

Let η_0 be the smallest of these numbers, then

$$\|x - x_0\| < \eta_0 \Rightarrow \sqrt{\{\|f_1(x) - f_1(x_0)\|^2 + \ldots + \|f_k(x) - f_k(x_0)\|^2\}} < \eta$$
$$\Rightarrow \|f(x) - f(x_0)\| < \epsilon.$$

Fundamental theorem. *Let A be a set in $\mathbf{R}^n$ and let f be a mapping of A into $\mathbf{R}^m$. A necessary and sufficient condition for f to be continuous in A is that the inverse image of every open set in $\mathbf{R}^m$ be open relative to A, or, equivalently, that the inverse image of every closed set in $\mathbf{R}^m$ be closed relative to A.*†

Firstly, suppose f is continuous and let $G \subset \mathbf{R}^m$ be an open set; let $f^{-1}(G)$ be the inverse image of G, that is, the set of points x of A such that $f(x) \in G$. Consider any point

$$x_0 \in f^{-1}(G);$$

there exists a number $\epsilon > 0$ such that

$$B_\epsilon(f(x_0)) \subset G,$$

and there exists a number $\eta > 0$ such that

$$x \in A \quad \text{and} \quad d(x_0, x) < \eta \Rightarrow d(f(x_0), f(x)) < \epsilon \Rightarrow f(x) \in G.$$

Thus we can assign to every point x_0 of $f^{-1}(G)$, an open ball

$$B_{x_0} = B_\eta(x_0)$$

such that

$$A \cap B_{x_0} \subset f^{-1}(G).$$

The set

$$B = \bigcup_{x_0 \in f^{-1}(G)} B_{x_0}$$

is a union of open sets, and hence is an open set of $\mathbf{R}^n$ and

$$A \cap B = f^{-1}(G).$$

† More generally, a mapping f of a topological space E into a topological space F is said to be continuous at a point x_0 if, for every open set V of F containing $f(x_0)$, there exists an open set U of E containing x_0 and satisfying

$$x \in U \Rightarrow f(x) \in V.$$

f is said to be continuous if it is continuous at every point of E. It can be proved that for f to be continuous it is necessary and sufficient that the inverse image of every open set of F be an open set of E.

Conversely, if the inverse image of every open set is open, let x_0 be any point of A and let ϵ be a number > 0. Then the set

$$f^{-1}[B_\epsilon(f(x_0))]$$

is the inverse image of an open set of $\mathbf{R}^m$ of the form $A \bigcap B$, where B is an open set of $\mathbf{R}^n$. Hence there exists a number $\eta > 0$, such that $B_\eta(x_0) \subset B$: hence

$$x \in A \quad \text{and} \quad d(x_0, x) < \eta \Rightarrow x \in A \bigcap B$$
$$\Rightarrow d(f(x_0), f(x)) < \epsilon.$$

EXAMPLE 1. A plane

$$E_f^\alpha = \{x | x \in \mathbf{R}^n \quad \text{and} \quad f(x) = \alpha\},$$

which is the inverse image of the closed set $\{\alpha\} \subset \mathbf{R}$, is itself closed since f is linear and therefore continuous.

EXAMPLE 2. If we note that, in $\mathbf{R}$, every interval of the form $]-\infty, \alpha[$ or $]\alpha, +\infty[$ is open, we see that every closed half-space

$$H_f^\alpha = \{x | x \in \mathbf{R}^n \quad \text{and} \quad f(x) \leqslant \alpha\}$$

(where f is a linear form) is a closed set, and that every open half-space

$$G_f^\alpha = \{x | x \in \mathbf{R}^n \quad \text{and} \quad f(x) < \alpha\}$$

(where f is a linear form) is an open set.

EXAMPLE 3. If we note that the distance

$$d(x, y) = \|x - y\|$$

is, according to the Theorem on composite functions, a continuous numerical function defined on $\mathbf{R}^n \times \mathbf{R}^n = \mathbf{R}^{2n}$, it can be seen that every sphere

$$S_\lambda(x_0) = \{x | x \in \mathbf{R}^n \quad \text{and} \quad d(x_0, x) = \lambda\}$$

is a closed set.

EXAMPLE 4. If G is an open set of $\mathbf{R}^n$, the set λG is open, if $\lambda \neq 0$; for if we write

$$f(x) = \frac{1}{\lambda} x,$$

f is a continuous mapping of $\mathbf{R}^n$ into $\mathbf{R}^n$ and thus

$$\lambda G = f^{-1}(G).$$

For the same reasons, if F is a closed set, λF is a closed set; notice that this is true even if $\lambda = 0$.

EXAMPLE 5. If A is any set in $\mathbf{R}^n$ and if G is an open set in $\mathbf{R}^n$, the set $A+G$ is open. For, if a is any point of $\mathbf{R}^n$, then the set $G+\{a\}$ is the inverse image of G by the continuous mapping f defined by $f(x) = x-a$. It follows that

$$A+G = \bigcup_{a \in A} [\{a\}+G]$$

is an open set.

EXAMPLE 6. If the sets $A \subset \mathbf{R}^p$ and $B \subset \mathbf{R}^q$ are open, the set $A \times B \subset \mathbf{R}^{p+q}$ is open. In fact the projections π_1 and π_2, that is to say, the mappings π_1 and π_2 of $\mathbf{R}^p \times \mathbf{R}^q$ into $\mathbf{R}^p$ and $\mathbf{R}^q$ defined respectively by

$$\pi_1(x,y) = x \quad \text{and} \quad \pi_2(x,y) = y$$

are continuous; thus

$$A \times B = \pi_1^{-1}(A) \bigcap \pi_2^{-1}(B).$$

Similarly if A and B are closed, $A \times B$ is closed.

2.4. COMPACT SETS

DEFINITION. A set $A \subset \mathbf{R}^n$ is said to be *compact* if from every family $(G_i)_{i \in I}$ of open sets whose union contains A, we can extract a finite subfamily $G_{i_1}, G_{i_2}, \ldots, G_{i_m}$ whose union contains A, or in other words, if from every family of sets open relative to A whose union is equal to A, a finite subfamily can be found whose union equals A.†

Theorem 1. *Every compact set is closed.*

Let A be a compact set, and consider a point $x_0 \notin A$. To every point x of A we can assign a number $\rho_x > 0$ with

$$\rho_x < d(x_0, x),$$

then

$$A \subset \bigcup_{x \in A} B_{\rho_x}(x).$$

There exist points $x_1, x_2, \ldots, x_m \in A$ such that

$$A \subset \bigcup_{i=1}^{m} B_{\rho_{x_i}}(x_i).$$

† More generally, a topological space E is said to be compact if it is separable and if from every family of open sets whose union equals E we can find a finite subfamily whose union equals E.

Hence the set A is contained in the closed set

$$\bigcup_{i=1}^{m} \overline{B_{\rho_{x_i}}(x_i)}:$$

this set does not contain x_0, thus $x_0 \notin \overline{A}$.

Theorem 2. *If A is a compact set in $\mathbf{R}^n$ and if f is a continuous mapping of A into $\mathbf{R}^m$, then the image $f(A)$ is a compact set of $\mathbf{R}^m$.*

Let $(G_i)_{i \in I}$ be a family of open sets in $\mathbf{R}^m$ whose union contains $f(A)$: the sets

$$(f^{-1}(G_i))_{i \in I}$$

are open relative to A and their union is equal to A. Then there exist indices $i_1, i_2, \ldots, i_k$ such that

$$\bigcup_{p=1}^{k} f^{-1}(G_{i_p}) = A.$$

Hence we have

$$\bigcup_{p=1}^{k} (G_{i_p}) \supset f(A).$$

EXAMPLE. Consider a compact set $A \subset \mathbf{R}^p \times \mathbf{R}^q$. The sets

$$\pi_1(A) = \{x \mid x \in \mathbf{R}^p \text{ and there exists } y \in \mathbf{R}^q \text{ such that } (x, y) \in A\}$$

and

$$\pi_2(A) = \{y \mid y \in \mathbf{R}^q \text{ and there exists } x \in \mathbf{R}^p \text{ such that } (x, y) \in A\}$$

are compact, since the projections π_1 and π_2 are continuous mappings. In particular, given the sets

$$A_1 \subset \mathbf{R}^{n_1}, A_2 \subset \mathbf{R}^{n_2}, \ldots, A_k \subset \mathbf{R}^{n_k}:$$

if the product

$$A = A_1 \times A_2 \times \ldots \times A_k$$

is compact, then the sets are compact. A converse of this proposition will be given later (in Theorem 5).

Theorem 3. *A set $A \subset \mathbf{R}^n$ is compact if and only if it possesses the following property:*

If $(F_i)_{i \in I}$ is a family of sets, closed relative to A whose intersection is empty, there exists a finite subfamily $F_{i_1}, F_{i_2}, \ldots, F_{i_m}$ whose intersection is empty.

Firstly, if A has this property, and if $(G_i)_{i\in I}$ is a family of open sets whose union contains A, then

$$\bigcap_{i\in I} F_i = \emptyset,$$

writing

$$F_i = A \cap \complement G_i \quad \text{for } i \in I;$$

hence there exist indices $i_1, i_2, \ldots, i_m$ such that

$$\bigcap_{k=1}^{m} F_{i_k} = \emptyset,$$

and

$$\bigcup_{k=1}^{m} G_{i_k} \supset A.$$

Thus we see that A is compact.

Conversely, if A is compact and if $(F_i)_{i\in I}$ is a family of sets closed relative to A, that is (since A is closed), of closed sets contained in A, whose intersection is empty, then writing

$$G_i = \complement F_i \quad \text{for } i \in I,$$

we have

$$\bigcup_{i\in I} G_i \supset A;$$

hence there exist indices $i_1, i_2, \ldots, i_m$ such that

$$\bigcup_{k=1}^{m} G_{i_k} \supset A$$

which implies that

$$\bigcap_{k=1}^{m} F_{i_k} = \emptyset.$$

Corollary. *Every closed set contained in a compact set is compact.*

Given the closed set F contained in the compact set K, it is enough to observe that if the sets $(F_i)_{i\in I}$ are closed relative to A, then they are closed sets contained in K.

Theorem 4. *A set* $A \subset \mathbf{R}^n$ *is compact if and only if every sequence of points in* A *has a limit point in* A.

Let A be compact and let $a_1, a_2, \ldots, a_p, \ldots$ be a sequence of points in A. Then let us write

$$A_p = \{a_p, a_{p+1}, a_{p+2}, \ldots\}$$

and notice that the set of limit points is simply

$$\bigcap_{p=1}^{\infty} \overline{A}_p.$$

If this set were empty, there would exist indices $p_1, p_2, \ldots, p_m$ such that

$$\bigcap_{k=1}^{m} \bar{A}_{p_k} = \emptyset,$$

which is impossible since

$$p \geqslant p_1, p_2, \ldots, p_m \Rightarrow a_p \in \bigcap_{k=1}^{m} A_{p_k} \subset \bigcap_{k=1}^{m} \bar{A}_{p_k}.$$

Conversely, suppose that every sequence of points of A has a limit point in A and let $(G_i)_{i \in I}$ be a family of open sets whose union contains A.

We first show that there exists a number $\rho > 0$ such that for any $x \in A$, there is at least one open set G_i containing the open ball $B_\rho(x)$. For, if this were not so, A would include a sequence $x_1, x_2, \ldots, x_p, \ldots$ such that

$$B_{1/p}(x_p) \not\subset G_i$$

for every integer p and $i \in I$. Let x_0 be a limit point of this sequence: there would exist at least one index $i_0 \in I$ such that $x_0 \in G_{i_0}$; in these circumstances a number $\lambda > 0$ would exist such that

$$B_\lambda(x_0) \subset G_{i_0}.$$

Let p_0 be an integer such that

$$\frac{1}{p_0} \leqslant \frac{\lambda}{2}:$$

there would exist at least one integer $p \geqslant p_0$ such that

$$x_p \in B_{\lambda/2}(x_0),$$

and we would thus have

$$B_{1/p}(x_p) \subset B_{\lambda/2}(x_p) \subset B_\lambda(x_0) \subset G_{i_0},$$

which is impossible.

Let $\rho > 0$ be a number with the properties indicated above. Suppose there does not exist a finite subfamily $G_{i_1}, G_{i_2}, \ldots, G_{i_m}$ whose union contains A; we shall derive a contradiction. Let x_1 be a point of A, and G_{i_1} an open set such that

$$B_\rho(x_1) \subset G_{i_1};$$

let x_2 be a point of A such that $x_2 \notin G_{i_1}$ and choose $i_2 \in I$ with

$$B_\rho(x_2) \subset G_{i_2};$$

let x_3 be a point of A with

$$x_3 \notin G_{i_1} \cup G_{i_2}$$

and choose $i_3 \in I$ such that

$$B_\rho(x_3) \subset G_{i_3},$$

and so on. We have thus constructed a sequence $x_1, x_2, \ldots, x_p, \ldots$, of points of A; this sequence cannot have limit points since

$$q > p \Rightarrow x_q \notin G_{i_p} \Rightarrow x_q \notin B_\rho(x_\rho) \Rightarrow d(x_p, x_q) \geqslant \rho.$$

We thus have the contradiction indicated.

Corollary. *If F is a closed set and K is a compact set in $\mathbf{R}^n$, the set $K+F$ is closed.*

If a point x_0 belongs to the closure of $K+F$, then x_0 must belong to $K+F$. For we can find a sequence $x_1, x_2, \ldots, x_p, \ldots$ of points of $K+F$ whose limit is x_0; then we can find a sequence $y_1, y_2, \ldots, y_p, \ldots$ of points of K and a sequence $z_1, z_2, \ldots, z_p, \ldots$ of points of F such that

$$x_p = y_p + z_p; \quad \text{for every } p.$$

There exists at least one subsequence $y_{p_1}, y_{p_2}, \ldots, y_{p_k}, \ldots$ of the first sequence which tends to a limit $y_0 \in K$; in these conditions, the sequence $z_{p_1}, z_{p_2}, \ldots, z_{p_k}, \ldots$ tends to the limit $x_0 - y_0$. Hence $x_0 - y_0 \in F$ and

$$x_0 = y_0 + (x_0 - y_0) \in K + F.$$

Theorem 5. *If the sets $A_1, A_2, \ldots, A_k$, contained respectively in $\mathbf{R}^{n_1}, \mathbf{R}^{n_2}, \ldots, \mathbf{R}^{n_k}$ are compact, their product $A_1 \times A_2 \times \ldots \times A_k$ is compact.*

It is easy to see that if this theorem is true for $k = 2$ then it is true for all k. We shall therefore prove it for $k = 2$. For this, consider a sequence $(x_1, y_1), (x_2, y_2), \ldots, (x_p, y_p), \ldots$ of points of $A_1 \times A_2$. There exists at least one subsequence $x_{p_1}, x_{p_2}, \ldots, x_{p_m}, \ldots$ of the sequence $x_1, x_2, \ldots, x_p, \ldots$ which tends to a limit $x_0 \in A_1$ and there exists at least one subsequence

$$y_{p_{m_1}}, \ldots, y_{p_{m_2}}, \ldots, y_{p_{m_n}}, \ldots$$

of the sequence $y_{p_1}, y_{p_2}, \ldots, y_{p_m}$ which tends to a limit $y_0 \in A_2$. In these conditions the subsequence

$$(x_{p_{m_1}}, y_{p_{m_1}}), (x_{p_{m_2}}, y_{p_{m_2}}), \ldots, (x_{p_{m_n}}, y_{p_{m_n}}), \ldots$$

of the initial sequence tends to the limit

$$(x_0, y_0) \in A_1 \times A_2.$$

Thus we see that $A_1 \times A_2$ is compact.

Corollary. *If A and B are two compact sets in $\mathbf{R}^n$, the set $A+B$ is compact.*

The set $A \times B$ is compact and the sum $A+B$ is the continuous mapping of $\mathbf{R}^n \times \mathbf{R}^n$ into $\mathbf{R}^n$. Thus $A+B$, the image of $A \times B$ by this mapping, is compact.

DEFINITION. A set $A \subset \mathbf{R}^n$ is said to be *bounded* if there exists a number $\alpha > 0$ such that

$$x \in A \Rightarrow \|x\| \leqslant \alpha.$$

Lemma. *In* **R** *every closed interval* $[a,b]$ *is compact.*

Let $(G_i)_{i \in I}$ be a family of open sets whose union contains the interval $[a,b]$. Consider the set A of points x of $[a,b]$ which have the following property: there exists a finite subfamily $G_{i_1}, G_{i_2}, \ldots, G_{i_m}$ whose union contains $[a,x]$; we shall show that $b \in A$. Now, A is not empty since $a \in A$; let c be the least upper bound of the set A and let G_{i_0} be an open set of the family containing c. There exists a number $\epsilon > 0$, such that

$$|x-c| < \epsilon \Rightarrow x \in G_{i_0};$$

now we can find a point $x_1 \in A$, with $|x_1 - c| < \epsilon$ and there exists a finite subfamily $G_{i_1}, G_{i_2}, \ldots, G_{i_k}$ whose union contains $[a, x_1]$. We then see that we cannot have $c < b$: for if this occurs, let us take a point x_2 such that

$$c < x_2 < \begin{cases} b \\ c+\epsilon; \end{cases}$$

the union of the sets $G_{i_0}, G_{i_1}, G_{i_2}, \ldots, G_{i_k}$ contains $[a, x_2]$ and we consequently have $x_2 \in A$ which is impossible. Thus $c = b$ and, on the other hand, since the union of the sets $G_{i_0}, G_{i_1}, G_{i_2}, \ldots, G_{i_k}$ contains $[a,c]$, we have $c \in A$.

Theorem 6. *A set* $A \subset \mathbf{R}^n$ *is compact if and only if it is closed and bounded.*

We have already seen that a compact set is a closed set. Suppose then that A is closed.

Firstly, if A is not bounded, it is easy to construct a sequence $x_1, x_2, \ldots, x_p, \ldots$ of points of A which has no limit point: for instance it is enough to choose these points in such a way that

$$\|x_{p+1}\| \geqslant \|x_p\| + 1, \quad \text{for every } p.$$

Conversely if A is bounded, we can find two numbers a and b such that every point

$$\mathbf{x} = (x^1, x^2, \ldots, x^n)$$

of A satisfies

$$a \leqslant x^i \leqslant b \quad \text{for } i = 1, 2, \ldots, n.$$

The closed set A is then contained in the set

$$[a,b]^n = [a,b] \times [a,b] \times [a,b] \times \ldots \times [a,b],$$

which is compact, being a direct product of compact sets. Hence A is compact.

EXAMPLE 1. Every closed ball is compact.

EXAMPLE 2. The set $\mathbf{P}_n$ of n-tuples $(p^1, p^2, \ldots, p^n)$ which satisfy

$$p^1, p^2, \ldots, p^n \geqslant 0 \quad \text{and} \quad p^1 + p^2 + \ldots + p^n = 1,$$

is bounded since

$$(p^1, p^2, \ldots, p^n) \in \mathbf{P}_n \Rightarrow 0 \leqslant p^i \leqslant 1, \quad \text{for } i = 1, 2, \ldots, n.$$

It is also closed, being the intersection of the plane

$$\{\mathbf{x} | \mathbf{x} = (x^1, x^2, \ldots, x^n) \in \mathbf{R}^n \quad \text{and} \quad x^1 + x^2 + \ldots + x^n = 1\}$$

and of the closed half-planes

$$\{\mathbf{x} | \mathbf{x} = (x^1, x^2, \ldots, x^n) \in \mathbf{R}^n \quad \text{and} \quad x^i \geqslant 0\}, \quad i = 1, 2, \ldots, n.$$

Hence $\mathbf{P}^n$ is a compact set.

Theorem 7. *If a set $A \subset \mathbf{R}^n$ is compact, its convex hull $[A]$ is compact.*

We know (cf. Theorem 6, page 23) that every point x of $[A]$ can be expressed in the form

$$x = p^1 a_1 + p^1 a_2 + \ldots + p^{n+1} a_{n+1},$$

with

$$a_1, a_2, \ldots, a_{n+1} \in A \quad \text{and} \quad (p^1, p^2, \ldots p^{n+1}) \in \mathbf{P}_{n+1}.$$

The set

$$\mathbf{P}_{n+1} \times A^{n+1}$$

which is the product of $(n+2)$ compact sets, is compact, and the mapping φ of this set into $\mathbf{R}^n$ defined by

$$\varphi(\mathbf{p}; a_1, a_2, \ldots, a_{n+1}) = p^1 a_1 + p^2 a_2 + \ldots + p^{n+1} a_{n+1}$$

is continuous. Thus we see that the set

$$[A] = \varphi(\mathbf{P}_{n+1} \times A^{n+1})$$

is compact.

EXAMPLE. The convex hull of a finite set,

$$A = \{a_1, a_2, \ldots, a_m\}$$

is called a convex polyhedron. As every finite set is obviously compact, we see that every convex polyhedron is compact.

2.5. NUMERICAL SEMICONTINUOUS FUNCTIONS

DEFINITION. Let A be a set in $\mathbf{R}^n$ and let f be a numerical function defined in A. f is said to be *lower semicontinuous*, if for any number λ, the set

$$\{x | x \in A \quad \text{and} \quad f(x) > \lambda\}$$

is open relative to A, or, equivalently, if the set

$$\{x | x \in A \quad \text{and} \quad f(x) \leqslant \lambda\}$$

is closed relative to A. f is said to be *upper semicontinuous*, if $(-f)$ is lower semicontinuous; or, in other words, if for every number λ, the set

$$\{x | x \in A \quad \text{and} \quad f(x) \geqslant \lambda\}$$

is closed relative to A.

Theorem 1. *For a numerical function f defined in the set $A \subset \mathbf{R}^n$ to be continuous, it is necessary and sufficient that it be both upper and lower semicontinuous.*

Firstly, suppose f is continuous and let λ be any number. The sets

$$\{x | x \in A \quad \text{and} \quad f(x) \leqslant \lambda\} \quad \text{and} \quad \{x | x \in A \quad \text{and} \quad f(x) \geqslant \lambda\},$$

which are inverse images of the closed sets $]-\infty, \lambda]$ and $[\lambda, +\infty[$ in $\mathbf{R}$ are closed relative to A.

Conversely, if f is both upper and lower semicontinuous. Consider any point $x_0 \in A$ and let ϵ be a number > 0. The set

$$\{x | x \in A \quad \text{and} \quad |f(x) - f(x_0)| < \epsilon\},$$

which is the intersection of the two sets

$$\{x | x \in A \quad \text{and} \quad f(x) > f(x_0) - \epsilon\}$$

and

$$\{x | x \in A \quad \text{and} \quad f(x) < f(x_0) + \epsilon\},$$

is open relative to A. It follows that there exists a number $\eta > 0$, such that

$$x \in A \quad \text{and} \quad d(x_0, x) < \eta \Rightarrow |f(x) - f(x_0)| < \epsilon.$$

Theorem 2. *Let $(f_i)_{i \in I}$ be a family of numerically valued lower semicontinuous functions, defined in the set $A \subset \mathbf{R}^n$. Their least upper bound*

$$f = \sup_{i \in I} f_i$$

if it exists, is lower semicontinuous.

For if we take any number λ, the set

$$\{x|f(x) \leqslant \lambda\} = \bigcap_{i \in I} \{x|f_i(x) \leqslant \lambda\}$$

is a closed set (relative to A).

Corollary. *If a family* $(f_i)_{i \in I}$ *of numerically valued functions, which are upper semicontinuous have a greatest lower bound* f, *then* f *is upper semicontinuous.*

NOTE. The above theorem shows in particular that every least upper bound of continuous functions is lower semicontinuous. Consider for instance the family $(f_a)_{a \in]0,1]}$ of numerically valued functions defined on $[0,1]$ by

$$f_a(x) = \begin{cases} \dfrac{x}{a} & \text{if } 0 \leqslant x \leqslant a \\ 1 & \text{if } a \leqslant x \leqslant 1; \end{cases}$$

these functions are continuous, but their least upper bound, f, defined by

$$f(x) = \begin{cases} 0 & \text{if } x = 0 \\ 1 & \text{if } 0 < x \leqslant 1 \end{cases}$$

is not continuous. It is only lower semicontinuous. However, the least upper bound f, of a *finite* family $f_1, f_2, \ldots, f_m$ of continuous functions, must be continuous. For, consider any point $x_0 \in A$ and let ϵ be any number > 0; there exist numbers $\eta_1, \eta_2, \ldots, \eta_m \geqslant 0$ such that

$$d(x_0, x) < \eta_i \Rightarrow |f_i(x) - f_i(x_0)| < \epsilon \quad \text{for } i = 1, 2, \ldots, m.$$

Let η be the smallest of these numbers; then

$$\begin{aligned} d(x_0, x) < \eta &\Rightarrow |f_i(x) - f_i(x_0)| < \epsilon \quad \text{for } i = 1, 2, \ldots, m. \\ &\Rightarrow |f(x) - f(x_0)| < \epsilon. \end{aligned}$$

Theorem 3. *A lower (upper) semicontinuous function* f *defined on a compact set* $A \subset \mathbf{R}^n$ *attains its minimum (maximum) at a point* $x_0 \in A$.

The set

$$\bigcap_{\lambda \in R} \{x|x \in A \quad \text{and} \quad f(x) \leqslant \lambda\}$$

is clearly empty. It follows that there exist numbers $\lambda_1, \lambda_2, \ldots, \lambda_m$ such that

$$\bigcap_{i=1}^{m} \{x|x \in A \quad \text{and} \quad f(x) \leqslant \lambda_i\} = \varnothing.$$

Let λ_0 be the smallest of these numbers; then

$$x \in A \Rightarrow f(x) > \lambda_0.$$

Thus it follows that $f(x)$ is bounded below in A; let α be its greatest lower bound. Let $\alpha_1, \alpha_2, \ldots, \alpha_m$ be numbers $> \alpha$ and let α_0 be the smallest of these. There exists at least one point $x \in A$ such that

$$\alpha \leqslant f(x) < \alpha_0.$$

Thus we see that, whatever the numbers $\alpha_1, \alpha_2, \ldots, \alpha_m > \alpha$,

$$\bigcap_{i=1}^{m} \{x | x \in A \quad \text{and} \quad f(x) \leqslant \alpha_i\} \neq \emptyset,$$

hence

$$\bigcap_{\lambda > \alpha}^{m} \{x | x \in A \quad \text{and} \quad f(x) \leqslant \lambda\} \neq \emptyset.$$

Let x_0 be a point belonging to the latter set: then necessarily

$$f(x_0) = \alpha = \min_{x \in A} f(x).$$

3. Properties of convex sets and functions in the space $\mathbf{R}^n$

3.1. SEPARATION THEOREMS

DEFINITION. The plane E_f^α is said to *separate* two non-empty sets A and B if

$$x \in A \Rightarrow f(x) \leqslant \alpha$$

and

$$x \in B \Rightarrow f(x) \geqslant \alpha.$$

It is said to separate the sets *strictly* if

$$x \in A \Rightarrow f(x) < \alpha$$

and

$$x \in B \Rightarrow f(x) > \alpha.$$

Lemma 1. *If C is a closed convex non-empty set in $\mathbf{R}^n$ and not containing the origin, there exists a linear form f and a positive number α such that*

$$x \in C \Rightarrow f(x) > \alpha.$$

For, let $B_\lambda(\mathbf{0})$ be a closed ball with centre at the origin and meeting C; the set $C \cap B_\lambda(\mathbf{0})$ is compact. Hence the continuous function $g(x) = \|x\|$ attains its greatest lower bound in this set at a point x_0. $\|x_0\| > 0$ since $x_0 \in C$; on the other hand, we have

$$x \in C \cap B_\lambda(0) \Rightarrow \|x\| \geqslant \|x_0\|,$$

hence *a fortiori*

$$x \in C \Rightarrow \|x\| \geqslant \|x_0\|.$$

We shall show that for every point $x \in C$,

$$\langle x_0, x\rangle \geqslant \|x_0\|^2;$$

this will prove the stated proposition, for $f(x) = \langle x_0, x\rangle$ is indeed a linear function.

Let y be any point of C. If

$$\epsilon = \|x_0\|^2 - \langle x_0, y\rangle,$$

and we suppose $\epsilon > 0$, we shall get a contradiction. For, if t is any number, then

$$\begin{aligned}\|(1-t)\,x_0 + ty\|^2 &= (1-t)^2\,\|x_0\|^2 + 2t(1-t)\,\langle x_0, y\rangle + t^2\,\|y\|^2 \\ &= \|x_0\|^2 - 2t\|x_0\|^2 + t^2\|x_0\|^2 + 2t(1-t)\,[\|x_0\|^2 - \epsilon] + t^2\|y\|^2 \\ &= \|x_0\|^2 - 2t(1-t)\,\epsilon + t^2\,[\|y\|^2 - \|x_0\|^2].\end{aligned}$$

Now, ϵ being positive, it is possible to choose t so that

$$\frac{t}{1-t}[\|y\|^2 - \|x_0\|^2] < 2\epsilon \quad \text{and} \quad 0 < t < 1;$$

and we then have at the same time

$$\|(1-t)\,x_0 + ty\|^2 - \|x_0\|^2 < -2t(1-t)\,\epsilon + t2\epsilon(1-t) = 0$$

and

$$(1-t)\,x_0 + ty \in C,$$

which is a contradiction. The proposition is thus proved.

Lemma 2. *If C is a non-empty convex set not containing the origin, there exists a linear form f not identically zero such that*

$$x \in C \Rightarrow f(x) \geqslant 0.$$

To every point $x \in C$, we assign the closed set

$$A_x = \{y \,|\, \|y\| = 1 \quad \text{and} \quad \langle y, x\rangle \geqslant 0\}.$$

Let $x_1, x_2, \ldots, x_k$ be any finite family of points of C. The convex polyhedron generated by this family of points is closed (since it is compact) and does not contain the origin; by Lemma 1, there is a vector y such that $\langle y, x_i\rangle > 0$ for all i; we can take y so that $\langle y, y\rangle = 1$, and then

$$\bigcap_{i=1}^{k} A_{x_i} \neq \varnothing.$$

As the sets A_x are contained in the unit sphere $S_1(\mathbf{0})$, which is compact, we have, by Theorem 3 on page 51

$$\bigcap_{x \in C} A_x \neq \varnothing.$$

Hence there is at least one point a, satisfying

$$a \in \bigcap_{x \in C} A_x;$$

the function $f(x) = \langle a, x\rangle$ is thus the linear form required.

First separation theorem. *If C and C' are two non-empty, convex, disjoint sets, there exists a plane E_f^α which separates them.*

For, $C+(-C')$ is convex and does not contain the origin (since $C \cap C' = \emptyset$), hence there exists, according to Lemma 2, a linear form f, not identically zero, such that

$$c \in C' \quad \text{and} \quad c' \in C' \Rightarrow f(c) - f(c') = f(c-c') \geqslant 0.$$

Thus we have

$$\inf_{c \in C} f(c) \geqslant \sup_{c' \in C'} f(c').$$

Second separation theorem. *If C and C' are two non-empty, convex, disjoint sets where C is compact and C' is closed, there exists a plane E_f^α which strictly separates them.*

For the set $(-C')$ is closed and convex, hence, since C is convex and compact, $C+(-C')$ is convex and closed. On the other hand, $\mathbf{0} \notin C+(-C')$ (since $C \cap C' = \emptyset$). Hence there exists, by Lemma 1, a linear form f and a number $\lambda > 0$, such that:

$$x \in C+(-C') \Rightarrow f(x) > \lambda.$$

We thus have

$$c \in C \quad \text{and} \quad c' \in C' \Rightarrow f(c) - f(c') > \lambda > 0;$$

hence

$$\inf_{c \in C} f(c) \geqslant \sup_{c' \in C'} f(c') + \lambda > \sup_{c' \in C'} f(c').$$

Now let α be such that

$$\sup_{c' \in C'} f(c') < \alpha < \inf_{c \in C} f(c):$$

E_f^α is the required plane.

NOTE. In $\mathbf{R}^2$ consider the two closed convex sets

$$C = \{\mathbf{x} = (x^1, x^2) \mid x^1 \leqslant 0\}$$

and

$$C' = \{\mathbf{x} = (x^1, x^2) \mid x^1, x^2 \geqslant 0 \quad \text{and} \quad x^1 x^2 \geqslant 1\}.$$

Neither of these sets is compact. The plane whose equation is $x^1 = 0$ separates them, but there does not exist a plane which separates them strictly.

DEFINITION. The intersection of closed convex sets which contain A is called the *closed-convex hull* of the set A, and is denoted by $\bar{c}[A]$. This set $\bar{c}[A]$ is itself convex and closed and it contains A.

EXAMPLE 1. In **R** consider the set of points

$$1, \frac{1}{2}, \frac{1}{3}, \ldots, \frac{1}{n}, \ldots$$

Its convex hull is the interval $]0, 1]$, its closed-convex hull is the closed interval $[0, 1]$.

EXAMPLE 2. If A is a finite set in $\mathbf{R}^n$, the convex polyhedron $[A]$ is closed, since it is compact (see page 49). In this case

$$\bar{c}[A] = [A].$$

Corollary. *The closed-convex hull of a set A is equal to the intersection of the closed half-spaces which contain it.*

The hull is clearly contained in this intersection. Conversely if x_0 is a point which does not belong to $\bar{c}[A]$, there exists, according to the Second separation theorem, a closed half-space which contains $\bar{c}[A]$, and hence A, but which does not contain x_0.

3.2. THEOREM ON SUPPORTING PLANES. POLYTOPES†

A plane E_f^α is said to be a *supporting plane* of a non-empty set A if the plane meets the set A and if all the points of A are on the same side of the plane.

If A is compact, there exists for every linear form f not identically zero, at least one supporting plane whose equation is $f(x) = \alpha$: for this we have only to take

$$\alpha = \min_{x \in A} f(x)$$

or

$$\alpha = \max_{x \in A} f(x).$$

Theorem of supporting planes. *If C is a non-empty convex set which is compact, every supporting plane of C contains a vertex of C.*

We shall suppose that the theorem is true for $\dim C < p$, and show that it is true for $\dim C = p$. There are two cases:

(a) If $p = 0$, C reduces to a point, which is a vertex and is contained in every supporting plane.

(b) If $p > 0$, every supporting plane E_f^α which does not contain C (and there are such supporting planes) is equally a supporting plane for the non-empty convex compact set $E_f^\alpha \cap C$, whose dimension is less than p.

† Polytope has been used to translate the French word: *tronçon*, but there is no implication here that the region is necessarily bounded.

Hence it contains a vertex x_0 of that set: x_0 is also a vertex of C. It goes without saying that every supporting plane containing C also contains a vertex of C. Therefore every supporting plane contains a vertex of C.

DEFINITION. The set of vertices of a convex set C is called the *profile* of C, and is denoted by $\ddot{C}$.

Corollary (Krein and Milman's theorem). *Every convex, compact, non-empty set C is equal to the closed-convex hull of its profile $\ddot{C}$.*

We have $\ddot{C} \subset C$, hence

$$\bar{c}[\ddot{C}] \subset \bar{c}[C] = C.$$

Conversely, it may be shown that we cannot have $x_0 \in C$ and $x_0 \notin \bar{c}[\ddot{C}]$. For, there would then exist a linear form f such that

$$x \in \bar{c}[\ddot{C}] \Rightarrow f(x) > f(x_0).$$

But this is impossible, since the supporting plane whose equation is

$$f(x) = \min_{x \in C} f(x)$$

must meet $\ddot{C}$.

DEFINITION. The intersection T of a finite number of closed half-spaces

$$H_{f_1}^{\alpha_1}, H_{f_2}^{\alpha_2}, \ldots, H_{f_m}^{\alpha_m}$$

is called a *polytope*† of $\mathbf{R}^n$: it is a closed convex set. The planes $E_{f_1}^{\alpha_1}, E_{f_2}^{\alpha_2}, \ldots, E_{f_m}^{\alpha_m}$ are the *generating planes* of T.

Theorem. *For a point of a polytope to be a vertex, it is necessary and sufficient that the intersection of the generating planes passing through this point should reduce to this point.*

For, consider a point $a \in T$. For a to be a vertex, it is necessary and sufficient that, for any $u \in \mathbf{R}^n$ with $u \neq 0$, at least one of the functions of λ

$$f_i(a+\lambda u) - \alpha_i \quad (i = 1, 2, \ldots, m)$$

should vanish for $\lambda = 0$ but should not always be zero; this proves the theorem.

Corollary 1. *The profile of a polytope is finite.*

For, the family of subsets of the set of generating planes is finite. To every vertex we can assign an element of this family, namely the set of generating

† See footnote on p. 56.

planes passing through the vertex. According to the theorem, to every pair of distinct vertices there correspond distinct elements of this family. The set of vertices is therefore finite.

Corollary 2. *Every bounded non-empty polytope is a convex polyhedron.*

For, a bounded non-empty polytope is equal to a closed convex hull of its profile, which is finite.

Properties of generating planes passing through a vertex.

Given a vertex a of a polytope T, and the generating planes

$$E^{\alpha_{i_1}}_{f_{i_1}}, E^{\alpha_{i_2}}_{f_{i_2}}, \ldots, E^{\alpha_{i_k}}_{f_{i_k}}$$

passing through a; we shall study the polytope T' which is the intersection of the closed half-spaces

$$H^{\alpha_{i_1}}_{f_{i_1}}, H^{\alpha_{i_2}}_{f_{i_2}}, \ldots, H^{\alpha_{i_k}}_{f_{i_k}},$$

in order to bring out certain properties needed later in describing the simplex method (Chapter 5, 5.3). For convenience, we take the origin at the point a. We then have

$$\alpha_{i_1} = \alpha_{i_2} = \ldots = \alpha_{i_k} = 0.$$

T' is obviously a convex cone containing T and issuing from the origin, the origin being a vertex. If $u \in T'$ and $-u \in T'$, then necessarily

$$f_{i_h}(u) = 0 \quad \text{for } h = 1, 2, \ldots, k,$$

hence $u = 0$, since the intersection of the generating planes passing through the origin, contains only the origin. It is assumed that T' does not reduce to the origin.

Consider the compact set

$$K = \{x | x \in T' \quad \text{and} \quad \|x\| = 1\}.$$

It is contained in the set $T' - \{0\}$, which is convex (cf. Theorem 7, Chapter 1, p. 24); its convex hull $[K]$, which is compact (cf. Theorem 7, Chapter 2, p. 49), therefore does not contain the origin. It follows that there exists a linear numerical function f and a number $\alpha > 0$ such that $f(x) \geqslant \alpha$ for $x \in K$.

Let T'' be the intersection of the polytope T' with the closed half-space

$$\{x | f(x) \leqslant \alpha\},$$

and let x be any point of T'', then

$$\frac{1}{\|x\|} x \in K,$$

hence

$$\frac{f(x)}{||x||} \geqslant \alpha \text{ and consequently } ||x|| \leqslant \frac{1}{\alpha} f(x) \leqslant 1;$$

T'' is thus a convex polyhedron, since it is bounded.

Let $a_1, a_2, \ldots, a_p$ be the vertices of T'' other than the origin: they satisfy

$$f(a_1) = f(a_2) = \ldots = f(a_p) = \alpha;$$

we shall show that T' is precisely the convex hull of the union of the half-lines

$$D^+_{a_1}, D^+_{a_2}, \ldots, D^+_{a_p}.$$

For, this convex hull is a cone containing T'' and contained in T'; if x is a point of T' which does not belong to T'', then $f(x) > \alpha$, so that if we write

$$x' = \frac{\alpha}{f(x)} x \quad \text{and} \quad \lambda = \frac{f(x)}{\alpha} > 0,$$

we have $x = \lambda x'$, with $x' \in T''$ and $\lambda > 0$.

We shall identify the half-lines

$$D^+_{a_1}, D^+_{a_2}, \ldots, D^+_{a_p}.$$

For this let us first note that if a point $x \in T'$ with $x \neq \mathbf{0}$ is such that the line D_x is the only line having x as an internal point with respect to T', the same holds good for all points of the form λx, with $\lambda > 0$; in this case we shall say that the half-line D^+_x is an edge of T'. We shall show that the edges of T' are the half-lines

$$D^+_{a_1}, D^+_{a_2}, \ldots, D^+_{a_p}.$$

Let T' be an edge and x a point on this edge satisfying $||x|| = 1$; we have $f(x) \geqslant \alpha > 0$. The point

$$x' = \frac{\alpha}{f(x)} x$$

belongs to this edge and satisfies $f(x') = \alpha$. x' is not an internal point of the line $D_{x'}$ with respect to T''; as $D^+_{x'}$ is an edge of T', it follows that x' is a vertex of T'', so that the edge $D^+_{x'}$ is equal to one of the half-lines

$$D^+_{a_1}, D^+_{a_2}, \ldots, D^+_{a_p}.$$

Conversely, let $a_i \neq \mathbf{0}$ be a vertex of T''. a_i cannot be expressed in the form

$$a_i = \lambda x + \lambda' x',$$

with

$$x, x' \in T', \quad x, x' \notin D_{a_i}, \quad \lambda, \lambda' > 0 \quad \text{and} \quad \lambda + \lambda' = 1;$$

for, if the above were true x and x' could be expressed in the form $x = \mu y$ and $x' = \mu' y'$ with

$$\mu, \mu' > 0 \quad \text{and} \quad f(y) = f(y') = \alpha;$$

and we would then have

$$a_i = \lambda \mu y + \lambda' \mu' y',$$

with

$$\lambda\mu, \lambda' \mu' > 0, \quad y, y' \in T'', \quad y, y' \neq a_i$$

and

$$\alpha = f(a_i) = \lambda\mu f(y) + \lambda' \mu' f(y') = \alpha(\lambda\mu + \lambda' \mu'),$$

hence

$$\lambda\mu + \lambda' \mu' = 1;$$

a_i would not then be a vertex of T'', which is impossible. Thus we see that $D^+_{a_i}$ is an edge of T'.

We can therefore state the following propositions.

Proposition 1. *T' is equal to the convex hull of the union of its edges, which are finite in number.*

Proposition 2. *For a half-line D^+_x contained in T' to be an edge, it is necessary and sufficient that the intersection of generating planes which contain it should reduce to the line D_x.*

3.3. INTERSECTIONS OF CONVEX SETS

Here we shall study certain combinatorial properties of families of convex sets, to be used subsequently.

Intersection theorem (Berge [3]). *Let $C_1, C_2, \ldots, C_m$ ($m \geqslant 2$) be closed convex sets in $\mathbf{R}^n$ whose union is convex; if the intersection of every $m-1$ of these is non-empty, then their intersection is non-empty.*

We can always reduce the problem to the case where the sets C_i are compact. It suffices to take the points $a_1, a_2 \ldots, a_m$ with

$$a_i \in \bigcap_{j \neq i} C_j,$$

and to write

$$A = \{a_1, a_2, \ldots, a_m\}$$

and

$$C'_i = [A] \bigcap C_i \quad (i = 1, 2, \ldots, m).$$

We shall therefore prove the theorem for compact convex sets C_i.

Firstly, the theorem is true for $m = 2$. Let C_1 and C_2 be convex sets with

$$C_1 \neq \varnothing, C_2 \neq \varnothing \quad \text{and} \quad C_1 \bigcup C_2 \text{ convex.}$$

If C_1 and C_2 were disjoint there would exist a plane which strictly separated them. There would then be points of $C_1 \bigcup C_2$ on both sides of the plane; hence there would be points on this plane, since $C_1 \bigcup C_2$ is convex. This is impossible since the plane must not meet either C_1 or C_2.

Secondly, if the theorem is true for $m = p(p \geqslant 2)$, *it is true for* $m = p+1$. Let $C_1, C_2, \ldots, C_{p+1}$ be the convex sets; put

$$C = \bigcap_{i=1}^{p} C_i.$$

By hypothesis, $C \neq \varnothing$ and $C_{p+1} \neq \varnothing$: if the two sets are disjoint, there exists a plane P which strictly separates them. Suppose

$$C_i' = P \bigcap C_i \quad (i = 1, 2, \ldots, p).$$

Then

$$\bigcup_{i=1}^{p} C_i' = P \bigcap \left(\bigcup_{i=1}^{p} C_i \right) = P \bigcap \left(\bigcup_{i=1}^{p+1} C_i \right),$$

since

$$P \bigcap C_{p+1} = \varnothing.$$

The set

$$\bigcup_{i=1}^{p} C_i'$$

is thus convex.

On the other hand, the intersection of any $p-1$ of the sets $C_1, C_2, \ldots, C_p$ contains C and meets C_{p+1} and consequently meets P. It follows that any $p-1$ of the sets $C_1', C_2', \ldots, C_p'$ has a non-empty intersection and hence from the induction hypothesis, their intersection is not empty. Thus

$$C \bigcap P \neq \varnothing,$$

which is impossible.

Corollary 1. *Let* $C_1, C_2, \ldots, C_m$ $(m \geqslant 2)$ *be closed convex sets in* $\mathbf{R}^n$. *If their intersection is empty and if the intersection of any* $m-1$ *of them is non-empty, their union is not convex.*

Corollary 2. *Let* $C_1, C_2, \ldots, C_m$ $(m \geqslant 1)$ *be closed convex sets in* $\mathbf{R}^n$. *If a convex set* C *meets the intersection of any* $m-1$ *of these but not their intersection, then it is not contained in their union.*

In the case where $m = 1$, the intersection of any $m-1$ of these convex sets is identical with the intersection of an empty family of sets, namely with $\mathbf{R}^n$.

If, then

$$C \bigcap \mathbf{R}^n = C \neq \emptyset$$

and if $C \bigcap C_1 = \emptyset$, clearly, we cannot have $C \subset C_1$.

In the case where $m \geqslant 2$, let $a_1, a_2, \ldots, a_m$ be points of C satisfying

$$a_i \in \bigcap_{j \neq i} C_j.$$

Suppose

$$A = \{a_1, a_2, \ldots, a_m\}$$

and

$$C'_i = [A] \bigcap C_i \quad (i = 1, 2, \ldots, m).$$

According to Corollary 1, the union of the C'_i is not convex. Hence there exists a point of $[A]$ which does not belong to this union. This point belongs to C and does not belong to the union of the C_i.

Corollary 3 (Helly's theorem). *Let $C_1, C_2, \ldots, C_m$ (with $m > n+1$) be convex sets in $\mathbf{R}^n$. If the intersection of any $n+1$ of these is non-empty, the intersection*

$$\bigcap_{i=I}^{m} C_i$$

is non-empty.

Let us suppose that the intersection of any p $(n+1 \leqslant p \leqslant m)$ of these is non-empty and show that the intersection of any $p+1$ of these, for example $C_1, C_2, \ldots, C_{p+1}$, is non-empty.

For, let $a_1, a_2, \ldots, a_{p+1}$ be points with

$$a_i \in \bigcap_{\substack{j \neq i \\ 1 \leqslant j \leqslant p+1}} \quad \text{for } i = 1, 2, \ldots, p+1.$$

We call C'_i the convex polyhedron included in C_i, generated by the points a_j with $j \neq i$. The intersection of every p of these closed convex sets C'_1, $C'_2, \ldots, C'_{p+1}$ is non-empty. On the other hand, by Theorem 6 (Chapter 1, p. 23) their union is equal to a convex polyhedron generated by the points $a_1, a_2, \ldots, a_{p+1}$, given that $p \geqslant n+1$. Thus it follows that their intersection is non-empty.

3.4. MINIMAX THEOREM. FARKAS–MINKOWSKI THEOREM

Fundamental theorem. *Let $C \subset \mathbf{R}^n$ be a convex set and $f_1, f_2, \ldots, f_m$ convex functions in C. If the system*

$$f_k(x) < 0 \quad \text{for } k = 1, 2, \ldots, m$$

has no solution in C, *there exists a function of the form*

$$f(x) = \sum_{i=1}^{n+1} p_i f_{k_i}(x),$$

with

$$p_1, p_2, \ldots, p_{n+1} \geqslant 0, \quad p_1 + p_2 + \ldots + p_{n+1} = 1$$

such that

$$\inf_{x \in C} f(x) \geqslant 0.$$

For, let G be the set of points

$$\boldsymbol{\xi} = (\xi_1, \xi_2, \ldots, \xi_m) \in \mathbf{R}^m$$

for which there exists a point $x \in C$ satisfying

$$f_i(x) < \xi_i \quad \text{for } i = 1, 2, \ldots, m.$$

The set G does not contain the origin. On the other hand, it is convex, for if $\boldsymbol{\xi}$ and $\boldsymbol{\xi}'$ are two points of G, if λ and λ' are two numbers with $\lambda, \lambda' \geqslant 0$ and $\lambda + \lambda' = 1$, and if x and x' are two points of C satisfying

$$f_i(x) < \xi_i \quad \text{and} \quad f_i(x') < \xi_i' \quad \text{for } i = 1, 2, \ldots, m,$$

the point

$$\lambda x + \lambda' x' \in C$$

satisfies

$$f_i(\lambda x + \lambda' x') \leqslant \lambda f_i(x) + \lambda' f_i(x') < \lambda \xi_i + \lambda' \xi_i' \quad \text{for } i = 1, 2, \ldots, m;$$

it follows that the point $\lambda \boldsymbol{\xi} + \lambda' \boldsymbol{\xi}'$ belongs to G.

According to the First separation theorem there exist coefficients $p_1, p_2, \ldots, p_m$, not all equal to zero, such that

$$\sum_{i=1}^{m} p_i \xi_i \geqslant 0$$

for every point

$$\boldsymbol{\xi} = (\xi_1, \xi_2, \ldots, \xi_m) \in G.$$

Note that if x is any point of C and if $\lambda_1, \lambda_2, \ldots, \lambda_m$ are positive numbers, the point $\boldsymbol{\xi}$ defined by

$$\xi_i = f_i(x) + \lambda_i \quad \text{for } i = 1, 2, \ldots, m,$$

belongs to G, therefore

$$\sum_{i=1}^{m} p_i f_i(x) + \sum_{i=1}^{m} p_i \lambda_i \geqslant 0$$

for all $\lambda_1, \lambda_2, \ldots, \lambda_m > 0$. It follows, on the one hand, that

$$\sum_{i=1}^{m} p_i f_i(x) \geqslant 0 \quad \text{for all } x \in C,$$

and on the other, that $p_1, p_2, \ldots, p_m \geqslant 0$; we can suppose that $\sum p_i = 1$, by dividing p_i by the number $p_1 + p_2 + \ldots + p_m > 0$. If $m \leqslant n+1$ the theorem is proved.

In the case where $m > n+1$, we can make at least $m-(n+1)$ of the numbers $p_1, p_2, \ldots, p_m$ zero. For we can write

$$C_i = \{x | x \in C \quad \text{and} \quad f_i(x) < 0\} \quad \text{for } i = 1, 2, \ldots, m.$$

As the intersection of the sets $C_1, C_2, \ldots, C_m$ is empty, there exist, according to Helly's theorem (cf. 3.3, page 62 above), indices $i_1, i_2, \ldots, i_{n+1}$ such that the intersection of the sets $C_{i_1}, C_{i_2}, \ldots, C_{i_{n+1}}$ is empty, the system

$$f_{i_k}(x) < 0 \quad \text{for } k = 1, 2, \ldots, n+1$$

has no solution in C, so that there exist numbers $q_1, q_2, \ldots, q_{n+1} \geqslant 0$ with

$$q_1 + q_2 + \ldots + q_{n+1} = 1$$

such that

$$\sum_{k=1}^{n+1} q_k f_{i_k}(x) \geqslant 0 \quad \text{for all } x \in C.$$

Corollary (Bohnenblust, Karlin, Shapley [4]). *Let C be a compact convex set in $\mathbf{R}^n$ and let $(f_k | k \in K)$ be a family (finite or infinite) of convex functions which are lower semicontinuous in C. If the system*

$$f_k(x) \leqslant 0 \quad \text{for } k \in K$$

had no solution in C, then there exists a function of the form

$$f(x) = \sum_{i=1}^{n+1} p_i f_{k_i}(x),$$

with

$$p_1, p_2, \ldots, p_{n+1} \geqslant 0 \quad \text{and} \quad p_1 + p_2 + \ldots + p_{n+1} = 1,$$

such that

$$\inf_{x \in C} f(x) > 0.$$

The system

$$f_k(x) \leqslant \epsilon \quad (\text{for every } k \in K \text{ and for every } \epsilon > 0)$$

has no solutions in C. The sets

$$C_{k,\epsilon} = \{x | x \in C \quad \text{and} \quad f_k(x) \leqslant \epsilon\}$$

are closed and contained in the compact set C and their intersection is empty. Hence we can choose a finite number of such sets so that their intersection is empty. Thus we obtain indices $k_1, k_2, \ldots, k_m$ and numbers $\epsilon_1, \epsilon_2, \ldots, \epsilon_m > 0$ such that the system

$$f_{k_i}(x) - \epsilon_i \leqslant 0 \quad \text{for } i = 1, 2, \ldots, m,$$

has no solution in C; thus there exist indices $i_1, i_2, \ldots, i_{n+1}$ and numbers $p_1, p_2, \ldots, p_{n+1} > 0$ with

$$p_1 + p_2 + \ldots + p_{n+1} = 1$$

such that

$$\sum_{r=1}^{n+1} p_r f_{k_{i_r}}(x) \geqslant \sum_{r=1}^{n+1} p_r \epsilon_{i_r} \quad \text{for all } x \in C;$$

hence we have

$$\inf_{x \in C} \sum_{r=1}^{n+1} p_r f_{k_{i_r}}(x) \geqslant \sum_{r=1}^{n+1} p_r \epsilon_{i_r} > 0.$$

Minimax theorem (Von Neumann). *Let $A \subset \mathbf{R}^m$ and $B \subset \mathbf{R}^n$ be two non-empty compact convex sets and let $f(x,y)$ be a numerical function defined in $\mathbf{R}^m \times \mathbf{R}^n = \mathbf{R}^{m+n}$ which is upper semicontinuous and concave with respect to x, and lower semicontinuous and convex with respect to y; then there exists an ordered pair (x_0, y_0) with $x_0 \in A$ and $y_0 \in B$ such that*

$$f(x, y_0) \leqslant f(x_0, y_0) \leqslant f(x_0, y)$$

for all $x \in A$ and all $y \in B$.

Such an ordered pair is called a *saddle point* or *equilibrium point*.

Note first that for every value of y the function $f(x,y)$ of x reaches its least upper bound in A, since it is upper semicontinuous. Consider now the function of y, equal to

$$\max_{x \in A} f(x, y);$$

this is a least upper bound of functions which are lower semicontinuous, hence it is itself lower semicontinuous and reaches its greatest lower bound at a point $y_0 \in B$.

We write

$$\alpha = \max_{x \in A} f(x, y_0) = \min_{y \in B} \max_{x \in A} f(x, y),$$

and define similarly a point x_0 of A and a number β by

$$\beta = \min_{y \in B} f(x_0, y) = \max_{x \in A} \min_{y \in B} f(x, y).$$

We shall show that $\alpha = \beta$ (hence the name 'minimax' theorem). It then follows easily that

$$f(x, y_0) \leqslant \alpha = \beta \leqslant f(x_0, y)$$

for every $x \in A$ and $y \in B$; this implies $f(x_0, y_0) = \alpha$, so that the pair (x_0, y_0) is the required equilibrium point.

Firstly, for every $x' \in A$ and $y' \in B$, we have

$$\max_{x \in A} f(x, y') - \min_{y \in B} f(x', y) = \max_{\substack{x \in A \\ y \in B}} [f(x, y') - f(x', y)] \geqslant f(x', y') - f(x', y') = 0;$$

hence

$$\min_{y' \in B} \max_{x \in A} f(x, y') \ - \ \max_{x' \in A} \min_{y \in B} f(x', y) \ = \ \min_{\substack{x' \in A \\ y' \in B}} \max_{\substack{x \in A \\ y \in B}} [f(x, y') - f(x', y)] \ \geqslant \ 0,$$

this is, $\alpha \geqslant \beta$.

Secondly, we shall now show that $\beta \geqslant \alpha$ also, from which we deduce that $\alpha = \beta$. Let $\epsilon > 0$ be any number; consider the family $(g_x | x \in A)$ of functions of y defined by

$$g_x(y) \ = \ f(x, y) - \alpha + \epsilon.$$

The system

$$g_x(y) \leqslant 0 \quad \text{for every } x \in A$$

has no solution in B, for the system implies

$$\max_{x \in A} f(x, y) \ \leqslant \ \alpha - \epsilon \ < \ \alpha,$$

which is not possible when $y \in B$.

According to the preceding corollary there exists a function of the form

$$g(y) \ = \ \sum_{i=1}^{r} p_i g_{x_i}(y),$$

with

$$p_1, p_2, \ldots, p_r \geqslant 0, \quad p_1 + p_2 + \ldots + p_r = 1,$$

satisfying

$$g(y) > 0 \quad \text{for every } y \in B.$$

Thus

$$f\left(\sum_{i=1}^{r} p_i x_i, y\right) \geqslant \sum_{i=1}^{r} p_i f(x_i, y) > \alpha - \epsilon$$

for every $y \in B$; therefore

$$\beta = \max_{x \in A} \min_{y \in B} f(x, y) \geqslant \min_{y \in B} f\left(\sum_{i=1}^{r} p_i x_i, y\right) > \alpha - \epsilon.$$

Thus $\beta > \alpha - \epsilon$ for every $\epsilon > 0$, hence the inequality $\beta \geqslant \alpha$.

We shall now prove the well-known theorem of Farkas–Minkowski [9] in a slightly more general form.

Farkas–Minkowski theorem. *Let $f(x)$, $g_1(x)$, $g_2(x), \ldots, g_m(x)$ be concave functions defined in $\mathbf{R}^n$ and let $q \leqslant m$ be such that the functions $g_i(x)$ $(q < i \leqslant m)$ are linear affine. If the system*

$$g_i(x) \geqslant 0 \quad \textit{for } i = 1, 2, \ldots, m$$

$$f(x) > 0$$

has no solution $x \in \mathbf{R}^n$ and if the system

$$g_i(x) = \begin{cases} > 0 & \textit{for } 1 \leqslant i \leqslant q \\ \geqslant 0 & \textit{for } q < i \leqslant m \end{cases}$$

has a solution, then there exist numbers $y_1, y_2, \ldots, y_m \geqslant 0$ not all equal to zero such that

$$f(x) + \sum_{i=1}^{m} y_i g_i(x) \leqslant 0 \quad \textit{for every } x \in \mathbf{R}^n.$$

According to the fundamental theorem, there exists a function $g(x)$ of the form

$$g(x) = p_0 f(x) + \sum_{i=1}^{m} p_i g_i(x),$$

with

$$p_0, p_1, \ldots, p_m \geqslant 0 \quad \text{and} \quad p_0 + p_1 + \ldots + p_m = 1,$$

such that

$$g(x) \leqslant 0 \quad \text{for every } x \in \mathbf{R}^n.$$

If $p_0 \neq 0$, we put $y_i = p_i/p_0$ and the theorem is proved. We shall now show that if $p_0 = 0$ we have a contradiction. For, let x_0 be a solution of the second system: we have at the same time

$$g(x_0) \leqslant 0 \quad \text{and} \quad g(x_0) = \sum_{i=1}^{m} p_i g_i(x_0) \geqslant 0;$$

hence

$$g(x_0) = 0$$

and $p_i = 0$ for $1 \leqslant i \leqslant q$.

$g(x)$ is therefore a non-positive linear affine function which vanishes at x_0, hence

$$g(x) = 0 \quad \text{for every } x \in \mathbf{R}^n.$$

We can always suppose that, if we omit any one of the inequalities $g_i(x) \geqslant 0$ in the first system, the system becomes consistent. In these conditions the $m-q$ closed convex sets

$$C_i = \{x | g_i(x) \geqslant 0\} \quad (i = q+1, \ldots, m);$$

their intersection does not meet the convex set

$$C = \{x | f(x) > 0 \quad \text{and} \quad g_i(x) \geqslant 0, \quad \text{for } 1 \leqslant i \leqslant q\},$$

but the intersection of any $m-q-1$ of these sets meets the convex set. It follows, according to Corollary 2 (Chapter 3, 3.3), that their union does not contain C; in other words, there exists a point $x_1 \in C$ such that

$$g_i(x_1) < 0 \quad \text{for } i = q+1, \ldots, m.$$

Thus

$$g(x_1) = \sum_{i=q+1}^{m} p_i g_i(x_1) < 0,$$

which is impossible.

3.5. SION'S THEOREM

We shall now give a recent generalization of the Minimax theorem. This section is not indispensable for what follows and may be omitted at first reading.

A numerical function f defined on the convex set $C \subset \mathbf{R}^n$ is said to be *quasi-convex* in C if, for any number α the set

$$\{x | x \in C \quad \text{and} \quad f(x) < \alpha\}$$

is convex. f is said to be *quasi-concave* if $(-f)$ is quasi-convex.

EXAMPLE 1. If f is a convex function then

$$\begin{cases} f(x) < \alpha \\ f(x') < \alpha \end{cases} \Rightarrow f(px+p'x') \leqslant pf(x)+p'f(x') < \alpha,$$

f is therefore quasi-convex.

EXAMPLE 2. If, in $\mathbf{R}$, $f(t)$ is an increasing (or decreasing) function it is both quasi-convex and quasi-concave.

EXAMPLE 3. If in $\mathbf{R}$, $f(t)$ is a decreasing function from $-\infty$ to t_0 and increasing from t_0 to $+\infty$, it is quasi-convex.

Minimax theorem (Sion [16]). *If $A \subset \mathbf{R}^m$ and $B \subset \mathbf{R}^n$ are two compact convex sets and if $f(x,y)$ is a numerical function defined on $A \times B$, upper semicontinuous and quasi-concave with respect to x, lower semicontinuous and quasi-convex with respect to y, then there exists a point $x_0 \in A$ and a point $y_0 \in B$ such that*

$$f(x, y_0) \leqslant f(x_0, y_0) \leqslant f(x_0, y)$$

for every $x \in A$ and $y \in B$.

This theorem generalizes Von Neumann's minimax theorem (cf. preceding section).

It is enough here to show that

$$\max_{x\in A}\min_{y\in B} f(x,y) \geqslant \min_{y\in B}\max_{x\in A} f(x,y)$$

the rest of the proof being the same as for Von Neumann's theorem.

For this, we consider two numbers γ_1 and γ_2 satisfying

$$\gamma_1 < \min_{y\in B}\max_{x\in A} f(x,y)$$

and

$$\gamma_2 > \max_{x\in A}\min_{y\in B} f(x,y),$$

and show that $\gamma_1 < \gamma_2$.

For, we assign to every $x \in A$, the compact convex set

$$B_x = \{y | y \in B \quad \text{and} \quad f(x,y) < \gamma_1\};$$

similarly we assign to every $y \in B$, the compact convex set

$$A_y = \{x | x \in A \quad \text{and} \quad f(x,y) \geqslant \gamma_2\}.$$

Then

$$\bigcap_{x\in A} B_x = \bigcap_{y\in B} A_y = \emptyset.$$

Hence there exist points $x_1, x_2, \ldots, x_p \in A$ such that

$$\bigcap_{i=1}^{p} B_{x_i} = \emptyset,$$

and also points $y_1, y_2, \ldots, y_q \in B$ such that

$$\bigcap_{j=1}^{q} A_{yj} = \emptyset.$$

Consider the family $\mathscr{F}$ of ordered pairs (I, J) with

$$I \subset \{1,2,\ldots,p\}, \quad J \subset \{1,2,\ldots,q\}, \quad (I \neq \emptyset \text{ and } J \neq \emptyset),$$

such that the intersection of

$$(B_{x_i})_{i\in I}$$

does not meet the convex polyhedron generated by $(y_j)_{j\in J}$, and the intersection of

$$(A_{y_j})_{j\in J}$$

does not meet the convex polyhedron generated by $(x_i)_{i\in I}$.

This family is finite and non-empty; let (I_0, J_0) be a minimal element, that is to say, such that

$$(I,J) \in \mathscr{F}, I \subset I_0 \quad \text{and} \quad J \subset J_0 \Rightarrow I = I_0 \quad \text{and} \quad J = J_0.$$

Let r be the number of elements in I_0 and s the number of elements in J_0. Let A' be the convex polyhedron generated by

$$(x_i)_{i \in I_0},$$

and B' the convex polyhedron generated by

$$(y_j)_{j \in J_0}.$$

The intersection of the sets

$$(A_{y_j})_{j \in J_0}$$

does not meet A', but the intersection of any $s-1$ of these meets A', since (I_0, J_0) is minimal. It follows (cf. Corollary 2, Chapter 3, 3.3) that A' is not contained in the union of the

$$(A_{y_j})_{j \in J_0}.$$

Let x_0 be a point of A' not belonging to this union, then

$$f(x_0, y_j) < \gamma_2 \quad \text{for } j \in J_0,$$

and since $f(x, y)$ is quasi-convex in y, we have

$$f(x_0, y) < \gamma_2 \quad \text{for } y \in B'.$$

In the same way, there exists a point y_0 in B' such that

$$f(x, y_0) > \gamma_1 \quad \text{for } x \in A'.$$

Therefore

$$\gamma_1 < f(x_0, y_0) < \gamma_2,$$

which proves the theorem.

4. Programming and associated problems

4.1. DIFFERENTIABLE FUNCTIONS

A numerical function

$$f(\mathbf{x}) = f(x^1, x^2, \ldots, x^n)$$

defined in $\mathbf{R}^n$ is said to be *differentiable at a point* $\mathbf{x}_0$ if there exists a point $\boldsymbol{\delta}\mathbf{f}(\mathbf{x}_0)$ of $\mathbf{R}^n$ called the *gradient at* $\mathbf{x}_0$, such that the function

$$\beta_{\mathbf{x}_0}(\mathbf{u}) = \frac{f(\mathbf{x}_0+\mathbf{u})-f(\mathbf{x}_0)-\langle\boldsymbol{\delta}\mathbf{f}(\mathbf{x}_0),\mathbf{u}\rangle}{\|\mathbf{u}\|},$$

defined for all non-zero $\mathbf{u}$ in $\mathbf{R}^n$, tends to 0 when $\mathbf{u}$ tends to $\mathbf{0}$. The function f is said to be *differentiable* if it is differentiable at every point of $\mathbf{R}^n$.

The function f is said to *have a partial derivative* with respect to x^i if

$$\frac{f(\mathbf{x}+h\boldsymbol{\delta}_i)-f(\mathbf{x})}{h}$$

tends to a limit when h tends to 0; this limit, denoted by f'_i, or $\partial f/\partial x^i$, is the *partial derivative* with respect to x^i.

Theorem 1. *Every differentiable function is continuous and has partial derivatives with respect to each of its variables.*

If f is differentiable, the difference

$$f(\mathbf{x}+\mathbf{u})-f(\mathbf{x}) = \langle\boldsymbol{\delta}\mathbf{f}(\mathbf{x}),\mathbf{u}\rangle+\beta_{\mathbf{x}}(\mathbf{u})\,\|\mathbf{u}\|$$

tends to 0 as $\mathbf{u}$ tends to $\mathbf{0}$.

On the other hand, the ratio

$$\frac{f(\mathbf{x}+h\boldsymbol{\delta}_i)-f(\mathbf{x})}{h} = \langle\boldsymbol{\delta}\mathbf{f}(\mathbf{x}),\boldsymbol{\delta}_i\rangle+\beta_{\mathbf{x}}(h\boldsymbol{\delta}_i)\frac{|h|}{h}$$

tends to

$$\langle\boldsymbol{\delta}\mathbf{f}(\mathbf{x}),\boldsymbol{\delta}_i\rangle = \frac{\partial f}{\partial x^i}(\mathbf{x})$$

as h tends to 0.

NOTE 1. Thus we see that

$$\boldsymbol{\delta}\mathbf{f} = \left(\frac{\partial f}{\partial x^1}, \frac{\partial f}{\partial x^2}, \ldots, \frac{\partial f}{\partial x^n}\right).$$

NOTE 2. The converse of this proposition is not true; consider for example in $\mathbf{R}^2$ the function $f(x,y)$, where

$$f(x,y) = \frac{xy}{\sqrt{(x^2+y^2)}} \quad \text{if } x \neq 0 \text{ or } y \neq 0,$$

$$f(x,y) = 0 \quad \text{if } x = y = 0.$$

It is continuous at the point $(0,0) = \mathbf{0}$ and it has partial derivatives

$$\frac{\partial f}{\partial x} = 0 \quad \text{and} \quad \frac{\partial f}{\partial y} = 0$$

at this point; however the ratio

$$\frac{f(x,y)}{\sqrt{(x^2+y^2)}} = \frac{xy}{x^2+y^2}$$

does not tend to 0 as (x,y) tends to $\mathbf{0}$.

Theorem 2. *If a function $f(\mathbf{x})$ has continuous partial derivatives with respect to each of its variables, it is differentiable.*

To simplify the writing we prove the theorem only for the case of a function $f(x,y)$ in $\mathbf{R}^2$. We have

$$\begin{aligned} \Delta f &= f(x+h,y+k) - f(x,y) \\ &= [f(x+h,y+k) - f(x+h,h)] + [f(x+h,y) - f(x,y)] \end{aligned}$$

and according to the Mean value theorem

$$\Delta f = kf_y'(x+h,y+\theta_1 k) + hf_x'(x+\theta_2 h,y), \quad \text{with } 0 \leqslant \theta_1, \theta_2 \leqslant 1.$$

The partial derivatives being continuous, we have

$$|\Delta f - hf_x' - kf_y'| = |h\epsilon_1 + k\epsilon_2| \leqslant [|\epsilon_1| + |\epsilon_2|]\sqrt{(h^2+k^2)},$$

where ϵ_1 and ϵ_2 tend to 0 as (h,k) tends to $\mathbf{0}$.

Theorem 3. *If a convex function $f(\mathbf{x})$ has partial derivatives with respect to each of its variables, it is differentiable.*

Let $\mathbf{x}_0$ be a point of $\mathbf{R}^n$. Since

$$\varphi_{\mathbf{x}_0}(\mathbf{u}) = f(\mathbf{x}_0+\mathbf{u})-f(\mathbf{x}_0)-\sum_{i=1}^{n}\frac{\partial f}{\partial x^i}u^i$$

is a convex function of $\mathbf{u}$, we have

$$\varphi_{\mathbf{x}_0}(\mathbf{u}) = \varphi_{\mathbf{x}_0}\left(\frac{\sum nu^i\boldsymbol{\delta}_i}{n}\right) \leqslant \frac{1}{n}\sum_{i=1}^{n}\varphi(nu^i\boldsymbol{\delta}_i)$$
$$= \sum_{i=1}^{n} u^i\epsilon_i \leqslant \left(\sum_{i=1}^{n}|\epsilon_i|\right)\|\mathbf{u}\|,$$

where the numbers $\epsilon_1, \epsilon_2, \ldots, \epsilon_n$ are defined by

$$\epsilon_i = \frac{\varphi(nu^i\boldsymbol{\delta}_i)}{nu^i} = \frac{f(\mathbf{x}_0+nu^i\boldsymbol{\delta}_i)-f(\mathbf{x}_0)}{nu^i}-\frac{\partial f}{\partial x^i}$$

and tend to 0 as $\mathbf{u}$ tends to $\mathbf{0}$.

We also have

$$\varphi(\mathbf{0}) \leqslant \frac{\varphi(\mathbf{u})+\varphi(-\mathbf{u})}{2} \quad \text{and} \quad \varphi(\mathbf{0}) = 0,$$

hence

$$\varphi(\mathbf{u}) \geqslant -\varphi(-\mathbf{u}) \geqslant -\left(\sum_{i=1}^{n}|\epsilon_i'|\right)\|\mathbf{u}\|,$$

where the numbers $\epsilon_1', \epsilon_2', \ldots, \epsilon_n'$ tend to 0 as $\mathbf{u}$ tends to $\mathbf{0}$. Thus we see that the ratio

$$\frac{\varphi(\mathbf{u})}{\|\mathbf{u}\|}$$

tends to 0 as $\mathbf{u}$ tends to $\mathbf{0}$.

Theorem 4. *If the functions $f_1(\mathbf{x}), f_2(\mathbf{x}), \ldots, f_m(\mathbf{x})$ are differentiable in $\mathbf{R}^n$ and if the function $\varphi\ (z_1, z_2, \ldots, z_m)$ is differentiable in $\mathbf{R}^m$, the function*

$$g(\mathbf{x}) = \varphi[f_1(\mathbf{x}), f_2(\mathbf{x}), \ldots, f_m(\mathbf{x})]$$

is differentiable in $\mathbf{R}^n$.

We have

$$\Delta z_k = f_k(\mathbf{x}_0+\mathbf{u})-f_k(\mathbf{x}_0) = \sum_{i=1}^{n}\frac{\partial f_k}{\partial x^i}u^i+\beta_k(\mathbf{u})\,\|\mathbf{u}\|$$

and

$$\Delta g = g(\mathbf{x}_0+\mathbf{u})-g(\mathbf{x}_0)$$
$$= \varphi(z_1+\Delta z_1, z_2+\Delta z_2, \ldots, z_m+\Delta z_m)-\varphi(z_1, z_2, \ldots, z_m),$$

writing $z_k = f_k(\mathbf{x}_0)$; hence

$$\Delta g = \sum_{k=1}^{m} \frac{\partial \varphi}{\partial z_k} \Delta z_k + \gamma(\mathbf{\Delta z}) \|\mathbf{\Delta z}\|$$

$$= \sum_{i=1}^{m} u^i \sum_{k=1}^{m} \frac{\partial \varphi}{\partial z_k} \cdot \frac{\partial f_k}{\partial x^i} + \|\mathbf{u}\| \left(\sum_{k=1}^{m} \frac{\partial \varphi}{\partial z_k} \cdot \beta_k(\mathbf{u}) + \gamma(\mathbf{\Delta z}) \frac{\|\mathbf{\Delta z}\|}{\|\mathbf{u}\|} \right).$$

It is immediately clear that the last term in brackets tends to 0 as $\mathbf{u}$ tends to $\mathbf{0}$, therefore g is differentiable and we have

$$\frac{\partial g}{\partial x^i} = \sum_{k=1}^{m} \frac{\partial \varphi}{\partial z_k} \cdot \frac{\partial f_k}{\partial x^i}.$$

Theorem 5. *If a function $f(\mathbf{x})$ is differentiable and if $\mathbf{c}$ and $\mathbf{c}'$ are two points of $\mathbf{R}^n$, the function*

$$\varphi(\lambda) = f(\lambda \mathbf{c} + (1-\lambda)\mathbf{c}'),$$

defined for $\lambda \in \mathbf{R}$, has for its derivative

$$\varphi'(\lambda) = \langle \boldsymbol{\delta} \mathbf{f}(\lambda \mathbf{c} + (1-\lambda)\mathbf{c}'), \mathbf{c} - \mathbf{c}' \rangle.$$

If we put

$$\mathbf{x} = \lambda \mathbf{c} + (1-\lambda)\mathbf{c}' = \mathbf{c}' + \lambda(\mathbf{c} - \mathbf{c}'),$$

we have

$$\varphi(\lambda + \Delta\lambda) - \varphi(\lambda) = f(\mathbf{x} + \Delta\lambda(\mathbf{c} - \mathbf{c}')) - f(\mathbf{x})$$

$$= \Delta\lambda \langle \boldsymbol{\delta} \mathbf{f}(\mathbf{x}), \mathbf{c} - \mathbf{c}' \rangle + \beta(\Delta\lambda(\mathbf{c} - \mathbf{c}')) \, |\Delta\lambda| \, \|\mathbf{c} - \mathbf{c}'\|,$$

which shows that

$$\frac{\varphi(\lambda + \Delta\lambda) - \varphi(\lambda)}{\Delta\lambda}$$

tends to $\langle \boldsymbol{\delta} \mathbf{f}(\mathbf{x}), \mathbf{c} - \mathbf{c}' \rangle$ when $\Delta\lambda$ tends to 0.

Lemma. *Let $\varphi(\lambda)$ be a differentiable numerical function defined in $\mathbf{R}$.*

1. *If $\varphi'(\lambda)$ is increasing in an interval, then $\varphi(\lambda)$ is convex in that interval.*
2. *If $\varphi(\lambda)$ is convex in the interval $[0,1]$, then*

$$\varphi'(0) \leqslant \varphi(1) - \varphi(0) \leqslant \varphi'(1).$$

1. Let λ_1 and λ_2 be any two numbers in this interval and let λ lie between these two numbers: for example suppose that $\lambda_1 < \lambda < \lambda_2$. Then

$$\varphi(\lambda) - \varphi(\lambda_1) = (\lambda - \lambda_1)\varphi'(\lambda'), \quad \text{with } \lambda_1 \leqslant \lambda' \leqslant \lambda$$

and

$$\varphi(\lambda_2) - \varphi(\lambda) = (\lambda_2 - \lambda)\varphi'(\lambda''), \quad \text{with } \lambda \leqslant \lambda'' \leqslant \lambda_2;$$

hence

$$\frac{\varphi(\lambda)-\varphi(\lambda_1)}{\lambda-\lambda_1} = \varphi'(\lambda') \leqslant \varphi'(\lambda'') = \frac{\varphi(\lambda_2)-\varphi(\lambda)}{\lambda_2-\lambda}.$$

That is,

$$(\lambda_2-\lambda)\,\varphi(\lambda)-(\lambda_2-\lambda)\,\varphi(\lambda_1) \leqslant (\lambda-\lambda_1)\,\varphi(\lambda_2)-(\lambda-\lambda_1)\,\varphi(\lambda),$$

or, again

$$(\lambda_2-\lambda_1)\,\varphi(\lambda) \leqslant (\lambda_2-\lambda)\,\varphi(\lambda_1)+(\lambda-\lambda_1)\,\varphi(\lambda_2).$$

If we write

$$\lambda = \alpha_1\lambda_1+\alpha_2\lambda_2,$$

where α_1, $\alpha_2 \geqslant 0$ and $\alpha_1+\alpha_2 = 1$, we have

$$\varphi(\alpha_1\lambda_1+\alpha_2\lambda_2) \leqslant \alpha_1\varphi(\lambda_1)+\alpha_2\varphi(\lambda_2).$$

2. Let λ be a number such that $0<\lambda<1$; then

$$\varphi(\lambda)-\varphi(\lambda 1+(1-\lambda)\,0) \leqslant \lambda\varphi(1)+(1-\lambda)\,\varphi(0);$$

hence

$$\frac{\varphi(\lambda)-\varphi(0)}{\lambda} \leqslant \varphi(1)-\varphi(0) \leqslant \frac{\varphi(\lambda)-\varphi(1)}{\lambda-1}.$$

As λ tends to 0, we get

$$\varphi'(0) \leqslant \varphi(1)-\varphi(0);$$

and as λ tends to 1,

$$\varphi(1)-\varphi(0) \leqslant \varphi'(1).$$

Fundamental theorem. *Let f be a differentiable function defined in $\mathbf{R}^n$, and let C be a convex set in $\mathbf{R}^n$.*

Firstly, for f to be convex in C, it is necessary and sufficient that for every $\mathbf{c}$, $\mathbf{c}' \in C$,

$$\langle \boldsymbol{\delta}\mathbf{f}(\mathbf{c}')-\boldsymbol{\delta}\mathbf{f}(\mathbf{c}), \mathbf{c}'-\mathbf{c}\rangle \geqslant 0 \tag{i}$$

Secondly, if f is convex in C and if $\mathbf{c}$ *and* $\mathbf{c}'$ *are two points in C, then*

$$\langle \boldsymbol{\delta}\mathbf{f}(\mathbf{c}), \mathbf{c}'-\mathbf{c}\rangle \leqslant f(\mathbf{c}')-f(\mathbf{c}).$$

Let $\mathbf{c}$, $\mathbf{c}'$ be any two points of C and consider the function

$$\varphi(\lambda) = f(\lambda\mathbf{c}+(1-\lambda)\,\mathbf{c}').$$

Firstly, suppose that the condition (i) is satisfied and let λ_1, λ_2 be two numbers such that $0 \leqslant \lambda_1 < \lambda_2 \leqslant 1$, let us put

$$\mathbf{c}_1 = \lambda_1\mathbf{c}+(1-\lambda_1)\,\mathbf{c}' \quad \text{and} \quad \mathbf{c}_2 = \lambda_2\mathbf{c}+(1-\lambda_2)\,\mathbf{c}'.$$

We have

$$\langle \boldsymbol{\delta}\mathbf{f}(\mathbf{c}_2) - \boldsymbol{\delta}\mathbf{f}(\mathbf{c}_1), \mathbf{c}_2 - \mathbf{c}_1 \rangle \geqslant 0;$$

now

$$\mathbf{c}_2 - \mathbf{c}_1 = (\lambda_2 - \lambda_1)(\mathbf{c} - \mathbf{c}');$$

hence

$$\langle \boldsymbol{\delta}\mathbf{f}(\mathbf{c}_2) - \boldsymbol{\delta}\mathbf{f}(\mathbf{c}_1), \mathbf{c} - \mathbf{c}' \rangle \geqslant 0$$

and consequently

$$\varphi'(\lambda_1) = \langle \boldsymbol{\delta}\mathbf{f}(\mathbf{c}_1), \mathbf{c} - \mathbf{c}' \rangle \leqslant \langle \boldsymbol{\delta}\mathbf{f}(\mathbf{c}_2), \mathbf{c} - \mathbf{c}' \rangle = \varphi'(\lambda_2).$$

Thus $\varphi'(\lambda)$ is increasing in $[0, 1]$, hence $\varphi(\lambda)$ is convex in this interval. Conversely, if $\varphi(\lambda)$ is convex, then

$$\varphi'(0) \leqslant \varphi(1) - \varphi(0) \leqslant \varphi'(1),$$

that is to say

$$\langle \boldsymbol{\delta}\mathbf{f}(\mathbf{c}'), \mathbf{c} - \mathbf{c}' \rangle \leqslant f(\mathbf{c}) - f(\mathbf{c}') \leqslant \langle \boldsymbol{\delta}\mathbf{f}(\mathbf{c}), \mathbf{c} - \mathbf{c}' \rangle;$$

hence

$$\langle \boldsymbol{\delta}\mathbf{f}(\mathbf{c}') - \boldsymbol{\delta}\mathbf{f}(\mathbf{c}), \mathbf{c}' - \mathbf{c} \rangle \geqslant 0$$

and

$$\langle \boldsymbol{\delta}\mathbf{f}(\mathbf{c}), \mathbf{c}' - \mathbf{c} \rangle \leqslant f(\mathbf{c}') - f(\mathbf{c}).$$

4.2. KUHN AND TUCKER MULTIPLIERS

Here we shall study the programming problem as follows:

Problem 1. *Given the numerical functions f, g^1, $g^2, \ldots, g^n$ defined in $\mathbf{R}^m$, find a point $\mathbf{x}$ of $\mathbf{R}^m$, subject to*

$$g^j(\mathbf{x}) \geqslant 0 \quad \text{for } j = 1, 2, \ldots, n$$

and such that $f(\mathbf{x})$ is a maximum.

The inequalities $g^j(\mathbf{x}) \geqslant 0$ are called the *constraints* of the programme. The function f is called the *gain function* of the programme. The set of points which satisfy the constraints is called the *domain* and is denoted by D. The programme is said to be *bounded* if $f(x)$ is bounded above in the domain.

NOTE. If a condition of the form $g(\mathbf{x}) \leqslant 0$ is imposed on $\mathbf{x}$, it is enough to write $-g(\mathbf{x}) \geqslant 0$. If it is required to impose a condition on $\mathbf{x}$ of the form $g(\mathbf{x}) = 0$, it is enough to write $g(\mathbf{x}) \geqslant 0$ and $-g(\mathbf{x}) \geqslant 0$.

The aim of this section is to study the connexions between this problem and certain other problems which we shall now enumerate.

Problem 2 (*Local Maximum Problem*). *Find an* $\mathbf{x} \in D$ *which possesses the following property: for every point* $\mathbf{u} \in \mathbf{R}^m$, *a number* $\lambda_0 > 0$ *can be found such that*

$$\left.\begin{matrix} 0 \leqslant \lambda \leqslant \lambda_0 \\ \mathbf{x}+\lambda\mathbf{u} \in D \end{matrix}\right\} \Rightarrow f(\mathbf{x}+\lambda\mathbf{u}) \leqslant f(\mathbf{x}).$$

Problem 3. *Given the differentiable functions* $f, g^1, \ldots, g^n$, *find an* $\mathbf{x} \in D$ *such that* $\langle \boldsymbol{\delta}\mathbf{f}, \mathbf{u}\rangle \leqslant 0$ *for every point* $\mathbf{u} \in \mathbf{R}^m$ *for which*

$$g^j(\mathbf{x}) = 0 \Rightarrow \langle \boldsymbol{\delta}\mathbf{g}^j, \mathbf{u}\rangle \geqslant 0.$$

Problem 4 (*Lagrange's Problem*). *Given the differentiable functions* $f, g^1, \ldots, g^n$, *find an* $\mathbf{x} \in D$ *and a* $\mathbf{y} = (y_1, y_2, \ldots, y_n) \geqslant \mathbf{0}$ *such that*

$$\sum_j y_j g^j(\mathbf{x}) = 0,$$

$$\frac{\partial f}{\partial x^i} + \sum_j y_j \frac{\partial g^j}{\partial x^i} = 0 \quad \textit{for } i = 1, 2, \ldots, m.$$

Problem 5. *Find a point*

$$\bar{\mathbf{x}} = (\bar{x}^1, \bar{x}^2, \ldots, \bar{x}^m) \in \mathbf{R}^m$$

and a point

$$\bar{\mathbf{y}} = (\bar{y}_1, \bar{y}_2, \ldots, \bar{y}_n) \geqslant \mathbf{0}$$

such that the pair $(\bar{\mathbf{x}}, \bar{\mathbf{y}})$ *is a saddle point of the function*

$$F(\mathbf{x}, \mathbf{y}) = f(\mathbf{x}) + \sum_j y_j g^j(\mathbf{x}),$$

that is to say, such that,

$$F(\mathbf{x}, \bar{\mathbf{y}}) \leqslant F(\bar{\mathbf{x}}, \bar{\mathbf{y}}) \leqslant F(\bar{\mathbf{x}}, \mathbf{y})$$

for every $\mathbf{x} \in \mathbf{R}^m$ *and* $\mathbf{y} = (y_1, y_2, \ldots, y_n) \geqslant \mathbf{0}$.

The function $F(\mathbf{x}, \mathbf{y})$ is called a *Lagrangian function*.

Proposition 1. *Every solution of Problem 1 is a solution of Problem 2. If* $(\bar{\mathbf{x}}, \bar{\mathbf{y}})$ *is a solution of Problem 5, then* $\bar{\mathbf{x}}$ *is a solution of Problem 1.*

The first part of the proposition is obvious.

If $(\bar{\mathbf{x}}, \bar{\mathbf{y}})$ is a solution of Problem 5, we have

$$g^j(\bar{\mathbf{x}}) \geqslant 0 \quad \text{for } j = 1, 2, \ldots, n;$$

For, if we had $g^{j_0}(\bar{\mathbf{x}}) < 0$ for some index j_0, then upon setting

$$z_j = \begin{cases} \bar{y}_j & \text{for } j \neq j_0 \\ \bar{y}_j + 1 & \text{for } j = j_0 \end{cases} \geqslant 0,$$

we would have

$$F(\bar{\mathbf{x}}, \mathbf{z}) = F(\bar{\mathbf{x}}, \bar{\mathbf{y}}) + g^{j_0}(\bar{\mathbf{x}}) < F(\bar{\mathbf{x}}, \bar{\mathbf{y}}),$$

contradicting the definition of the pair $(\bar{\mathbf{x}}, \bar{\mathbf{y}})$.

On the other hand, if a point $\mathbf{x}$ satisfies

$$g^j(\mathbf{x}) \geqslant 0 \quad \text{for } j = 1, 2, \ldots, n,$$

then

$$f(\mathbf{x}) \leqslant F(\mathbf{x}, \bar{\mathbf{y}}) \leqslant F(\bar{\mathbf{x}}, \bar{\mathbf{y}}) \leqslant F(\bar{\mathbf{x}}, \mathbf{0}) = f(\bar{\mathbf{x}}).$$

Proposition 2. *If the functions $f, g^1, g^2, \ldots, g^n$ are differentiable, every solution of Problem 5 is a solution of Problem 4, and Problems 3 and 4 are equivalent.*

Firstly, let $(\bar{\mathbf{x}}, \bar{\mathbf{y}})$ be a solution of Problem 5. Then by definition

$$\bar{y}_j \geqslant 0 \quad \text{for } j = 1, 2, \ldots, n.$$

Referring to the proof of Proposition 1, we see that

$$g^j(\bar{\mathbf{x}}) \geqslant 0 \quad \text{for } j = 1, 2, \ldots, n,$$

and

$$\sum_j \bar{y}_j g^j(\bar{\mathbf{x}}) = F(\bar{\mathbf{x}}, \bar{\mathbf{y}}) - f(\bar{\mathbf{x}}) = 0.$$

On the other hand, we must have for every $\mathbf{u} \in \mathbf{R}^m$ and every $\lambda > 0$

$$F(\bar{\mathbf{x}} + \lambda \mathbf{u}, \bar{\mathbf{y}}) \leqslant F(\bar{\mathbf{x}}, \bar{\mathbf{y}}),$$

that is

$$\frac{F(\bar{\mathbf{x}} + \lambda \mathbf{u}, \bar{\mathbf{y}}) - F(\bar{\mathbf{x}}, \bar{\mathbf{y}})}{\lambda} \leqslant 0.$$

As λ tends to zero, we obtain

$$\left\langle \boldsymbol{\delta}\mathbf{f} + \sum_j \bar{y}_j \boldsymbol{\delta}\mathbf{g}^j, \mathbf{u} \right\rangle \leqslant 0$$

for every $\mathbf{u} \in \mathbf{R}^m$; this implies

$$\boldsymbol{\delta}\mathbf{f} + \sum_j \bar{y}_j \boldsymbol{\delta}\mathbf{g}^j = 0.$$

The pair $(\bar{\mathbf{x}}, \bar{\mathbf{y}})$ is therefore a solution of Problem 4.

Secondly, let $(\bar{\mathbf{x}}, \bar{\mathbf{y}})$ be a solution of Problem 4 and let $J \subset \{1, 2, \ldots, n\}$, be defined by

$$j \in J \Leftrightarrow g^j(\bar{\mathbf{x}}) = 0.$$

The terms $\bar{y}_j g^j(\bar{\mathbf{x}})$ must all be zero since they are all non-negative and their sum is zero, therefore

$$j \notin J \Rightarrow \bar{y}_j = 0;$$

hence

$$\boldsymbol{\delta}\mathbf{f} = -\sum_{j=1}^{n} \bar{y}_j \boldsymbol{\delta}\mathbf{g}^j = -\sum_{j \in J} \bar{y}_j \boldsymbol{\delta}\mathbf{g}^j.$$

Thus we see that if $\mathbf{u} \in \mathbf{R}^m$ satisfies

$$\langle \boldsymbol{\delta}\mathbf{g}^j, \mathbf{u} \rangle \geqslant 0 \quad \text{for } j \in J,$$

it necessarily satisfies

$$\langle \boldsymbol{\delta}\mathbf{f}, \mathbf{u} \rangle \geqslant 0.$$

$\bar{\mathbf{x}}$ is consequently a solution of Problem 3.

Thirdly, let $\bar{\mathbf{x}}$ be a solution of Problem 3, we define the set J similarly by

$$j \in J \Leftrightarrow g^j(\bar{\mathbf{x}}) = 0.$$

The system

$$\langle \boldsymbol{\delta}\mathbf{g}^j, \mathbf{u} \rangle \geqslant 0 \quad \text{for } j \in J$$

$$\langle \boldsymbol{\delta}\mathbf{f}, \mathbf{u} \rangle > 0$$

has no solution $\mathbf{u} \in \mathbf{R}^m$, while the system

$$\langle \boldsymbol{\delta}\mathbf{g}^j, \mathbf{u} \rangle \geqslant 0 \quad \text{for } j \in J$$

has the solution $\mathbf{u} = \mathbf{0}$.

According to Farkas's Theorem (see page 67), there exist numbers $\lambda_j \geqslant 0$ $(j \in J)$ such that

$$\langle \boldsymbol{\delta}\mathbf{f}, \mathbf{u} \rangle + \sum_{j \in J} \lambda_j \langle \boldsymbol{\delta}\mathbf{g}^j, \mathbf{u} \rangle \leqslant 0$$

for every $\mathbf{u} \in \mathbf{R}^m$, which implies that

$$\boldsymbol{\delta}\mathbf{f} + \sum_{j \in J} \lambda_j \boldsymbol{\delta}\mathbf{g}^j = 0.$$

Define $\bar{\mathbf{y}} = (y_1, y_2, \ldots, y_m)$ by

$$\bar{y}_i = \begin{cases} \lambda_j & \text{for } j \in J, \\ 0 & \text{for } j \notin J. \end{cases}$$

The pair $(\bar{\mathbf{x}}, \bar{\mathbf{y}})$ is a solution of Problem 4.

Proposition 3. *If the functions f, g^1, $g^2, \ldots,$ g^n are differentiable and if f is concave, every solution of Problem 3 is a solution of Problem 2.*

Let $\bar{\mathbf{x}}$ be a solution of Problem 3; as before let us denote by J the set of indices j for which $g^j(\bar{\mathbf{x}}) = 0$. If $\mathbf{u}$ is any point of $\mathbf{R}^m$, two cases can arise.

CASE I. There is at least one index $j_0 \in J$ for which $\langle \boldsymbol{\delta}\mathbf{g}^{j_0}, \mathbf{u}\rangle < 0$; then we can find a number $\lambda_0 > 0$ such that

$$0 < \lambda \leqslant \lambda_0 \Rightarrow g^{j_0}(\bar{\mathbf{x}}+\lambda\mathbf{u}) < g^{j_0}(\bar{\mathbf{x}}) = 0;$$

in this case, we cannot at the same time have $0 \leqslant \lambda \leqslant \lambda_0$ and $\mathbf{x}+\lambda\mathbf{u} \in D$ unless $\lambda = 0$.

CASE II. For every $j \in J$, we have $\langle \boldsymbol{\delta}\mathbf{g}^j, \mathbf{u}\rangle \geqslant 0$: $\bar{\mathbf{x}}$ being a solution of Problem 3, we have $\langle \boldsymbol{\delta}\mathbf{f}, \mathbf{u}\rangle \leqslant 0$, and, since f is concave,

$$f(\bar{\mathbf{x}}+\lambda\mathbf{u}) \leqslant f(\bar{\mathbf{x}})+\lambda\langle \boldsymbol{\delta}\mathbf{f}, \mathbf{u}\rangle \leqslant f(\bar{\mathbf{x}}) \quad \text{for every } \lambda > 0.$$

In both cases, we see that we can find a number $\lambda_0 > 0$ such that

$$\left.\begin{array}{r} 0 \leqslant \lambda \leqslant \lambda_0 \\ \bar{\mathbf{x}}+\lambda\mathbf{u} \in D \end{array}\right\} \Rightarrow f(\bar{\mathbf{x}}+\lambda\mathbf{u}) \leqslant f(\bar{\mathbf{x}}).$$

$\bar{\mathbf{x}}$ is thus a solution of Problem 2.

NOTE. It can be shown, using trivial examples, that if f is not concave, a solution $\bar{\mathbf{x}}$ of Problem 3 is not necessarily a solution of Problem 2.

EXAMPLE 1. Find $x \in \mathbf{R}$ such that $f(x) = x^2$ is maximized.

EXAMPLE 2. Find $x \in \mathbf{R}$ such that $f(x) = x^3$ is maximized.

In these two examples, Problem 2 has no solution, while Problem 3 has the solution $\bar{x} = 0$.

What is more unexpected, and should be noted, is that in certain special cases a solution of Problem 2 cannot be a solution of Problem 3, as is shown in the following example.

EXAMPLE 3. Find

$$\mathbf{x} = (x_1, x_2) \in \mathbf{R}^2$$

subject to

$$g_1(\mathbf{x}) = x_1 \geqslant 0,$$

$$g_2(\mathbf{x}) = x_2 \geqslant 0,$$

$$g_3(\mathbf{x}) = (1-x_1)^3 - x_2 \geqslant 0,$$

and such that $f(\mathbf{x}) = x_1$ is maximized.

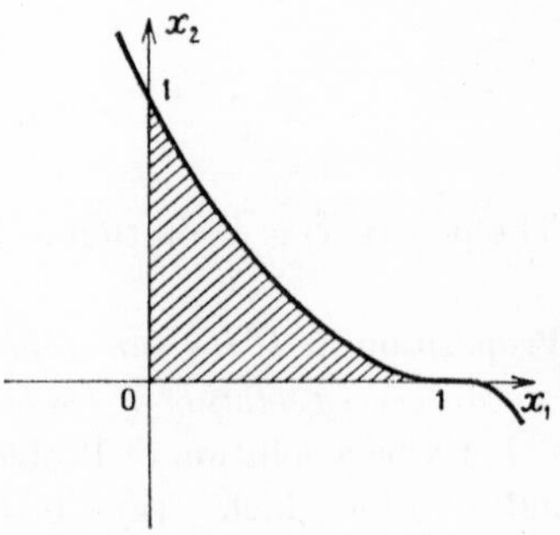

In the accompanying figure the shaded region represents the set of points $\mathbf{x}$ which satisfy the constraints, and we see that Problems 1 and 2 have the unique solution $\bar{\mathbf{x}} = (1,0)$. Now we have

$$g_1(\bar{\mathbf{x}}) = 1, \quad g_2(\bar{\mathbf{x}}) = 0, \quad g_3(\bar{\mathbf{x}}) = 0,$$

and the point $\mathbf{u} = (1,0)$ satisfies

$$\langle \boldsymbol{\delta}\mathbf{g}_2, \mathbf{u}\rangle = \langle \boldsymbol{\delta}\mathbf{g}_3, \mathbf{u}\rangle = 0$$

and

$$\langle \boldsymbol{\delta}\mathbf{f}, \mathbf{u}\rangle = 1 > 0.$$

Therefore $\bar{\mathbf{x}}$ is not a solution of Problem 3.

Proposition 4. *If the functions f, g^1, $g^2, \ldots, g^n$ are concave, every solution of Problem 2 is a solution of Problem 1.*

Let $\bar{\mathbf{x}}$ be a solution of Problem 2, and $\mathbf{x}$ be a point of $\mathbf{R}^m$ satisfying

$$g^j(\mathbf{x}) \geqslant 0 \quad \text{for } j = 1, 2, \ldots, n.$$

Every point of the form

$$\bar{\mathbf{x}} + \lambda(\mathbf{x} - \bar{\mathbf{x}}) = \lambda\mathbf{x} + (1-\lambda)\,\bar{\mathbf{x}},$$

with $0 < \lambda < 1$, satisfies

$$g^j(\lambda\mathbf{x} + (1-\lambda)\,\bar{\mathbf{x}}) \geqslant \lambda g^j(\mathbf{x}) + (1-\lambda)\, g^j(\bar{\mathbf{x}}) \geqslant 0$$

for $j = 1, 2, \ldots, n$.

Choosing λ sufficiently small, we have

$$f(\lambda\mathbf{x} + (1-\lambda)\,\bar{\mathbf{x}}) \leqslant f(\bar{\mathbf{x}}),$$

which implies that

$$f(\bar{\mathbf{x}}) > \lambda f(\mathbf{x}) + (1-\lambda) f(\bar{\mathbf{x}}),$$

hence

$$f(\bar{\mathbf{x}}) \geqslant f(\mathbf{x}).$$

Kuhn and Tucker theorem. *If the functions f, g^1, $g^2, \ldots, g^n$ are concave and if there exists at least one point $\mathbf{x}$ satisfying the constraints and such that $g^j(\mathbf{x}) \neq 0$ for all the functions $g^j(\mathbf{x})$ which are not linear affine, Problems 1, 2 and 5 are equivalent. If, moreover, the functions f, g^1, $g^2, \ldots, g^n$ are differentiable all five problems are equivalent.*

Given the above four propositions, it is enough to show that if $\bar{\mathbf{x}}$ is a solution of Problem 1, there exists a point $\bar{\mathbf{y}} \in \mathbf{R}^n$ such that $(\bar{\mathbf{x}}, \bar{\mathbf{y}})$ is a solution of Problem 5. The system

$$g^j(\mathbf{x}) \geqslant 0,$$

$$f(\mathbf{x}) - f(\bar{\mathbf{x}}) > 0,$$

has no solution; according to Farkas's Theorem there exists a point

$$\bar{\mathbf{y}} = (\bar{y}_1, \bar{y}_2, \ldots, \bar{y}_n) \in \mathbf{R}^n,$$

with $\bar{y}_1, \bar{y}_2, \ldots, \bar{y}_n \geqslant 0$ such that

$$f(\mathbf{x}) - f(\bar{\mathbf{x}}) + \sum_j \bar{y}_j g^j(\mathbf{x}) \leqslant 0$$

for every $\mathbf{x} \in \mathbf{R}^m$, that is to say, such that

$$F(\mathbf{x}, \bar{\mathbf{y}}) \leqslant f(\bar{\mathbf{x}})$$

for every $\mathbf{x} \in \mathbf{R}^m$. Also

$$f(\bar{\mathbf{x}}) \leqslant F(\bar{\mathbf{x}}, \mathbf{y})$$

for every

$$\mathbf{y} = (y_1, y_2, \ldots, y_n) \quad \text{with } y_1, y_2, \ldots, y_n \geqslant 0$$

hence,

$$F(\mathbf{x}, \bar{\mathbf{y}}) \leqslant f(\bar{\mathbf{x}}) \leqslant F(\bar{\mathbf{x}}, \mathbf{y}),$$

for every $\mathbf{x} \in \mathbf{R}^m$ and $y_1, y_2, \ldots, y_n \geqslant 0$. Putting $\mathbf{x} = \bar{\mathbf{x}}$ and $\mathbf{y} = \bar{\mathbf{y}}$ we see that

$$f(\bar{\mathbf{x}}) = F(\bar{\mathbf{x}}, \bar{\mathbf{y}}).$$

$(\bar{\mathbf{x}}, \bar{\mathbf{y}})$ is thus a solution of Problem 5.

This theorem is a slight generalization of the well-known result of H. W. Kuhn and A. W. Tucker [13].

NOTE. Consider the problem which consists in finding $\mathbf{x} = (x_1, x_2) \in \mathbf{R}^2$, subject to

$$g_1(\mathbf{x}) = x_2 - x_1^2 \geqslant 0,$$

$$g_2(\mathbf{x}) = -x_2 \geqslant 0,$$

and such that

$$f(\mathbf{x}) = ax_1 + bx_2$$

is maximized ($a \neq 0$).

The functions f and g_2 are linear affine and we can verify that $g_1(x)$ is concave. However, the system

$$g_1(\mathbf{x}) \geqslant 0,$$

$$g_2(\mathbf{x}) \geqslant 0,$$

has only the solution $\mathbf{x} = (0,0)$: this solution does not satisfy $g_1(\mathbf{x}) \neq 0$, and the conditions postulated in the Kuhn and Tucker Theorem are not all satisfied; $\bar{\mathbf{x}} = (0,0)$ is clearly the unique solution of Problems 1 and 2. Now $\mathbf{u} = (a, 0)$ satisfies

$$\langle \boldsymbol{\delta}\mathbf{g}_1, \mathbf{u} \rangle = \langle \boldsymbol{\delta}\mathbf{g}_2, \mathbf{u} \rangle = 0$$

and

$$\langle \boldsymbol{\delta}\mathbf{f}, \mathbf{u} \rangle = a^2 > 0.$$

Thus Problem 3 has no solution; according to Proposition 2, Problems 4 and 5 also have no solutions.

It is often convenient to put Problems 1 and 5 in the following forms.

Problem 1′. *If $f, g^1, g^2, \ldots, g^r$ are concave functions and $g^{r+1}, \ldots, g^n$ are linear affine functions, find an $\mathbf{x} \in \mathbf{R}^m$ subject to*

$$g^j(\mathbf{x}) \geqslant 0 \quad \text{for } j = 1, 2, \ldots, r$$
$$g^j(\mathbf{x}) = 0 \quad \text{for } j = r+1, \ldots, n$$

and such that $f(\mathbf{x})$ is maximized.

Problem 5′. *Find an $\mathbf{x} \in \mathbf{R}^m$, non-negative numbers $y_1, y_2, \ldots, y_r$ and numbers $y_{r+1}, y_{r+2}, \ldots, y_n$, subject to*

$$g^j(\mathbf{x}) \geqslant 0 \quad \text{for } j = 1, 2, \ldots, r,$$
$$g^j(\mathbf{x}) = 0 \quad \text{for } j = r+1, \ldots, n,$$
$$\sum_{j=1}^{n} y_j g^j(\mathbf{x}) = 0,$$

and such that the function

$$F(\boldsymbol{\xi}) = f(\boldsymbol{\xi}) + \sum_{j=1}^{n} y_j g^j(\boldsymbol{\xi})$$

reaches its maximum in $\mathbf{R}^m$ at the point $\boldsymbol{\xi} = \mathbf{x}$.

Corollary. *If there exists a point $\mathbf{x}$, satisfying the constraints and such that $g^j(\mathbf{x}) \neq 0$ for all the functions g^j which are not linear affine, Problems 1′ and 5′ are equivalent.*

For, if we replace each of the equalities $g^j(\mathbf{x}) = 0$ by the two inequalities $g^j(\mathbf{x}) \geqslant 0$ and $-g^j(\mathbf{x}) \geqslant 0$, we see that Problem 1′ is equivalent to the problem of finding the numbers

$$y_1, y_2, \ldots, y_r, y'_{r+1}, \ldots, y'_n, y''_{r+1}, \ldots, y''_n \geqslant 0$$

and a point $\mathbf{x} \in \mathbf{R}^m$ such that the function

$$F(\boldsymbol{\xi}) = f(\boldsymbol{\xi}) + \sum_{j=1}^{r} y_j g^j(\boldsymbol{\xi}) + \sum_{j=r+1}^{n} (y'_j - y''_j)\, g^j(\boldsymbol{\xi})$$

reaches its maximum in $\mathbf{R}^m$ at the point $\boldsymbol{\xi} = \mathbf{x}$, and such that

$$\sum_{j=1}^{r} y_j g^j(\mathbf{x}) + \sum_{j=r+1}^{n} (y'_j - y''_j)\, g^j(\mathbf{x}) \leqslant \sum_{j=1}^{r} \eta_j g^j(\mathbf{x}) + \sum_{j=r+1}^{n} (\eta'_j - \eta''_j)\, g^j(\mathbf{x})$$

for all numbers:

$$\eta_1, \eta_2, \ldots, \eta_r, \quad \eta'_{r+1}, \ldots, \eta'_n, \quad \eta''_{r+1}, \ldots, \eta''_n \geqslant 0.$$

If we note that every number η can be expressed in the form $\eta' - \eta''$ with $\eta', \eta'' \geqslant 0$, we see that the latter condition is equivalent to the system of conditions

$$g^j(\mathbf{x}) \geqslant 0 \quad \text{for } j = 1, 2, \ldots, r,$$

$$g^j(\mathbf{x}) = 0 \quad \text{for } j = r+1, \ldots, n,$$

$$\sum_{j=1}^{n} y_j g^j(\mathbf{x}) = 0,$$

on writing

$$y_j = y_j' - y_j'' \quad \text{for } j = r+1, \ldots, n.$$

Problem 1′ is thus equivalent to Problem 5′.

NOTE. The condition

$$\sum_{j=1}^{n} y_j g^j(x) = 0$$

can also be written as

$$\sum_{j=1}^{r} y_j g^j(x) = 0,$$

since

$$g^j(x) = 0 \quad \text{for } j = r+1, \ldots, n.$$

5. Convex programmes with linear constraints

In this chapter we shall be concerned only with the following problem.

To find numbers $x^1, x^2, \ldots, x^p \geqslant 0, x^{p+1}, x^{p+2}, \ldots, x^m$ *subject to*

$$\sum_{i=1}^{m} a_i^j x^i \leqslant b^j \quad \textit{for } j = 1, 2, \ldots, r$$

$$\sum_{i=1}^{m} a_i^j x^i = b^j \quad \textit{for } j = r+1, \ldots, n$$

and such that the concave function

$$f(\mathbf{x}) = f(x^1, x^2, \ldots, x^m)$$

is maximized.

The domain of such a programming problem is a polytope (cf. Chapter 3, 3.2).

5.1. ASSOCIATED PROBLEM

Such a programming problem is equivalent to the following (of the form 5′): to find a point $\mathbf{x} \in \mathbf{R}^m$ satisfying the constraints and numbers $y_1, y_2, \ldots, y_r \geqslant 0$, $y_{r+1}, \ldots, y_n$ of any sign and $x'_1, x'_2, \ldots, x'_p \geqslant 0$ such that

$$\sum_{j=1}^{n} y_j \left(b^j - \sum_{i=1}^{m} a_i^j x^i\right) + \sum_{i=1}^{p} x'_i x^i = 0 \tag{1}$$

and such that

$$F(\boldsymbol{\xi}) = f(\boldsymbol{\xi}) + \sum_{j=1}^{n} y_j \left(b^j - \sum_{i=1}^{m} a_i^j \xi^i\right) + \sum_{i=1}^{p} x'_i \xi^i \tag{2}$$

reaches its maximum in $\mathbf{R}^m$ for $\boldsymbol{\xi} = \mathbf{x}$.

Notice that condition (1) is equivalent to the conditions

$$\sum_{j=1}^{n} y^j\left(b^j - \sum_{i=1}^{m} a_i^j x^i\right) = 0 \tag{1'}$$

and

$$\sum_{i=1}^{p} x_i' x^i = 0. \tag{1''}$$

Also notice that the problem of finding $x^1, x^2, \ldots, x^p \geqslant 0, x^{p+1}, \ldots, x^m$ such that the function

$$\varphi(\mathbf{x}) = f(\mathbf{x}) + \sum_{j=1}^{n} y_j\left(b^j - \sum_{i=1}^{m} a_i^j x^i\right)$$

is maximized, (where $y_1, y_2, \ldots, y_n$ are given) is equivalent to the problem of finding $x^1, x^2, \ldots, x^p \geqslant 0, x^{p+1}, \ldots, x^m$ and $x_1', x_2', \ldots, x_p' \geqslant 0$ satisfying (1″) and (2). Thus, we see that the initial programming problem is equivalent to the following problem.

Associated problem. *Find numbers* $x^1, x^2, \ldots, x^p \geqslant 0, x^{p+1}, \ldots, x^m$ *subject to*

$$\sum_{i=1}^{m} a_i^j x^i \leqslant b^j \quad \textit{for } j = 1, 2, \ldots, r,$$

$$\sum_{i=1}^{m} a_i^j x^i = b^j \quad \textit{for } j = r+1, \ldots, n;$$

and numbers

$$y_1, y_2, \ldots, y_r \geqslant 0, \quad y_{r+1}, \ldots, y_n$$

subject to

$$\sum_{j=1}^{n} y_j\left(b^j - \sum_{i=1}^{m} a_i^j x^i\right) = 0,$$

such that for any

$$\xi^1, \xi^2, \ldots, \xi^p \geqslant 0, \quad \xi^{p+1}, \ldots, \xi^m,$$

we have

$$f(\mathbf{x}) + \sum_{j=1}^{n} y_j\left(b^j - \sum_{i=1}^{m} a_i^j x^i\right) \geqslant f(\boldsymbol{\xi}) + \sum_{j=1}^{n} y_j\left(b^j - \sum_{i=1}^{m} a_i^j \xi^i\right).$$

NOTE. If f is differentiable, the last condition can be replaced by the following set of conditions:

$$\frac{\partial f}{\partial x^i} \leqslant \sum_{j=1}^{n} a_i^j y_j \quad \text{for } i = 1, 2, \ldots, p$$

$$\frac{\partial f}{\partial x^i} = \sum_{j=1}^{n} a_i^j y_j \quad \text{for } i = p+1, \ldots, m$$

$$\sum_{i=1}^{m} x^i\left[\sum_{j=1}^{n} a_i^j y_j - \frac{\partial f}{\partial x^i}\right] = 0.$$

5.2. DUALITY IN LINEAR PROGRAMMING

If the function to be maximized is linear of the form

$$f(\mathbf{x}) = c_1 x^1 + c_2 x^2 + \ldots + c_m x^m,$$

then, in view of the preceding note, we can replace the last condition of the associated problem by the following conditions:

$$\sum_{j=1}^{n} a_i^j y_j \geqslant c_i \quad \text{for } i = 1, 2, \ldots, p,$$

$$\sum_{j=1}^{n} a_i^j y_j = c_i \quad \text{for } i = p+1, \ldots, m,$$

$$\sum_{i=1}^{m} x^i \left(c_i - \sum_{j=1}^{n} a_i^j y_j \right) = 0.$$

Consider now the following programming problem.

Dual programme. *Find numbers*

$$y_1, y_2, \ldots, y_r \geqslant 0, \quad y_{r+1}, \ldots, y_n$$

subject to

$$\sum_{j=1}^{n} a_i^j y_j \geqslant c_i \quad \textit{for } i = 1, 2, \ldots, p,$$

$$\sum_{j=1}^{n} a_i^j y_j = c_i \quad \textit{for } i = p+1, \ldots, m,$$

and such that

$$g(\mathbf{y}) = \sum_{j=1}^{n} b^j y_j$$

is minimized.

First we notice that if two points $\mathbf{x} \in \mathbf{R}^m$ and $\mathbf{y} \in \mathbf{R}^n$, belong to the domains of the initial programme and the dual programme, respectively, then

$$\sum_{i=1}^{m} c_i x^i \leqslant \sum_{i=1}^{m} \sum_{j=1}^{n} a_i^j x^i y_j \leqslant \sum_{j=1}^{n} b^j y_j.$$

It clearly follows that *if the domain of one of the programmes is non-empty, then the domain of the other is bounded.* This result is important, for we shall show in the following paragraph that if a linear programme has a non-empty and bounded domain, it has a solution.

We see, on the other hand, that if two points $\mathbf{x}$ and $\mathbf{y}$ belonging to the respective domains of the two programmes, satisfy

$$\sum_{i=1}^{m} c_i x^i = \sum_{j=1}^{n} b^j y_j,$$

7

then they are solutions of the respective programmes. It is obvious that this last equality will hold if and only if the pair $(\mathbf{x}, \mathbf{y})$ is a solution of the associated problem. Finally we know that if $\mathbf{x}$ is a solution of the initial problem, there exists a point $\mathbf{y} \in \mathbf{R}^n$ such that the pair $(\mathbf{x}, \mathbf{y})$ is a solution of the associated problem. Thus we can state:

Duality theorem. *If two points* $\mathbf{x}$ *and* $\mathbf{y}$ *belong to the respective domains of the initial programme and of the dual programme, then the following three propositions are equivalent:*

(1) $\mathbf{x}$ *and* $\mathbf{y}$ *are respective solutions of the two programmes.*
(2) *The pair* $(\mathbf{x}, \mathbf{y})$ *is a solution of the associated problem.*
(3) $\sum_{i=1}^{m} c_i x^i = \sum_{j=1}^{n} b^j y_j.$

5.3. THE SIMPLEX METHOD

Here we shall only describe the principles of this method, due to G. Dantzig, which enables us to solve linear programmes. For the actual procedure of calculations, we refer the reader to other works (for example [15] or [17]).

The problem is to find a point x of a polytope T that maximizes a linear affine function $f(x)$. Suppose we know a vertex a of this polytope;† we can take this point as the origin and associate with it a polytope T' as indicated in Chapter 3, 3.2. If we omit the trivial case where T' reduces to this vertex – in this case T also reduces to this vertex – we have necessarily one of the two following situations.

FIRST CASE. For every point x belonging to one of the edges of T', we have $f(x) \leqslant f(0)$. In this case, we have

$$x \in T \Rightarrow x \in T' \Rightarrow f(x) \leqslant f(0),$$

and the vertex in question is the solution.

SECOND CASE. There exists a point x_0 belonging to an edge such that $f(x_0) > f(0)$. Let λx_0 be any point with $\lambda \geqslant 0$ of this edge; we have

$$f(\lambda x_0) - f(0) = \lambda[f(x_0) - f(0)].$$

(a) If

$$D^+_{x_0} \subset T,$$

then the domain of the programme is not bounded.

† When we do not know any vertex of the polytope T, it is necessary to find one, before applying the algorithm described here. There is a simple method for this, called the method of 'artificial variables', but we shall not describe it here.

(b) If, on the contrary, there exists a number $\lambda_0 \geqslant 0$ such that

$$\lambda x_0 \in T \quad \text{for } \lambda \leqslant \lambda_0$$

and

$$\lambda x_0 \notin T \quad \text{for } \lambda > \lambda_0,$$

then there exists a generating plane E_f^α of the polytope T, whose intersection with $D_{x_0}^+$ reduces to a point $\lambda_0 x_0$ and such that $\lambda x \notin H_f^\alpha$ for $\lambda > \lambda_0$. This generating plane does not pass through the origin; for if it did we would then have, by definition, $T' \subset H_f^\alpha$ and consequently

$$D_{x_0}^+ \subset H_f^\alpha.$$

Thus the point $a_1 = \lambda_0 x_0$ satisfies $f(a_1) > f(a)$ and is a vertex of T since the intersection of the generating planes containing $D_{a_1}^+$ and of the plane H_f^α reduces to a point a. We can repeat this process starting again from a_1, and so on.

The set of vertices of T being finite, at some stage we shall necessarily arrive at one of the two cases 1 or 2a; thus the problem will then be solved.

NOTE 1. Given a vertex, there are in general exactly n generating planes passing through this vertex. The edges of T' should then be looked for, according to Proposition 2 of page 60, among the n intersections of $n-1$ by $n-1$ of these generating planes. In the case where there are more than n generating planes passing through this vertex, we can clearly look for the edges among the intersections of generating planes which reduce to straight lines passing through this vertex; but in this case there exist other more rapid methods of which the most common is the so-called ϵ method which the reader may find described in the works cited above.

NOTE 2. The technique of the algorithm we have just described shows that if the domain of the programme is non-empty and bounded, it has a solution. For, at the end of the calculations we have necessarily Case 1, since we cannot have Case 2a.

5.4. NON-LINEAR PROGRAMMING

Here we give a method due to M. Frank and P. Wolfe [10], with which we can, by successive approximations, solve every programme with linear constraints whose function to be maximized is concave, provided that the following two conditions are satisfied:

Firstly, $f(x)$ is differentiable and its partial derivatives are continuous.

Secondly, for every x_0 in the domain T, the linear function $\langle \delta f(x_0), x\rangle$ is bounded in the domain (in particular this occurs when the polytope T is bounded).

Proposed method. We start by choosing a number ρ, with $0 < \rho \leqslant 1$. Then, starting with an arbitrary point $x_1 \in T$, construct a sequence $x_1, x_2, \ldots, x_k, \ldots$ of points of T in the following manner; knowing x_k use the simplex method – or any other method – find a vertex ξ^k of the polytope T which maximizes the linear form $\langle \delta f(x_k), \xi \rangle$, then choose a point x_{k+1} of the segment $[x_k, \xi_k]$ which satisfies

$$f(x_{k+1}) \geqslant f(x_k) + \rho \Big[\max_{x \in [x_k, \xi_k]} f(x) - f(x_k) \Big].$$

The points of this sequence all belong to the convex polyhedron generated by $x_1 \bigcup \ddot{T}$; hence, the increasing sequence formed by the numbers $f(x_1)$, $f(x_2), \ldots, f(x_k), \ldots$ is bounded: it tends to a limit μ. We now show that

$$\mu = \max_{x \in T} f(x).$$

Let x_0 be a limit point of the sequence. As the profile $\ddot{T}$ is finite, we can find a sub-sequence $x_{n_1}, x_{n_2}, \ldots, x_{n_k}, \ldots$ whose limit is x_0 and such that the associated vertices $\xi_{n_1}, \xi_{n_2}, \ldots, \xi_{n_k}, \ldots$ are all equal to the same vertex ξ_0.

Let λ be a number with $0 \leqslant \lambda \leqslant 1$; for any k, we have

$$f(x_{n_k} + \lambda(\xi_0 - x_{n_k})) - f(x_{n_k}) \leqslant \max_{x \in [x_{n_k}, \xi_0]} f(x) - f(x_{n_k})$$

$$\leqslant \frac{1}{\rho} [f(x_{n_k+1}) - f(x_{n_k})],$$

and, in the limit,

$$f(x_0 + \lambda(\xi_0 - x_0)) - f(x_0) \leqslant 0.$$

When λ tends to 0, we obtain

$$\langle \delta f(x_0), \xi_0 - x_0 \rangle \leqslant 0.$$

Now let x_0 be any point of the domain T. We have for every k

$$\langle \delta f(x_{n_k}), x - x_{n_k} \rangle \leqslant \langle \delta f(x_{n_k}), \xi_0 - x_{n_k} \rangle,$$

and, in the limit

$$\langle \delta f(x_0), x - x_0 \rangle \leqslant \langle \delta f(x_0), \xi_0 - x_0 \rangle \leqslant 0;$$

hence,

$$f(x) - f(x_0) \leqslant \langle \delta f(x_0), x - x_0 \rangle \leqslant 0.$$

We have

$$\mu = f(x_0) = \max_{x \in T} f(x)$$

NOTE. Let x_k be a point of the sequence. For any $x \in T$,

$$f(x) - f(x_k) \leqslant \langle \delta f(x_k), x - x_k \rangle \leqslant \langle \delta f(x_k), \xi_k - x_k \rangle.$$

In practice, if we decide to be satisfied with a point a of the domain, for which we would have

$$0 \leqslant \max_{x \in T} f(x) - f(a) < \epsilon,$$

then we shall stop computing as soon as we have

$$\langle \delta f(x_k), \xi_k - x_k \rangle < \epsilon$$

and we shall take $a = x_k$.

This eventuality will arise at some stage, since in the partial sequence which we have considered above, the expression

$$\langle \delta f(x_{n_k}), \xi_0 - x_{n_k} \rangle$$

tends to

$$\langle \delta f(x_0), \xi_0 - x_0 \rangle \leqslant 0.$$

5.5. QUADRATIC PROGRAMMING

We shall suppose here that the function to be maximized is a quadratic of the form

$$f(\mathbf{x}) = \sum_{i=1}^{m} c_i x^i - \tfrac{1}{2} \sum_{i,k} c_{ik} x^i x^k \quad (\text{with } c_{ik} = c_{ki})$$

and that it is concave, which implies, as may easily be seen, that the quadratic form

$$\sum_{i,k} c_{ik} x^i x^k$$

is positive.

For solving such a programme, we can use the method described in the preceding section, at least whenever the conditions there are satisfied.

But there are other methods having the advantage of yielding an exact result in a finite number of steps of computation. We shall describe one of these.†

Consider the polytope $T \subset \mathbf{R}^{m+n}$ formed by the ordered pairs $\mathbf{z} = (\mathbf{x}, \mathbf{y})$ with $\mathbf{x} \in \mathbf{R}^m$ and $\mathbf{y} \in \mathbf{R}^n$ satisfying

$$\left\{\begin{array}{l} y_j \\ \sum_{i=1}^{m} a_i^j x^i \end{array}\right. \left\{\begin{array}{l} \left.\begin{array}{l} \geqslant 0 \\ \leqslant b^j \end{array}\right\} \text{ for } j = 1, 2, \ldots, r \\ \left.\begin{array}{l} \text{of any sign} \\ = b^j \end{array}\right\} \text{ for } j = r+1, \ldots, n \end{array}\right.$$

† The method given here was originally due to Wolfe [10]. For other algorithms see [19] and [1].

and

$$\left\{\begin{array}{l} x^i \\ \\ \sum\limits_{j=1}^{n} a_i^j y_j \end{array}\right\} \left\{\begin{array}{l} \geqslant 0 \\ \geqslant c_i - \sum\limits_{k=1}^{m} c_{ik} x^k \end{array}\right\} \text{for } i = 1, 2, \ldots, p$$

$$\left.\begin{array}{l} \text{of any sign} \\ = c_i - \sum\limits_{k=1}^{m} c_{ik} x^k \end{array}\right\} \text{for } i = p+1, \ldots, m.$$

On the other hand, consider the concave function

$$\varphi(\mathbf{z}) = \sum_{j=1}^{n} y_j \left(\sum_{i=1}^{m} a_i^j x^i - b^j \right) + \sum_{i=1}^{m} x^i \left(c_i - \sum_{k=1}^{m} c_{ik} x^k - \sum_{j=1}^{n} a_i^j y_j \right)$$

$$= -\sum_{j=1}^{n} b^j y_j + \sum_{i=1}^{m} c_i x^i - \sum_{i,k} c_{ik} x^i x^k.$$

The problem associated with the given problem can be expressed thus: find $\mathbf{z} \in T$ such that $\varphi(\mathbf{z}) = 0$.

At this stage we shall make several comments.

1. We have $\varphi(\mathbf{z}) \leqslant 0$ for every $\mathbf{z} \in T$.

2. If the initial programme can be solved – and it is necessarily so when the initial domain is bounded† – there exists a point $\mathbf{z} \in T$ such that $\varphi(\mathbf{z}) = 0$. Here we shall assume that the initial programme has a solution, thus

$$\max_{z \in T} \varphi(\mathbf{z}) = 0.$$

The problem we have to deal with now is therefore the following: find $\mathbf{z} \in T$ such that $\varphi(\mathbf{z})$ is maximized.

† Let $\mathbf{z}_0 = (\mathbf{x}_0, \mathbf{y}_0) \in T$ and let $\mathbf{x}$ be any point of the initial domain. We have

$$\langle \delta f(\mathbf{x}_0), \mathbf{x} \rangle - \sum_{j=1}^{n} b^j y_{0j} = \sum_{i=1}^{m} x^i \left(c_i - \sum_{k=1}^{m} c_{ik} x_0^k - \sum_{j=1}^{n} a_i^j y_{0j} \right)$$

$$+ \sum_{j=1}^{n} y_{0j} \left(\sum_{i=1}^{m} a_i^j x^i - b^j \right) \leqslant 0;$$

hence

$$f(\mathbf{x}) \leqslant f(\mathbf{x}_0) + \langle \delta f(\mathbf{x}_0), \mathbf{x} - \mathbf{x}_0 \rangle \leqslant f(\mathbf{x}_0) + \sum_{j=1}^{n} b^j y_{0j} - \langle \delta f(\mathbf{x}_0), \mathbf{x}_0 \rangle$$

Thus we find that if T is non-empty, the domain of the programme is bounded. On the other hand, if the initial programme has a solution, it is evident that T is not empty. It can be shown that if the domain of the initial programme is non-empty and bounded, it has a solution.

Finally we see *the following three propositions are equivalent*:

1. *The programme has a solution.*
2. *The domain of the programme is bounded and non-empty.*
3. *T is not empty.*

3. Let $\mathbf{z}_0$ be any point of T; we shall show that the linear form $\langle \boldsymbol{\delta\varphi}(\mathbf{z}_0), \mathbf{z}\rangle$ is bounded in T. For, we have

$$\sum_{i=1}^{m} x^i \left(c_i - \sum_{k=1}^{m} c_{ik} x_0^k\right) \leqslant \sum_{i,j} a_i^j x^i y_{0j} \leqslant \sum_{j=1}^{n} b^j y_{0j}$$

and

$$\sum_{i=1}^{m} x_0^i \left(c_i - \sum_{k=1}^{m} c_{ik} x^k\right) \leqslant \sum_{i,j} a_i^j x_0^i y_j \leqslant \sum_{j=1}^{n} b^j y_j;$$

hence

$$\begin{aligned}\langle \boldsymbol{\delta\varphi}(\mathbf{z}_0), \mathbf{z}\rangle &= -\sum_{j=1}^{n} b^j y_j + \sum_{i=1}^{n} c_i x^i - 2\sum_{i,k} c_{ik} x^i x_0^k \\ &\leqslant \sum_{j=1}^{n} b^j y_{0j} - \sum_{i=1}^{m} c_i x_0^i.\end{aligned}$$

4. Hence it is possible to find the maximum of $\varphi(\mathbf{z})$ by carrying out the method described in the preceding paragraph. We shall show (it follows from the particular nature of this new programme) that this method leads to an exact result after a finite number of iterations.

Starting with an arbitrary point $\mathbf{z} \in T$ for which $\varphi(\mathbf{z}_1) \neq 0$, and constructing, as indicated, a sequence $\mathbf{z}_1, \mathbf{z}_2, \ldots, \mathbf{z}_k, \ldots$ of points of T, to which will be assigned the vertices $\boldsymbol{\zeta}_1, \boldsymbol{\zeta}_2, \ldots, \boldsymbol{\zeta}_k, \ldots$, we shall see that one of these vertices is the required point. For this, consider the finite set $A \subset \ddot{T}$ which they form. All points of the sequence belong to the convex polyhedron generated by $\{\mathbf{z}_1\} \bigcup A$. Let $\mathbf{z}_0$ be a limit point: $\mathbf{z}_0$ also belongs to this polyhedron and satisfies $\varphi(\mathbf{z}_0) = 0$. If $\mathbf{z}_0$ is one of the vertices of this polyhedron, then the stated property is thus proved. Otherwise, we can express $\mathbf{z}_0$ in the form

$$\mathbf{z}_0 = t\boldsymbol{\zeta} + (1-t)\,\mathbf{z},$$

with $\boldsymbol{\zeta} \in A$, $\mathbf{z} \in T$ and $0 < t < 1$. Let j be any index: one of the two linear affine functions

$$\sum_{i=1}^{m} a_i^j x^i - b^j \quad \text{and} \quad y_j$$

vanishes at the point $\mathbf{z}_0$ and it has the same sign at the two points $\boldsymbol{\zeta}$, $\mathbf{z} \in T$; hence it is zero at these two points. Similarly, let i be any index; one of the two linear affine functions

$$c_i - \sum_{k=1}^{m} c_{ik} x^k - \sum_{j=1}^{n} a_i^j y_j \quad \text{and} \quad x^i$$

which vanishes at the point $\mathbf{z}_0$, is also zero at the two points $\boldsymbol{\zeta}$ and $\mathbf{z}$. Thus we have $\varphi(\boldsymbol{\zeta}) = 0$, and this completes the proof of the property stated above.

5.6. CONJUGATE FUNCTIONS

Given a concave function φ in $\mathbf{R}^r$, let us find the condition under which the linear affine function

$$f(\xi) = \langle \eta, \xi \rangle - h,$$

defined by the parameters $\eta \in \mathbf{R}^r$ and $h \in \mathbf{R}$, satisfies

$$f(\xi) \geqslant \varphi(\xi) \quad \text{for every } \xi \in \mathbf{R}^r.$$

For $f(\xi)$ to possess this property, it is necessary and sufficient that the function

$$\langle \eta, \xi \rangle - \varphi(\xi)$$

be bounded below for $\xi \in \mathbf{R}^r$ and that

$$h \leqslant \inf_{\xi \in \mathbf{R}^r} [\langle \eta, \xi \rangle - \varphi(\xi)].$$

In the case where the function φ is such that the first of the two preceding conditions is satisfied for every $\eta \in \mathbf{R}^r$, the function

$$\psi(\eta) = \inf_{\xi \in \mathbf{R}^r} [\langle \eta, \xi \rangle - \varphi(\xi)]$$

is called the *conjugate function* of φ.

Proposition. *If the function $\varphi(\xi)$ has the conjugate function $\psi(\eta)$, the function*

$$\varphi_1(\xi) = \varphi(\xi) + \langle a, \xi \rangle + \alpha$$

has the conjugate function

$$\psi_1(\eta) = \psi(\eta - a) - \alpha.$$

We have

$$\psi(\eta - a) = \inf_{\xi \in \mathbf{R}^r} [\langle \eta - a, \xi \rangle - \varphi(\xi)]$$

$$= \alpha + \inf_{\xi \in \mathbf{R}^r} [\langle \eta, \xi \rangle - \varphi_1(\xi)].$$

Theorem 1. *If $\psi(\eta)$ is the conjugate function of a concave function $\varphi(\xi)$, then ψ is itself concave and the function $\varphi(\xi)$ is its conjugate.*

Firstly, let η, η' be two points in $\mathbf{R}^r$ and let λ, λ' be two numbers $\geqslant 0$ with $\lambda + \lambda' = 1$. Then for every $\xi \in \mathbf{R}^r$,

$$\psi(\eta) \leqslant \langle \eta, \xi \rangle - \varphi(\xi)$$

and

$$\psi(\eta') \leqslant \langle \eta', \xi \rangle - \varphi(\xi);$$

hence

$$\lambda \psi(\eta) + \lambda' \psi(\eta') \leqslant \langle \lambda \eta + \lambda' \eta', \xi \rangle - \varphi(\xi).$$

Thus

$$\lambda\psi(\eta)+\lambda'\psi(\eta') \leqslant \psi(\lambda\eta+\lambda'\eta'),$$

which shows that $\psi(\eta)$ is concave.

Secondly, let ξ_0 be any point of $\mathbf{R}^r$: then for every $\eta \in \mathbf{R}^r$,

$$\psi(\eta) \leqslant \langle \xi_0, \eta\rangle - \varphi(\xi_0),$$

that is,

$$\varphi(\xi_0) \leqslant \langle \xi_0, \eta\rangle - \psi(\eta).$$

We shall now show that there exists a point η_0 such that

$$\varphi(\xi_0) = \langle \xi_0, \eta_0\rangle - \psi(\eta_0);$$

we shall then have

$$\varphi(\xi_0) = \inf_{\eta \in \mathbf{R}^r} [\langle \xi_0, \eta\rangle - \psi(\eta)].$$

Consider in $\mathbf{R}^r \times \mathbf{R} = \mathbf{R}^{r+1}$, the convex set T_φ formed by the ordered pairs (ξ, ζ) where $\xi \in \mathbf{R}^r$ and $\zeta < \varphi(\xi)$. The point $(\xi_0, \varphi(\xi_0))$ does not belong to T_φ and hence there exists a linear form not identically zero

$$g(\xi, \zeta) = \langle a, \xi\rangle - \alpha\zeta \quad \text{with } a \in \mathbf{R}^r \text{ and } \alpha \in \mathbf{R}$$

such that

$$g(\xi, \zeta) \geqslant g(\xi_0, \varphi(\xi_0)) \quad \text{for every } (\xi, \zeta) \in T_\varphi.$$

α cannot be zero, for if it were, we would have

$$\langle a, \xi\rangle \geqslant \langle a, \xi_0\rangle \quad \text{for every } \xi \in \mathbf{R}^r,$$

whence $a = \mathbf{0}$ and $g(\xi, \zeta)$ would be identically zero. On the other hand, we have

$$g(\xi_0, \zeta) \geqslant g(\xi_0, \varphi(\xi_0)) \quad \text{for every } \zeta < \varphi(\xi_0),$$

which shows that α is positive. In these conditions, the point $\eta_0 = (1/\alpha)a$ satisfies

$$\langle \eta_0, \xi\rangle - \zeta \geqslant \langle \eta_0, \xi_0\rangle - \varphi(\xi_0) \quad \text{for every } (\xi, \zeta) \in T_\varphi.$$

We then have

$$\langle \eta_0, \xi\rangle - \varphi(\xi) \geqslant \langle \eta_0, \xi_0\rangle - \varphi(\xi_0) \quad \text{for every } \xi \in \mathbf{R}^r;$$

hence,

$$\langle \eta_0, \xi_0\rangle - \varphi(\xi_0) = \inf_{\xi \in \mathbf{R}^r} [\langle \eta_0, \xi\rangle - \varphi(\xi)] = \psi(\eta_0).$$

The property stated above is thus proved; hence $\psi(\eta)$ has $\varphi(\xi)$ as its conjugate function.

DEFINITION. If the function ψ is conjugate to the function φ, a point η is said to be *conjugate to* the point ξ if these two points satisfy

$$\varphi(\xi) + \psi(\eta) = \langle \xi, \eta\rangle.$$

The above proof has shown that for any point ξ_0 there exists a point η_0 conjugate to ξ_0. The role of the two functions φ and ψ being symmetrical, we also see that for every point η_0 there exists a point ξ_0, whose conjugate is η_0.

Theorem 2. *For a differentiable concave function $\varphi(\xi)$ defined in $\mathbf{R}^r$ to have a conjugate function, it is necessary and sufficient that it possesses the property that for every point $\eta \in \mathbf{R}^r$ there exists a point $\xi \in \mathbf{R}^r$ such that $\delta\varphi(\xi) = \eta$.*

Firstly, suppose that $\varphi(\xi)$ possesses this property and let η_0 be any point in $\mathbf{R}^r$; let ξ_0 be a point such that

$$\delta\varphi(\xi_0) = \eta_0.$$

We have

$$\langle \delta\varphi(\xi_0), \xi - \xi_0 \rangle \geqslant \varphi(\xi) - \varphi(\xi_0)$$

for every $\xi \in \mathbf{R}^r$; hence,

$$\langle \eta_0, \xi_0 \rangle - \varphi(\xi_0) \leqslant \langle \eta_0, \xi \rangle - \varphi(\xi)$$

for every $\xi \in \mathbf{R}^r$.

We see that $\varphi(\xi)$ has a conjugate function $\psi(\eta)$, and that

$$\psi(\eta_0) = \langle \eta_0, \xi_0 \rangle - \varphi(\xi_0).$$

Conversely if $\varphi(\xi)$ has a conjugate function $\psi(\eta)$, consider any point $\eta_0 \in \mathbf{R}^r$. Let ξ_0 be a point with η_0 as its conjugate and let u be any point of $\mathbf{R}^r$. Then for every $\lambda > 0$

$$\varphi(\xi_0 + \lambda u) \leqslant \langle \xi_0 + \lambda u, \eta_0 \rangle - \psi(\eta_0) = \varphi(\xi_0) + \lambda \langle u, \eta_0 \rangle;$$

hence, dividing by λ and letting λ tend to 0,

$$\langle \delta\varphi(\xi_0), u \rangle \leqslant \langle \eta_0, u \rangle.$$

Thus

$$\langle \delta\varphi(\xi_0) - \eta_0, u \rangle \leqslant 0,$$

for every $u \in \mathbf{R}^r$, which implies that

$$\delta\varphi(\xi_0) = \eta_0.$$

Corollary. *Let φ be a differentiable concave function which has a conjugate function ψ. For a point η to be conjugate to the point ξ, it is necessary and sufficient that*

$$\eta = \delta\varphi(\xi).$$

This follows immediately from the above proof.

EXAMPLE 1. Consider in **R**, the differentiable function

$$f(x) = \begin{cases} -(x+1)^2 & \text{for } x \leqslant -1, \\ 0 & \text{for } -1 \leqslant x \leqslant +1, \\ -(x-1)^2 & \text{for } x \geqslant +1, \end{cases}$$

we have

$$\delta f(x) = \begin{cases} -2(x+1) & \text{for } x \leqslant -1, \\ 0 & \text{for } -1 \leqslant x \leqslant +1, \\ -2(x-1) & \text{for } x \geqslant +1. \end{cases}$$

If y is a positive number, the point

$$x = -1-y/2 \text{ satisfies } \delta f(x) = y;$$

if y is a negative number, the point

$$x = 1-y/2 \text{ satisfies } \delta f(x) = y.$$

Hence we find that $f(x)$ has the conjugate function

$$g(y) = \begin{cases} -y-y^2/4 & \text{for } y \geqslant 0, \\ y-y^2/4 & \text{for } y \leqslant 0. \end{cases}$$

This function is not differentiable at the point $y=0$. This is due to the fact that this point is the conjugate, not of a single point but of every point x which satisfies $-1 < x \leqslant 1$.

EXAMPLE 2. In $\mathbf{R}^n$ consider a concave quadratic form (that is to say, a negative definite form)

$$f(\mathbf{x}) = \tfrac{1}{2} \sum_{i,k} c_{ik} x^i x^k \quad (\text{with } c_{ik} = c_{ki}).$$

For $f(\mathbf{x})$ to have a conjugate function, it is necessary and sufficient that the linear mapping of $\mathbf{R}^n$ into $\mathbf{R}^n$;

$$\boldsymbol{\delta}\mathbf{f}(\mathbf{x}) = \left(\frac{\partial f}{\partial x^1}, \frac{\partial f}{\partial x^2}, \ldots, \frac{\partial f}{\partial x^n}\right),$$

with

$$\frac{\partial f}{\partial x^i} = \sum_{k=1}^{n} c_{ik} x^k \quad \text{for } i = 1, 2, \ldots, n,$$

satisfy $\boldsymbol{\delta}\mathbf{f}(\mathbf{R}^n) = \mathbf{R}^n$, and hence that the square matrix formed by the numbers c_{ik} is regular.

Let c_{-1}^{ik} $(i, k = 1, 2, \ldots, n)$ be the inverse of this matrix, and let $g(\mathbf{y})$ be the conjugate function of $f(\mathbf{x})$. If $\mathbf{y}$ is conjugate to $\mathbf{x}$ we have

$$y_i = \sum_{k=1}^{n} c_{ik} x^k \quad \text{for } i = 1, 2, \ldots, n,$$

hence

$$f(\mathbf{x}) = \tfrac{1}{2}\langle \mathbf{x}, \mathbf{y} \rangle$$

and

$$g(\mathbf{y}) = \langle \mathbf{x}, \mathbf{y} \rangle - f(\mathbf{x}) = \tfrac{1}{2}\langle \mathbf{x}, \mathbf{y} \rangle = \tfrac{1}{2}\sum_{i,k} c_{-1}^{ik} y_i y_k.$$

If we now consider the concave quadratic function

$$f(\mathbf{x}) = \sum_{i=1}^{n} c_i x^i + \tfrac{1}{2}\sum_{i,k} c_{ik} x^i x^k,$$

we see (cf. page 94) that it has a conjugate function $g(\mathbf{y})$ if and only if the square matrix formed by the numbers c_{ik} is regular, and that, in this case, we have

$$g(\mathbf{y}) = \tfrac{1}{2}\sum_{i,k} c_{-1}^{ik}(y_i - c_i)(y_k - c_k).$$

5.7. DUALITY IN CERTAIN NON-LINEAR PROGRAMMES

The duality we shall consider here does not require any of the usual assumptions (cf. [7]) about the differentiability of the function to be maximized.

Given two concave conjugate functions φ and ψ defined in $\mathbf{R}^r$, consider the following two programmes:

Programme 1. *Find $x^1, x^2, \ldots, x^m$ and $\xi^1, \xi^2, \ldots, \xi^r$ subject to*

$$b^j - \sum_{i=1}^{m} a_i^j x^i - \sum_{h=1}^{r} \alpha_h^j \xi^h \geqslant 0 \quad \textit{for } j = 1, 2, \ldots, n$$

and such that

$$\sum_{=1}^{m} c_i x^i + \varphi(\xi^1, \xi^2, \ldots, \xi^r)$$

is maximized.

Programme 2. *Find $y_1, y_2, \ldots, y_n \geqslant 0$; $\eta_1, \eta_2, \ldots, \eta_r$ subject to*

$$\sum_{j=1}^{n} a_i^j y_j = c_i \quad \textit{for } i = 1, 2, \ldots, m,$$

$$\sum_{=1}^{n} \alpha_h^j y_j - \eta_h = 0 \quad \textit{for } h = 1, 2, \ldots, r$$

and such that

$$\sum_{j=1}^{n} b^j y_j - \psi(\eta_1, \eta_2, \ldots, \eta_r)$$

is minimized.

We shall show that these two problems are dual in the sense that their associated problems are equivalent.

The problem associated with the first programme is the following: Find

$$\mathbf{x} \in \mathbf{R}^m, \boldsymbol{\xi} \in \mathbf{R}^r \quad \text{and} \quad y_1, y_2, \ldots, y_n \geqslant 0$$

satisfying

$$b^j - \sum_{i=1}^{m} a_i^j x^i - \sum_{h=1}^{r} \alpha_h^j \xi^h \geqslant 0 \quad \text{for } j = 1, 2, \ldots, n, \tag{1}$$

$$\sum_{j=1}^{n} b^j y_j - \sum_{j=1}^{n} \sum_{i=1}^{m} a_i^j x^i y_j - \sum_{j=1}^{n} \sum_{h=1}^{r} \alpha_h^j \xi^h y_j = 0 \tag{2}$$

and such that

$$F(\mathbf{x}, \boldsymbol{\xi}) = \sum_{i=1}^{m} c_i x^i + \varphi(\boldsymbol{\xi}) + \sum_{j=1}^{n} b^j y_j - \sum_{j=1}^{n} \sum_{i=1}^{m} a_i^j x^i y_j - \sum_{j=1}^{n} \sum_{h=1}^{r} \alpha_h^j \xi^h y_j$$

satisfies

$$F(\mathbf{x}', \boldsymbol{\xi}') \leqslant F(\mathbf{x}, \boldsymbol{\xi}) \quad \text{for every } \mathbf{x}' \in \mathbf{R}^m \text{ and } \boldsymbol{\xi}' \in \mathbf{R}^r. \tag{3}$$

If we suppose

$$\sum_{j=1}^{n} \alpha_h^j y_j = \eta_h \quad \text{for } h = 1, 2, \ldots, r \tag{4}$$

and note that $F(\mathbf{x}, \boldsymbol{\xi})$ is the sum of a linear function of $\mathbf{x}$ and a concave function of $\boldsymbol{\xi}$, we see that condition (3) is equivalent to the two conditions

$$\sum_{j=1}^{n} a_i^j y_j = c_i \quad \text{for } i = 1, 2, \ldots, m \tag{3'}$$

and

$$\varphi(\boldsymbol{\xi}') - \langle \boldsymbol{\xi}', \boldsymbol{\eta}' \rangle \leqslant \varphi(\boldsymbol{\xi}) - \langle \boldsymbol{\xi}, \boldsymbol{\eta} \rangle \quad \text{for every } \boldsymbol{\xi}' \in \mathbf{R}^r. \tag{3''}$$

Now condition (3″) is equivalent to the condition

$$\varphi(\boldsymbol{\xi}) + \psi(\boldsymbol{\eta}) = \langle \boldsymbol{\xi}, \boldsymbol{\eta} \rangle. \tag{3'''}$$

Therefore we see that the first programme is equivalent to the following problem:

Programme 3. *Find* $\mathbf{x}\in\mathbf{R}^m$, $\boldsymbol{\xi}\in\mathbf{R}^r$, $\boldsymbol{\eta}\in\mathbf{R}^r$, *and* $y_1, y_2, \ldots, y_n \geqslant 0$ *subject to*

$$b^j - \sum_{i=1}^{m} a_i^j x^i - \sum_{h=1}^{r} \alpha_h^j \xi^h \geqslant 0 \quad \textit{for } j = 1,2,\ldots,n \tag{1}$$

$$\sum_{j=1}^{n} a_i^j y_j = c_i \quad \textit{for } i = 1,2,\ldots,m \tag{3'}$$

$$\sum_{j=1}^{n} \alpha_h^j y_j = \eta_h \quad \textit{for } h = 1,2,\ldots,r \tag{4}$$

$$\sum_{j=1}^{n} b^j y_j - \sum_{i=1}^{m} c_i x^i - \langle \boldsymbol{\xi}, \boldsymbol{\eta} \rangle = 0 \tag{2'}$$

and

$$\varphi(\boldsymbol{\xi}) + \psi(\boldsymbol{\eta}) = \langle \boldsymbol{\xi}, \boldsymbol{\eta} \rangle. \tag{3'''}$$

The problem associated with the second programme is the following: Find $y_1, y_2, \ldots, y_n \geqslant 0$, $\boldsymbol{\eta}\in\mathbf{R}^r$, $\mathbf{x}\in\mathbf{R}^m$ and $\boldsymbol{\xi}\in\mathbf{R}^r$ satisfying (3′) and (4) and such that

$$G(\mathbf{y}, \boldsymbol{\eta}) = -\sum_{j=1}^{n} b^j y_j + \psi(\boldsymbol{\eta}) + \sum_{i=1}^{m} x^i \left(-c_i + \sum_{j=1}^{n} a_i^j y_j \right) + \sum_{h=1}^{r} \xi^h \left(-\eta_h + \sum_{j=1}^{n} \alpha_h^j y_j \right)$$

satisfies $G(\mathbf{y}', \boldsymbol{\eta}') \leqslant G(\mathbf{y}, \boldsymbol{\eta})$ for every

$$\mathbf{y}' = (y_1', y_2', \ldots, y_n') \geqslant 0 \quad \text{and} \quad \boldsymbol{\eta}' \in \mathbf{R}^r. \tag{5}$$

If we note that $G(\mathbf{y}, \boldsymbol{\eta})$ is the sum of a linear function of $\mathbf{y}$ and a concave function of $\boldsymbol{\eta}$, we see that condition (5) is equivalent to the two conditions:

$$\sum_{j=1}^{n} (y_j' - y_j) \left(-b^j + \sum_{i=1}^{m} a_i^j x^i + \sum_{h=1}^{r} \alpha_h^j \xi^h \right) \leqslant 0 \quad \text{for every } y_1', y_2', \ldots, y_n' \geqslant 0 \tag{5'}$$

and

$$\psi(\boldsymbol{\eta}') - \langle \boldsymbol{\xi}, \boldsymbol{\eta}' \rangle \leqslant \psi(\boldsymbol{\eta}) - \langle \boldsymbol{\xi}, \boldsymbol{\eta} \rangle \quad \text{for any } \boldsymbol{\eta}' \in \mathbf{R}^r. \tag{5''}$$

Condition (5′) is equivalent to the set of two conditions (1) and (2), and condition (5″) is equivalent to condition (3‴). Thus we see that the second programme is also equivalent to Programme 3.

Duality theorem. *If* $(\mathbf{x}, \boldsymbol{\xi})$ *and* $(\mathbf{y}, \boldsymbol{\eta})$ *belong to the respective domains of the two programmes, then the three following propositions are equivalent:*

(1) $(\mathbf{x}, \boldsymbol{\xi})$ *and* $(\mathbf{y}, \boldsymbol{\eta})$ *are respectively the solutions of the two programmes.*

(2) *We have*

$$\sum_{j=1}^{n} b^j y_j - \sum_{i=1}^{m} c_i x^i = \langle \boldsymbol{\xi}, \boldsymbol{\eta} \rangle$$

and the points $\boldsymbol{\xi}$ *and* $\boldsymbol{\eta}$ *are conjugate.*

(3) *We have*

$$\sum_{i=1}^{m} c_i x^i + \varphi(\boldsymbol{\xi}) = \sum_{j=1}^{n} b^j y_j - \psi(\boldsymbol{\eta}).$$

For, we have

$$\sum_{j=1}^{n} b^j y_j \geqslant \sum_{j=1}^{n} \sum_{i=1}^{m} a_i^j x^i y_j + \sum_{j=1}^{n} \sum_{h=1}^{r} \alpha_h^j \xi^h y_j = \sum_{i=1}^{m} c_i x^i + \langle \boldsymbol{\xi}, \boldsymbol{\eta} \rangle;$$

hence, from the properties of conjugate functions, we have the double inequality

$$\sum_{j=1}^{n} b^j y_j - \sum_{i=1}^{m} c_i x^i \geqslant \langle \boldsymbol{\xi}, \boldsymbol{\eta} \rangle \geqslant \varphi(\boldsymbol{\xi}) + \psi(\boldsymbol{\eta}).$$

It follows immediately that propositions (2) and (3) are equivalent and that if proposition (3) is satisfied, so is proposition (1).

Finally, if $(\mathbf{x}, \boldsymbol{\xi})$ is a solution of Programme 1, there exists, by virtue of the equivalence of Programme 1 and Programme 3, a pair $(\mathbf{y}', \boldsymbol{\eta}')$ belonging to the domain of Programme 2 and such that

$$\sum_{i=1}^{m} c_i x^i + \varphi(\boldsymbol{\xi}) = \sum_{j=1}^{n} b^j y'_j - \psi(\boldsymbol{\eta}').$$

If then $(\mathbf{y}, \boldsymbol{\eta})$ is a solution of Programme 2 we necessarily have,

$$\sum_{j=1}^{n} b^j y_j - \psi(\boldsymbol{\eta}) \geqslant \sum_{i=1}^{m} c_i x^i + \varphi(\boldsymbol{\xi})$$

and

$$\sum_{j=1}^{n} b^j y_j - \psi(\boldsymbol{\eta}) \leqslant \sum_{j=1}^{n} b^j y'_j - \psi(\boldsymbol{\eta}');$$

hence,

$$\sum_{j=1}^{n} b^j y_j - \psi(\boldsymbol{\eta}) = \sum_{i=1}^{m} c_i x^i + \varphi(\boldsymbol{\xi}).$$

Thus we see that if proposition (1) is satisfied, so is proposition (3); the theorem is therefore proved.

6. Games of strategy

6.1. INTRODUCTION

The theory of games, conceived by Borel and developed by Von Neumann and Morgenstern, is important because it enables us to tackle certain situations of military or economic conflict. However it is really in the situations of games that we find examples which are the simplest and the most perfect from the point of view of the agreement between theory and reality.

EXAMPLE 1. Peter and Paul decide to play the following game: each one of them simultaneously indicates a number with the fingers of his right hand. If the two numbers are both even, or if they are both odd, Peter gives Paul 2 shillings. If Peter's number is even and Paul's odd, the latter gives Peter 3 shillings. Finally if Peter's number is odd and Paul's even, Paul gives Peter 1 shilling.

Such a game can be presented with the help of the following tableau, which shows how much Peter wins in different situations.

		PAUL	
		Even	Odd
PETER	Even	−2	+3
	Odd	+1	−2

EXAMPLE 2. Let us now imagine that this operation, which consists in two players indicating a number simultaneously, is carried out twice consecutively and that the payments are made in the following manner:

If the number of even digits is 0, 2 or 4 Peter gives Paul 2 shillings.
If the number of even digits is 1, Paul gives Peter 1 shilling.
If the number of even digits is 3, Paul gives Peter 3 shillings.

This game is more complicated than the preceding one, since each player has two moves instead of one only. However, each player can perfectly well begin by defining a strategy for himself, that is to say, a rule which tells him what he must do in any circumstance. It is possible to make a list of strategies from which Peter may choose, namely:

	1st move	2nd move
Strategy No. 1	Even	Even
Strategy No. 2	Even	Odd
Strategy No. 3	Odd	Even
Strategy No. 4	Odd	Odd
Strategy No. 5	Even	The same as Paul's first move
Strategy No. 6	Even	The opposite to Paul's first move
Strategy No. 7	Odd	The same as Paul's first move
Strategy No. 8	Odd	The opposite to Paul's first move

Paul's list of strategies is here the same as Peter's, except that *Paul* should be replaced by *Peter* in the definitions of strategies numbers 5, 6, 7 and 8. Once the two players have each chosen their strategies, the play of the game is perfectly defined. We know then the amount, positive or negative, that Paul has to pay Peter.

In the end, we see that the game can be represented by the following tableau, in which we write in the intersections of the ith row and jth column, the sum that Peter receives from Paul whenever Peter adopts strategy i and Paul adopts strategy j.

		PAUL							
	Strategy	No. 1	No. 2	No. 3	No. 4	No. 5	No. 6	No. 7	No. 8
PETER	No. 1	−2	+3	+3	−2	−2	+3	+3	−2
	No. 2	+3	−2	−2	+1	+3	−2	−2	+1
	No. 3	+3	−2	−2	+1	−2	+3	+1	−2
	No. 4	−2	+1	+1	−2	+1	−2	−2	+1
	No. 5	−2	+3	−2	+1	−2	+3	−2	+1
	No. 6	+3	−2	+3	−2	+3	−2	+3	−2
	No. 7	+3	−2	+1	−2	−2	+3	−2	+1
	No. 8	−2	+1	−2	+1	+1	−2	+1	−2

More generally, consider two players or two competitors or two enemies who confront each other; call them A and B. Suppose that the number of possible strategies is finite for these two adversaries: we can make a list of these and number them. A's strategies are numbered from 1 to m, those of B from 1 to n. We shall suppose that the result of the game, which depends on the strategy i of A and the strategy j of B, is the transfer from B to A of a certain sum, positive or negative, say a_i^j, of money, or any commodity. In these conditions the situation can be represented by a table of the numbers a_i^j, in which player A chooses row i and, at the same time, player B chooses column j, the resulting gain for A being a_i^j.

The present Chapter will be devoted to the study of this type of game.

6.2. STRICTLY DETERMINED GAMES (games with saddle points)

EXAMPLE 3. Consider the game defined by the following tableau.

		PLAYER B 1	2	3
PLAYER A	1	-1	$+2$	$+1$
	2	$+1$	$+1$	$+2$
	3	0	0	-1

Whatever A's strategies, B's strategy 1 is more advantageous than his strategy 2. B will therefore never choose column 2 and we get the following game:

		PLAYER B 1	2
PLAYER A	1	-1	$+1$
	2	$+1$	$+2$
	3	0	-1

At this stage, it is obvious that A should choose row 2 and that consequently B should choose column 1.

This game thus reduces to an operation which yields $+1$ to the player A.

EXAMPLE 4. Now consider the following game:

		PLAYER B 1	2	3
PLAYER A	1	$+4$	0	-5
	2	-7	-1	$+4$
	3	$+2$	$+1$	$+1$

Here, there do not appear to be the possibilities of simplification as there were in the preceding example. However, it can be seen that if A chooses row 3, he is certain to win at least $+1$, while if he chooses row 1 his winnings can drop to -5, and to -7 if he chooses row 2. Similarly, if B chooses column 2, he can be sure that A cannot win more than $+1$ while if he chooses column 1 or column 3, A can win $+4$.

A would be wise to play row 3 which guarantees him a win of 1, because he knows that B may, if he wants, compel him not to win more than 1; similarly B should choose column 2. The pair of strategies represented by row 3 and column 2 constitutes a position of equilibrium, which it is not in the interest of either player to abandon. We can say that this game yields $+1$ to player A.

We can describe formally the phenomena we have just observed. We have chosen a row i_0 for which the guaranteed win for player A is the maximum, that is, such that

$$\min_j a_{i_0}^j = \max_i \min_j a_i^j;$$

such a strategy is said to be *maximin*.

We have also chosen column j_0 such that

$$\max_i a_i^{j_0} = \min_j \max_i a_i^j;$$

such a strategy is said to be *minimax*.

It would have been logical at this stage to have had the double inequality

$$\max_i \min_j a_i^j = \min_j a_{i_0}^j \leqslant a_{i_0}^{j_0} \leqslant \max_i a_i^{j_0} = \min_i \max_j a_i^j;$$

but what is noteworthy is that we in fact found the equality

$$\max_i \min_j a_i^j = \min_j \max_i a_i^j.$$

In these conditions, the pair (i_0, j_0) satisfies

$$a_i^{j_0} \leqslant a_{i_0}^{j_0} \leqslant a_{i_0}^j \quad \text{for any } i \text{ and } j;$$

it constitutes what is called a *saddle-point* or *point of equilibrium*. The *value of the game* (for player A) is

$$\bar{\nu} = a_{i_0}^{j_0} = \max_i \min_j a_i^j = \min_j \max_i a_i^j.$$

NOTE. Conversely, if we have a saddle-point (i_0, j_0), we have

$$\max_i a_i^{j_0} = a_{i_0}^{j_0}$$

and

$$\max_i a_i^j \geqslant a_{i_0}^j \geqslant a_{i_0}^{j_0} \quad \text{for any } j;$$

consequently

$$\min_j \max_i a_i^j = a_{i_0}^{j_0},$$

similarly

$$\max_i \min_j a_i^j = a_{i_0}^{j_0}.$$

6.3. ELUDING GAMES (games without saddle points)

Let us go back to Example 1.

	PAUL (B)	
PETER (A)	-2	$+3$
	$+1$	-2

Here we have

$$\max_i \min_j a_i^j = -2$$

and

$$\min_i \max_j a_i^j = +1.$$

There is no point of equilibrium. The only gain which player A can be guaranteed with certainty is -2. Between this value and the value $+1$ which player B can force player A not to exceed, there is a margin of uncertainty upon which each of the two players will try to encroach by being cunning, that is to say:

By guessing as far as possible how the opponent is going to play.
By concealing his own intention.

Suppose now that player A decides to trust to luck in making his choice, associating a probability p^1 with row 1, a probability p^2 with row 2,..., a probability p^m with row m. A is said to have adopted a *mixed strategy* defined by the m-tuple $\mathbf{p} = (p^1, p^2, \ldots, p^m)$. He is thus assured of a gain at least equal to

$$\min_j \sum_i p^i a_i^j$$

in terms of mathematical expectation.

In the same way, if B adopts the mixed strategy defined by the n-tuple $\mathbf{q} = (q_1, q_2, \ldots, q_n)$, he is assured that the mathematical expectation of his loss will not exceed

$$\max_i \sum_j q_j a_i^j.$$

Von Neumann must take the credit for showing that in all cases one could play in this way, that is by trusting to luck without trying to guess the opponent's intentions. Indeed if A adopts the mixed strategy $\mathbf{p} \in \mathbf{P}_m$ the better to conceal his own choice, and if B adopts the mixed strategy $\mathbf{q} \in \mathbf{P}_n$, A's mathematical expectation of gain is

$$f(\mathbf{p}, \mathbf{q}) = \sum_{i,j} p^i q_j a_i^j.$$

Now, Von Neumann's theorem (see page 65) shows that there exists an ordered pair $(\bar{\mathbf{p}}, \bar{\mathbf{q}})$ such that

$$f(\mathbf{p}, \bar{\mathbf{q}}) \leqslant f(\bar{\mathbf{p}}, \bar{\mathbf{q}}) \leqslant f(\bar{\mathbf{p}}, \mathbf{q}),$$

for any $\mathbf{p} \in \mathbf{P}_m$, $\mathbf{q} \in \mathbf{P}_n$.

Thus we see that the games we are concerned with in this Chapter all reduce – except for eccentric behaviour by one of the players – to games of chance; this does not exclude the fact that, for some of these games – those studied in the preceding paragraph – this chance itself may reduce to certainty.

Before going on to the next paragraph, let us introduce the following terminology:

$\bar{\mathbf{p}}$ and $\bar{\mathbf{q}}$ are called *optimal strategies.*

$\bar{\nu} = f(\bar{\mathbf{p}}, \bar{\mathbf{q}})$ is the *value of the game* (for player A).

Pure strategies are those which consist in choosing a row or a column without trusting to luck. The pure strategy defined by row i_0 is clearly identical with the mixed strategy defined by

$$p^i = \begin{cases} 1 & \text{for } i = i_0, \\ 0 & \text{for } i \neq i_0, \end{cases}$$

that is, by

$$\mathbf{p} = \boldsymbol{\delta}_{i_0}.$$

6.4. SOLUTION OF A GAME BY LINEAR PROGRAMMING

We shall show that we can reduce the solution of a game to a linear programme.†

We have

$$\bar{\nu} = \min_j \sum_i \bar{p}^i a^i_j = \max_{p \in P_m} \min_j \sum_i p^i a^j_i.$$

To obtain $\bar{\mathbf{p}}$ and $\bar{\nu}$ it is enough to solve the following linear programme:

Find $p^1, p^2, \ldots, p^m \geqslant 0$ and u subject to

$$-\sum a^j_i p^i + u \leqslant 0 \quad \text{for } j = 1, 2, \ldots, n$$

$$p^1 + p^2 + \ldots + p^m = 1$$

and such that u is a maximum.

The programme which similarly enables us to obtain $\bar{\mathbf{q}}$ and $\bar{\nu}$ is the following:

Find $q_1, q_2, \ldots, q_n \geqslant 0$ and w *subject to*

$$-\sum_j a^j_i q_j + w \geqslant 0 \quad \text{for } i = 1, 2, \ldots, m$$

$$q_1 + q_2 + \ldots + q_n = 1$$

and such that w is a minimum.

It can be seen that these two problems are dual.

† Conversely, Dantzig [5] has shown that every linear programme can be reduced to a matrix game, cf. [14], page 419.

NOTE. If we add to all of the terms a_i^j the same constant a, the optimal strategies remain unchanged and the value of the game is increased by a. We may thus obtain the case where all the a_i^j are strictly positive. Hence the solutions of the two programmes are not changed if we add to the first, the condition $u > 0$ and to the second, the condition $w > 0$. Writing

$$x^i = p^i/u, \quad i = 1, 2, \ldots, m,$$

and

$$y_j = q_j/w, \quad j = 1, 2, \ldots, n,$$

we then obtain the two dual programmes:

to find $x^1, x^2, \ldots, x^m \geqslant 0$ subject to

$$\sum_i a_i^j x^i \geqslant 1 \quad \text{for } j = 1, 2, \ldots, n$$

and such that $x^1 + x^2 + \ldots + x^m$ is a minimum,

and find $y_1, y_2, \ldots, y_n \geqslant 0$ subject to

$$\sum_j a_i^j y_j \leqslant 1 \quad \text{for } i = 1, 2, \ldots, m$$

and such that $y_1 + y_2 + \ldots + y_n$ is a maximum.

6.5. SOLUTION OF A GAME BY SUCCESSIVE APPROXIMATIONS

We now ask the reader to forget the theory of games for a moment, while we prove a theorem which will be useful later.

DEFINITION. Consider a square table T of m^2 numbers a_i^j, antisymmetric with respect to the principal diagonal, that is to say, such that

$$a_i^j + a_j^i = 0 \quad \text{for } i, j = 1, 2, \ldots, m.$$

We say that the sequence $\mathbf{c}^0, \mathbf{c}^1, \mathbf{c}^2, \ldots$ of points of $\mathbf{R}^m$ is *compatible with this table* if it satisfies the following conditions:

$$c_i^0 \leqslant 0 \quad \text{for } i = 1, 2, \ldots, m$$

$$\mathbf{c}^{k+1} = \mathbf{c}^k + \mathbf{a}^{j_k},$$

where the index j_k is such that

$$c_{j_k}^k = \max_j c_j^k,$$

and where we write

$$\mathbf{a}^j = (a_1^j, a_2^j, \ldots, a_m^j).$$

Lemma 1. *For any k, at least one of the coordinates of $\mathbf{c}^k$ is negative or zero.*

For $k = 0$, this result follows by definition. For $k \geqslant 1$, we have

$$\sum_{\nu=0}^{k-1} c_{j_\nu}^k = \sum_{\nu=0}^{k-1} c_{j_\nu}^0 + \sum_{\nu=0}^{k-1} \sum_{\mu=0}^{k-1} a_{j_\nu}^{j_\mu}.$$

The first sum on the right-hand side is negative or zero; since the table T is antisymmetric, the second sum on the right-hand side is zero. Therefore $\mathbf{c}^k$ cannot have all its coordinates strictly positive.

Lemma 2. *Let k and k_1 be two integers. If for every i $(1 \leqslant i \leqslant m)$ there exists an integer ρ with $k \leqslant \rho \leqslant k+k_1$ such that $i = j_\rho$, then*

$$\max_i c_i^{k+k_1} \leqslant k_1 a,$$

where

$$a = \max_{i,j} a_i^j.$$

Let i_0 be such that $c_{i_0}^k \leqslant 0$ and let ρ, with $k \leqslant \rho \leqslant k+k_1$, be such that $i_0 = j_\rho$. We have

$$c_i^{k+k_1} \leqslant c_i^\rho + (k+k_1-\rho)\,a \leqslant c_{i_0}^\rho + (k+k_1-\rho)\,a$$

and

$$c_{i_0}^\rho \leqslant c_{i_0}^k + (\rho - k)\,a \leqslant (\rho - k)\,a;$$

hence

$$c_i^{k+k_1} \leqslant k_1 a \quad \text{for } i = 1, 2, \ldots, m.$$

Theorem. *There exists an integer $k(m;a,\epsilon)$, depending on m and the two numbers $a, \epsilon > 0$, such that for every antisymmetric square table of m^2 numbers a_i^j satisfying*

$$\max_{i,j} a_i^j \leqslant a,$$

and for every sequence $\mathbf{c}^0, \mathbf{c}^1, \mathbf{c}^2, \ldots$ compatible with T, we have

$$k \geqslant k(m;a,\epsilon) \Rightarrow \max_i c_i^k \leqslant k\epsilon.$$

The integer $k(m;a,\epsilon)$ obviously exists for $m = 1$. We shall suppose that it exists for $m < n$ and then show that $k(n;a,\epsilon)$ exists. For this, consider an antisymmetric square table T of n^2 elements a_i^j satisfying

$$\max_{i,j} a_i^j \leqslant a,$$

and any number $\epsilon > 0$.

1. Let η be a number > 0; write

$$k_1 = k(n-1;a,\eta).$$

We shall show, in the form of a lemma, that given any integer k, if there exists an index i_0 different from $j_k, j_{k+1}, \ldots, j_{k+k_1}$, then

$$\max_i c_i^{k+k_1} \leqslant \max_i c_i^k + k_1 \eta.$$

Suppose, for example, that $i_0 = n$ and consider the k_1+1 points of $\mathbf{R}^{n-1}$, say $\mathbf{c}'^s$ $(s = 0, 1, 2, \ldots, k_1)$ defined by

$$c_i'^s = c_i^{k+s} - \max_j c_j^k \quad i = 1, 2, \ldots, n-1.$$

We can easily verify that these points form the beginning of a sequence compatible with the table T' obtained by deleting the nth row and nth column from table T. We then have

$$\max_i c_i'^{k_1} = \max_i c_i^{k+k_1} - \max_j c_j^k \leqslant k_1 \eta.$$

2. Now let k be any integer, and let q and r be the quotient and the remainder, respectively, after dividing k by k_1. Let s be an integer such that $0 \leqslant s < q$: according to whether there is or is not an index i_0 $(1 \leqslant i_0 \leqslant n)$ with $i_0 \neq j_\rho$ for

$$\rho = sk_1 + r, sk_1 + r + 1, \ldots, (s+1)\,k_1 + r,$$

we have

$$\max_i c_i^{(s+1)\,k_1+r} \leqslant \max_i c_i^{sk_1+r} + k_1 \eta,$$

or

$$\max_i c_i^{(s+1)\,k_1+r} \leqslant k_1 a.$$

On the other hand

$$\max_i c_i^r \leqslant \max_i c_i^0 + ra \leqslant ra \leqslant k_1 a,$$

from which, finally, we have

$$\max_i c_i^k \leqslant qk_1 \eta + k_1 a \leqslant k(\eta + a/q).$$

Thus we see that if we write

$$k(n; a, \epsilon) = qk_1(n-1; a, \epsilon/2),$$

where q is an integer greater than $2a/\epsilon$, we have

$$k \geqslant k(n; a, \epsilon) \Rightarrow \max_i c_i^k \leqslant k\epsilon.$$

The theorem is thus proved.

Method of solving a game

Given a game represented by a tableau of m rows and n columns of numbers a_i^j, let $i_1, i_2, \ldots, i_k$ be a sequence of pure strategies of one of the players, say A. A mixed strategy *defined by this sequence* is one for which the probability associated with each of the m pure strategies of player A is proportional to the number of times this pure strategy appears in the sequence $i_1, i_2, \ldots, i_k$.

Case of a symmetric game

A game is said to be *symmetric* if we get the same game by permuting the two players, in other words, if the tableau of a_i^j is square and antisymmetric. The value of such a game is obviously zero.

Consider a sequence of pure strategies $i_0, i_1, \ldots, i_k, \ldots$, starting from an arbitrary strategy i_0, and taking i_{k+1} to be the best strategy – or one of the best – if the opponent adopts the mixed strategy defined by $i_0, i_i, \ldots, i_k$. Now let u_k be the minimum gain guaranteed by this mixed strategy. We have clearly $u_k \leqslant 0$. We shall show that u_k tends to 0 as k tends to infinity.

Let ϵ be any number > 0; the sequence $\mathbf{c}^0, \mathbf{c}^1, \mathbf{c}^2, \ldots$, defined by $\mathbf{c}^0 = 0$ and

$$\mathbf{c}^{k+1} = \sum_{\nu=0}^{k} \mathbf{a}^{i_\nu}$$

is compatible with the tableau of a_i^j, and we have, for sufficiently large k,

$$\max_i c_i^{k+1} \leqslant (k+1)\,\epsilon$$

and

$$u_k = -\frac{1}{k+1} \max_i c_i^{k+1} \geqslant -\epsilon.$$

Symmetrization of a game

Given a game defined by a tableau of m rows and n columns of numbers a_i^j, let us suppose that two players play the game once and then play it again interchanging their roles. We have thus defined a new game which is symmetric. The choice of a pure strategy in this game is identified with the choice of a row and then a column – or, for the other player, of a column and then a row – in the initial tableau. Therefore for each player there are mn possible strategies given by the ordered pairs (i, j) where $i = 1, 2, \ldots, m$ and $j = 1, 2, \ldots, n$.

If player A adopts the strategy (i, j) while player B adopts the strategy (i', j'), the gain of player A is

$$a_i^{j'} - a_{i'}^{j}.$$

It should be noted that if a player adopts the mixed strategy defined by the probabilities p_j^i, his gain is the same as if he adopts the mixed strategy defined by

$$p^i = \sum_{j=1}^{n} p_j^i \quad (i = 1, 2, \ldots, m),$$

when he has to choose a row, and the mixed strategy defined by

$$q_j = \sum_{i=1}^{m} p_j^i \quad (j = 1, 2, \ldots, n),$$

when he has to choose a column, and this remains true for any strategy (i', j') of the other player.

Thus, we have:

$$\sum_{i,j} p_j^i (a_i^{j'} - a_{i'}^j) = \sum_{i,j} p_j^i a_i^{j'} - \sum_{i,j} p_j^i a_{i'}^j = \sum_i p^i a_i^{j'} - \sum_j q_j a_{i'}^j.$$

Solution of any game

Given a game defined by the tableau of a_i^j, consider a sequence $i_0, i_1, \ldots, i_k, \ldots$ of pure strategies of player A and a sequence $j_0, j_1, \ldots, j_k, \ldots$ of pure strategies of player B starting with two arbitrary strategies i_0 and j_0 and taking i_{k+1} to be the best strategy – or one of the best – of A if B adopts the strategy defined by $j_0, j_1, \ldots, j_k$ and j_{k+1} to be the best strategy of B if A adopts the strategy defined by $i_0, i_1, \ldots, i_k$.

If we call u_k the minimum gain guaranteed to A by the strategy defined by $i_0, i_1, \ldots, i_k$, and w^k B's maximum loss when he adopts the strategy defined by $j_0, j_1, \ldots, j_k$, we have

$$u_k \leqslant \bar{v} \leqslant w^k,$$

where $\bar{v}$ is the value of the game.

Now we shall show that u_k and w^k tend to $\bar{v}$ as k tends to infinity. For this, it is enough to note on the one hand that in the symmetric game obtained from the given game, the sequence of strategies

$$(i_0, j_0), (i_1, j_1), \ldots, (i_k, j_k), \ldots$$

satisfies the condition defined above in the case of a symmetric game, and hence that the minimum gain guaranteed by the mixed strategy defined by the first k elements of this sequence tends to zero when k tends to infinity. On the other hand, this assured minimum gain is precisely $u_k - w^k$.

NOTE. In practice, if player A decides to be content with any mixed strategy which guarantees him a gain greater than $\bar{v} - \epsilon$ where ϵ is a positive number which he has chosen, he will stop computation as soon as he finds for two integers k_1 and k_2 a difference

$$w^{k_2} - u_{k_1} \leqslant \epsilon.$$

He will then know that the mixed strategy defined by $i_0, i_1, \ldots, i_{k_1}$ is appropriate for him.

Bibliography to Part I

[1] BEALE, E. M. L., 'On quadratic programming', *Nav. Res. Logist. Q.*, Sept. 1959.

[2] BERGE, C., *Espaces topologiques et fonctions multivoques*, Dunod, 1959.

[3] BERGE, C., 'Sur une propriété combinatoire des ensembles convexes', *C. R. Acad. Sci., Paris*, **248**, 2698, 1959.

[4] BOHNENBLUST, H. F., KARLIN, S., SHAPLEY, L., *Contributions to the theory of games*, Vol. 1, p. 181, Princeton University Press, 1950.

[5] DANTZIG, G. B., 'A proof of the equivalence of the programming problem and the game problem,' *Cowles Commission Monograph*, No. 13, 330, Wiley, 1951.

[6] DANTZIG, G. B., 'Constructive proof of the Min-Max theorem', *Pacif. J. Math.*, **6**, 25, 1956.

[7] DENNIS, J. B., *Mathematical programming and electrical networks*, Wiley, 1959.

[8] DRESHER, M., *Games of strategy*, Rand Corporation, 1961.

[9] FARKAS, J., 'Uber die theorie der einfachen ungleichungen', *J. reine angew. Math.*, **124**, 1–24, 1902.

[10] FRANK, M., WOLFE, P., 'An algorithm for quadratic programming', *Nav. Res. Logist. Q.*, March and June, 1956.

[11] GHOUILA-HOURI, A., 'Sur l'étude combinatoire des familles de convexes', *C. R. Acad. Sci., Paris*, **252**, 494, 1961.

[12] KARLIN, S., *Mathematical methods and theory in games, programming and economics*, Addison-Wesley, 1959.

[13] KUHN, H. W., TUCKER, A. W., 'Non-linear programming', *Proceedings of the 2nd Berkeley Symposium on Math. Stat. and Prob.*, 1951, p. 481.

[14] LUCE, R. D., RAIFFA, H., *Games and decisions*, Wiley, 1957.

[15] SIMONNARD, M., *Programmation linéaire*, Dunod, 1962.

[16] SION, M., 'Sur une généralisation du théorème minimax', *C. R. Acad. Sci., Paris*, **244**, 2120, 1957.

[17] VAJDA, S., *The theory of games and linear programming*, Methuen, 1956.

[18] VILLE, J., 'Sur la théorie générale des jeux où intervient l'habileté des joueurs', *Traité du calcul des probabilités et de ses applications*, by E. BOREL and J. VILLE, IV, 2, pp. 105–113, 1938.

[19] WOLFE, P., 'The simplex method for quadratic programming', *Rand report*, p. 1205, Santa-Monica, 1957.

PART TWO

Problems of Transportation and of Potential

7. Cycles and coboundaries of a graph

7.1. GENERAL REMARKS ON GRAPHS

We shall define here the principal concepts in the theory of finite graphs in as intuitive a manner as possible, without aiming at axiomatic rigour.

We say that we have a *graph* whenever we have:

Firstly, a set X whose elements will be represented on paper by points and which can stand for individuals, molecules, situations, localities, etc.

Secondly, a set U of (ordered) pairs (a,b) with $a \in X$, $b \in X$, which will be represented on paper by a continuous line joining the points a and b (with an arrow directed from a to b).

The graph G defined by the sets X and U is denoted by $G = (X, U)$.

Such diagrams are met with under different names in many fields: sociograms (psychology), simplexes (topology), electric circuits (physics), organization diagrams (economics), communication networks, genealogical trees, etc.; it is noteworthy that such varied disciplines should use the same theorems, and the main purpose of the theory of graphs is to forge a mathematical tool which applies as much to the behavioural sciences, information theory, the theory of games and transportation networks, as to the theory of sets, matrices or to other purely abstract fields.

The elements of X are the *vertices* of the graph; they are denoted by $a_1, a_2, \ldots, a_n$. The pairs of U are called the *arcs* of the graph; unless otherwise stated, there can be several distinct arcs going from one vertex a_i to another vertex a_j, in which case these arcs are denoted by: (a_i, a_j), $(a_i, a_j)'$, $(a_i, a_j)''$, ... Usually we shall denote the arcs of the graph by the integers $1, 2, \ldots, m$.

It is customary to write the number of elements of a finite set A by $|A|$; thus $|X| = n$, $|U| = m$.

A *subgraph* of a graph (X, U) is defined as the graph formed by a set $A \subset X$, and by the set of all the arcs of U joining two vertices of A; a *partial graph* of (X, U) is defined as the graph formed by all the vertices of X, and by the arcs of the set $V \subset U$. A *partial subgraph* is a partial graph of a subgraph. For example, if X is the set of towns in France and if U is the set of the roads, each counted twice (once for each direction), then the graph (X, U) represents the whole road map of France; the road map of main roads is a partial graph, while the road map of the province of Normandy is a subgraph.

Two arcs are said to be *adjacent* if they have a common vertex, two vertices are *adjacent* if they are distinct and are joined by an arc. An *edge* is a set of two adjacent vertices. If $(a_j, a_k) \in U$, we say that a_j is a *predecessor* of a_k and a_k a *successor* of a_j.

Finally, we say that an arc is *incident from a* if the vertex a is the initial vertex and if its terminal vertex is not a. We define in a similar way an arc *incident to a*. The concept can easily be extended; if A is a given set of vertices, we say that an arc is incident from A if it is of the form (a,b) with

$$a \in A, \quad b \notin A.$$

The set of arcs incident from a set A is denoted by $\omega^+(A)$, and the set of arcs incident to A by $\omega^-(A)$. The set of arcs

$$\omega^+(A) \cup \omega^-(A)$$

incident with A is denoted by $\omega(A)$.

A sequence of arcs in a graph, such that the terminal vertex of each arc coincides with the initial vertex of the succeeding arc, is defined as a *path*.

The *length* of a path $\mu = (u_1, u_2, \ldots, u_k)$ is the number of arcs in the sequence (say $l(\mu) = k$). The initial vertex of the first arc and the terminal vertex of the last arc of the path are called respectively the initial and terminal vertices of the path.

The concepts of *arc* and *path* allow us to characterize certain important types of graphs. Firstly, a graph (X, U) is said to be *symmetric* if

$$(a,b) \in U \Rightarrow (b,a) \in U.$$

In a symmetric graph two adjacent vertices a and b are always joined by two oppositely directed arcs.

A graph (X, U) is said to be *antisymmetric* if

$$(a,b) \in U \Rightarrow (b,a) \notin U$$

(every pair of adjacent vertices is joined in only one direction).

A graph (X, U) is said to be *complete* if

$$(a,b) \notin U \Rightarrow (b,a) \in U$$

(every pair of vertices is joined in at least one of the two directions).

Finally, a graph is said to be *strongly connected* if, for any two vertices a and b (with $a \neq b$), there exists a path directed from a to b.

For example, consider the following graph: X is a set of individuals, and we write $(a,b) \in U$ if one person a can send a message directly to person b.

In general, this graph is symmetric: this is so when communication is by radio, telephone, tom-tom, etc., but the graph is not always symmetric if the communication is by rocket signals or carrier pigeons. Moreover, in a well-designed communication network, every individual should be able to send a message to every other member of the organization, either directly or by successive retransmissions; in other words, the graph should be strongly connected.

EXAMPLE. Consider the graph of Figure 7.1 below with $n = 6$ vertices and $m = 10$ arcs

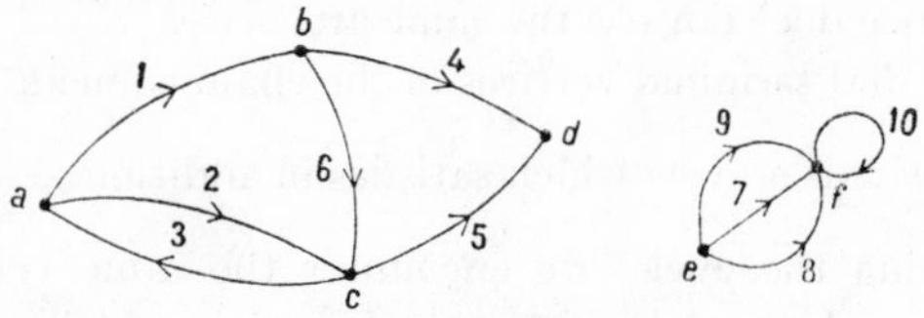

FIG. 7.1

If we write $A = \{a,b,c\}$, the subgraph generated by A is *complete* and *strongly connected*; we have:

$$\omega^+(A) = \{4,5\}, \quad \omega^-(A) = \emptyset.$$

The arc (f,f), for which the initial and terminal vertices coincide, is a *loop*.

Besides the ideas already given, which stem ultimately from the orientation of the arcs, we can define very similar non-oriented concepts. An *edge* is an unordered pair of adjacent vertices; edges such as $\{a,c\}$ and $\{e,f\}$ in the graph of Figure 7.1 are called *multiple edges* and the others are *simple edges*.

A *chain* is a sequence of arcs

$$\mu = (u_1, u_2, \ldots, u_k, u_{k+1}, \ldots, u_q)$$

such that each of its intermediate arcs u_k is attached to u_{k-1} at one of its extremities and to u_{k+1} at the other. A path is a chain, but the converse is not true.

A graph is *connected* if for every pair of distinct vertices there is a chain going from one to the other. A strongly connected graph is connected, but the converse is not true.

If a is a vertex, the set formed by a and all the vertices which can be joined by a chain to a is defined as a *connected component* (or *component*) of the graph. If a graph is connected, it has only one component; if a graph is not connected, then there are two vertices a and b which cannot be joined by any chain and the graph has at least two distinct components.

The graph of Figure 7.1 has two components: $\{a,b,c,d\}$ and $\{e,f\}$; as we see here, the different components of the graph *partition* the set X.

7.2. CYCLES AND COBOUNDARIES; LEMMA ON COLOURED ARCS

In a graph, we define a *cycle*† as a sequence of arcs $(u_1, u_2, \ldots, u_k, \ldots, u_q)$ such that:

1. Every arc u_k (with $1 < k < q$) is joined to the preceding arc u_{k-1} at one of its extremities and to the succeeding arc u_{k+1} at the other (in other words it is a *chain*).
2. The sequence does not use the same arc twice.
3. The initial and terminal vertices of the chain coincide.

An *elementary cycle* is a cycle which satisfies in addition:

4. In traversing the cycle, we encounter the same vertex only once (except, of course, the initial and terminal vertices which coincide).

For a given cycle μ, we denote by μ^+ the set of arcs oriented in a given sense and by μ^- the set of arcs oriented in the opposite sense. A *circuit* is a cycle in which all the arcs are oriented in the same sense.

If the arcs are numbered $1, 2, \ldots, m$, with every cycle we can associate a vector

$$\boldsymbol{\mu} = (\mu_1, \mu_2, \ldots, \mu_m),$$

with

$$\mu_i = \begin{cases} 0 & \text{if } i \notin \mu^+ \bigcup \mu^-, \text{ that is, if the arc } i \text{ is not used;} \\ +1 & \text{if } i \in \mu^+, \\ -1 & \text{if } i \in \mu^-. \end{cases}$$

In what follows, the cycle will be identified with the vector $\boldsymbol{\mu}$, which it defines, and when we say that a cycle $\boldsymbol{\mu}$ is the *sum* of the cycles $\boldsymbol{\mu}^1 + \boldsymbol{\mu}^2$, we shall mean the vector sum.

Property 1. *Every cycle* $\boldsymbol{\mu}$ *is a sum of elementary disjoint cycles* (*that is, without common arcs*).

This is obvious: if we traverse $\boldsymbol{\mu}$, an elementary cycle is defined every time we arrive at a vertex previously encountered.

† This definition differs slightly from that given in [2]. But we can consider that the word *cycle* here is an abbreviation for what would have been called in [2] a *simple cycle of a multigraph generated by the arcs*. On the other hand, the word cycle should not be taken in the sense of combinatorial topology (where we use the word *topological cycle* or *t-cycle*).

Property 2. *A cycle is elementary if and only if it is a minimal cycle (that is, if no other cycle can be obtained by deleting arcs).*

This is obvious.

If A is any set of vertices, we have seen that $\omega^+(A)$ denotes the set of arcs incident from A and $\omega^-(A)$ the set of arcs incident to A and we write

$$\omega(A) = \omega^+(A) \bigcup \omega^-(A).$$

A *coboundary*† is defined as a set of arcs of the form $\omega(A)$, which is non-empty and partitioned into two classes $\omega^+(A)$ and $\omega^-(A)$.

A coboundary will sometimes be denoted by $\boldsymbol{\omega}(A)$ (assuming the existence of two classes of which only one may be empty).

To every coboundary we can associate a vector

$$\boldsymbol{\omega} = (\omega_1, \omega_2, \ldots, \omega_m),$$

with

$$\omega_i = \begin{cases} 0 & \text{if } i \notin \omega(A) \\ +1 & \text{if } i \in \omega^+(A) \\ -1 & \text{if } i \in \omega^-(A). \end{cases}$$

In what follows, the coboundary $\omega(A)$ will be identified with the vector $\boldsymbol{\omega}$.

A coboundary is said to be *elementary* if it is formed by the set of arcs joining two connected subgraphs A_1 and A_2 with

$$\begin{cases} A_1, A_2 \neq \emptyset \\ A_1 \bigcap A_2 = \emptyset \\ A_1 \bigcup A_2 = C \end{cases}$$

where C is a connected component of the graph.

A cocircuit is a coboundary $\boldsymbol{\omega}(A)$ in which all the arcs are oriented in the same direction: either outwards from A or into A.

Property 1. *Every coboundary $\boldsymbol{\omega}$ is a sum of elementary disjoint coboundaries (that is, without common arcs).*

Let $\boldsymbol{\omega}$ be a coboundary of the form $\boldsymbol{\omega}(A)$, and let $A_1, A_2, \ldots, A_k$ be the different connected components of the subgraph generated by A. We have

$$\boldsymbol{\omega}(A) = \boldsymbol{\omega}(A_1) + \boldsymbol{\omega}(A_2) + \ldots + \boldsymbol{\omega}(A_k),$$

where the coboundaries $\boldsymbol{\omega}(A_1)$, $\boldsymbol{\omega}(A_2), \ldots,$ $\boldsymbol{\omega}(A_k)$ are mutually disjoint. We show that $\boldsymbol{\omega}(A_i)$ is a sum of disjoint elementary coboundaries.

† At the request of M. Berge the French word *cocycle* has been translated *coboundary*.

If C is the connected component containing A_i, the subgraph generated by $C-A_i$ has the components $C_1, C_2, \ldots$, and we have

$$\boldsymbol{\omega}(A_i) = -\boldsymbol{\omega}(C_1) - \boldsymbol{\omega}(C_2) - \ldots$$

$-\boldsymbol{\omega}(C_1)$ is an elementary coboundary since it joins two connected subgraphs C_1 and $A_i \bigcup C_2 \bigcup C_3 \ldots$; moreover $-\boldsymbol{\omega}(C_1)$, $-\boldsymbol{\omega}(C_2), \ldots$ are disjoint.

Property 2. *A coboundary is elementary if and only if it is minimal, (that is, if no other coboundary can be obtained by deleting arcs).*

Let $\boldsymbol{\omega}(A)$ be a minimal coboundary (hence A is contained in a connected component C) and let $A_1, A_2, \ldots, A_k$ be the connected components of the subgraph generated by $C-A$. If $k \geqslant 2$, $-\boldsymbol{\omega}(A_1)$ is a coboundary contained in $\boldsymbol{\omega}(A)$ and not equal to $\boldsymbol{\omega}(A)$, which is absurd, hence we have $k = 1$ and $\boldsymbol{\omega}(A)$ is an elementary coboundary.

Conversely, let $\boldsymbol{\omega}$ be an elementary coboundary which joins two connected subgraphs A_1 and A_2. If we delete some of its arcs but not all, $A_1 \bigcup A_2$ is not disconnected, hence we do not obtain a coboundary. Thus $\boldsymbol{\omega}$ is a minimal coboundary.

Lemma on coloured arcs (Minty, [31]). *Let the arcs $i = 1, 2, \ldots, m$ of a graph be coloured red, green or black and suppose that arc 1 is coloured black. One (and only one) of the following propositions is true:*

1. *An elementary cycle, in red and black only, and with all its black arcs oriented in the same direction, passes through arc 1.*
2. *An elementary coboundary, in green and black only, and with all its black arcs oriented in the same direction, passes through arc 1.*

We label vertices of the graph step by step by an iterative procedure. Let (a_1, b_1) be the arc 1.

1. Label the vertex b_1 the terminal vertex of the arc 1.
2. If a is a vertex which is already labelled, and b is a vertex yet to be labelled, we label b in the following cases:

There is a black arc from a to b,
There is a red arc from a to b or from b to a.

We continue this labelling procedure as long as possible; then one of the following alternatives will have arisen:

(1) the vertex a_1, which is the initial vertex of the arc 1, has been labelled: hence there necessarily exists a red and black cycle containing arc 1 with all the black arcs oriented in the same direction (hence there cannot be a black and green coboundary containing arc 1 with all black arcs in the same direction). This cycle is the sum of disjoint elementary cycles one of which contains the arc 1.

(2) the vertex a_1 has not been labelled: if A denotes the set of all vertices which are not labelled, $\boldsymbol{\omega}(A)$ contains only black arcs oriented from A or green arcs and we have a green and black coboundary $\boldsymbol{\omega}(A)$ containing arc 1 with all the black arcs oriented from A (hence there is no red and black cycle containing arc 1 with all black arcs oriented in the same direction). This coboundary is a sum of disjoint elementary coboundaries, one of which contains the arc 1.

Consequence. *Every arc belongs either to an elementary circuit or to an elementary cocircuit (but not to both).*

This follows on colouring all the arcs black and then applying the theorem.

We now introduce an important concept; we say that the cycles $\boldsymbol{\mu}_1, \boldsymbol{\mu}_2, \ldots, \boldsymbol{\mu}_k$ are *dependent* if there exists a relation of the form

$$r_1 \boldsymbol{\mu}^1 + r_2 \boldsymbol{\mu}^2 + \ldots + r_k \boldsymbol{\mu}^k = \mathbf{0},$$

where $r_1, r_2, \ldots, r_k$ are numbers not all zero; if such a relation does not exist the cycles are said to be *independent*.

A *fundamental basis of cycles* is defined as a set $\{\boldsymbol{\mu}^1, \boldsymbol{\mu}^2, \ldots, \boldsymbol{\mu}^k\}$ of elementary independent cycles, such that every other elementary cycle $\boldsymbol{\mu}$ can be expressed in the form

$$\boldsymbol{\mu} = r_1 \boldsymbol{\mu}^1 + r_2 \boldsymbol{\mu}^2 + \ldots + r_k \boldsymbol{\mu}^k$$

for any numbers $r_1, r_2, \ldots, r_k$. We say that k is the dimension of the vector sub-space of $\mathbf{R}^m$ generated by the cycles. We propose to determine this constant. Similarly we define a *basis of coboundaries* $\{\boldsymbol{\omega}^1, \boldsymbol{\omega}^2, \ldots, \boldsymbol{\omega}^l\}$ and we propose to determine the constant l.

EXAMPLE. Consider the graph below; we have different elementary cycles, namely:

$$\begin{aligned}
\boldsymbol{\mu}^1 &= (1,6,2) &&= [a\,b\,c\,a] \\
\boldsymbol{\mu}^2 &= (1,6,3) &&= [a\,b\,c\,a] \\
\boldsymbol{\mu}^3 &= (2,3) &&= [a\,c\,a] \\
\boldsymbol{\mu}^4 &= (1,4,5,2) &&= [a\,b\,d\,c\,a] \\
\boldsymbol{\mu}^5 &= (6,5,4) &&= [b\,c\,d\,b] \\
\boldsymbol{\mu}^6 &= (1,4,5,3) &&= [a\,b\,d\,c\,a].
\end{aligned}$$

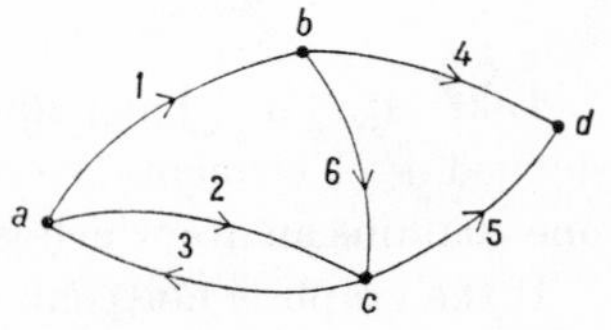

However, these cycles are not independent: the cycles $\boldsymbol{\mu}^1$, $\boldsymbol{\mu}^2$, $\boldsymbol{\mu}^3$, for instance, are dependent since

$$\boldsymbol{\mu}^1 - \boldsymbol{\mu}^2 + \boldsymbol{\mu}^3 = \mathbf{0}.$$

We may form a basis of cycles taking for example: $\boldsymbol{\mu}^2$, $\boldsymbol{\mu}^3$, $\boldsymbol{\mu}^6$.

The same considerations apply to coboundaries in the above graph. A coboundary $\boldsymbol{\omega}(A)$ can be denoted either by the indices of the arcs i preceded by a plus sign if $i \in \omega^+(A)$ and a minus sign if $i \in \omega^-(A)$, or by the set A. Here the elementary coboundaries are

$$\begin{aligned}
\boldsymbol{\omega}^1 &= \{a\} &&= (1, 2, -3)\\
\boldsymbol{\omega}^2 &= \{a\,b\} &&= (+6, +2, -3, +4)\\
\boldsymbol{\omega}^3 &= \{a\,c\} &&= (-6, +1, +5)\\
\boldsymbol{\omega}^4 &= \{a\,b\,c\} &&= (+4, +5)\\
\boldsymbol{\omega}^5 &= \{a\,b\,d\} &&= (+6, +2, -3, -5)\\
\boldsymbol{\omega}^6 &= \{a\,c\,d\} &&= (-6, +1, -4)
\end{aligned}$$

We can form a basis of coboundaries by taking, for example:

$$\boldsymbol{\omega}^1, \boldsymbol{\omega}^4, \boldsymbol{\omega}^5.$$

Theorem 1. *Let G be a graph with n vertices, m arcs, p connected components; the number of elements in the basis of cycles is $k(G) = m - n + p$; the number of elements in the basis of coboundaries is $l(G) = n - p$.†*

1. *There exist $n - p$ independent elementary coboundaries.*

Firstly, suppose the graph is connected ($p = 1$) and form $n - 1$ independent coboundaries step by step as follows:

Take an arbitrary vertex a_1 and let $A_1 = \{a_1\}$; the coboundary $\boldsymbol{\omega}(A_1)$ contains an elementary coboundary; let $[a_1, a_2]$ be an edge of this elementary coboundary with:

$$a_1 \in A_1, \quad a_2 \notin A_1.$$

Let $A_2 = A_1 \cup \{a_2\}$; the coboundary $\boldsymbol{\omega}(A_2)$ contains an elementary coboundary; let $[b, a_3]$ be an edge of this elementary coboundary with

$$b \in A_2, \quad a_3 \notin A_2.$$

Take $A_3 = A_2 \cup \{a_3\}$ and repeat this process; finally we shall have defined $n - 1$ elementary coboundaries; these are independent, since each one contains an arc which is not contained in the following ones.

If the graph is not connected, let $C_1, C_2, \ldots, C_p$ be the connected components. Then, using the above result, there exist

$$(|C_1| - 1) + (|C_2| - 1) + \ldots + (|C_p| - 1) = n - p$$

independent elementary coboundaries.

† $k(G)$ is also sometimes called the *cyclomatic number* and $l(G)$ the *cocyclomatic number* of the graph G.

2. *There exist $m-n+p$ independent elementary cycles.*

Let us write $k(G) = m-n+p$ and consider a series of partial graphs $G_0, G_1, \ldots, G_m = G$; the graph G_0 consists only of the vertices of G and every graph G_i is obtained from G_{i-1} by adjoining the arc i of G.

Firstly, we have $k(G_0) = 0$ and there are no cycles.

If the arc i closes a new cycle $\boldsymbol{\mu}^i$, we have

$$k(G_i) = k(G_{i-1})+1$$

since m increases by one but p remains the same.

Otherwise, we have:

$$k(G_i) = k(G_{i-1}),$$

since m increases and p decreases by one. We have therefore finally defined $k(G) = m-n+p$ cycles $\boldsymbol{\mu}^{i_1}, \boldsymbol{\mu}^{i_2}, \ldots, \boldsymbol{\mu}^{i_k}$.

Suppose there exists a linear relation of the form:

$$r_1\boldsymbol{\mu}^{i_1}+r_2\boldsymbol{\mu}^{i_2}+\ldots+r_t\boldsymbol{\mu}^{i_t} = \mathbf{0}$$

with $r_t \neq 0$ and $i_1 < i_2 < \ldots < i_t$.

This is impossible, for the cycle $\boldsymbol{\mu}^{i_t}$ contains the arc i_t which is not contained in the other cycles $\boldsymbol{\mu}^{i_1}, \ldots, \boldsymbol{\mu}^{i_{t-1}}$. Hence we have $k(G)$ independent cycles.

3. *There cannot exist more than $k(G) = m-n+p$ independent cycles, and there cannot exist more than $l(G) = n-p$ independent coboundaries.*

In $\mathbf{R}^m$ consider the vector space M generated by the cycles and the vector space Ω generated by the coboundaries.

If $\boldsymbol{\mu}$ is a cycle and $\boldsymbol{\omega} = \boldsymbol{\omega}(A)$ a coboundary, their scalar product

$$\langle \boldsymbol{\mu}, \boldsymbol{\omega} \rangle = \sum_{i=1}^{m} \mu_i \omega_i$$

is zero, for

$$\langle \boldsymbol{\mu}, \boldsymbol{\omega}(A) \rangle = \left\langle \boldsymbol{\mu}, \sum_{a\in A} \boldsymbol{\omega}(a) \right\rangle = \sum_{a\in A} \langle \boldsymbol{\mu}, \boldsymbol{\omega}(a) \rangle = 0.$$

Hence M and Ω are two orthogonal sub-spaces of $\mathbf{R}^m$ and consequently their dimensions satisfy:

$$\dim M + \dim \Omega \leqslant m.$$

On the other hand, from the above results, we also have

$$\dim M + \dim \Omega \geqslant k(G) + l(G) = m.$$

Hence equality holds and thus

$$\dim M = k(G)$$

and

$$\dim \Omega = l(G).$$

7.3. STRONGLY CONNECTED GRAPHS AND GRAPHS WITHOUT CIRCUITS

The duality we have demonstrated between cycles and coboundaries will be used repeatedly.

Notice that the concepts of *strongly connected graphs* and of *graphs without circuits* are dual. This can be seen more precisely from the following propositions:

Proposition 1. *For a connected graph G with at least one arc, the following conditions are equivalent:*

(1) *G is strongly connected;*
(2) *through every arc there is a circuit;*
(3) *G does not contain any cocircuit.*

(1) $\Rightarrow$ (2), for if (a,b) is an arc, there is a path directed from b to a, therefore a circuit must pass through (a,b).

(2) $\Rightarrow$ (3), for if G contained a cocircuit passing through an arc i, there would be no circuit with the arc i, according to the lemma on coloured arcs (where all the arcs are coloured black).

(3) $\Rightarrow$ (1): let G be a connected graph without cocircuits. We suppose G is not strongly connected and deduce a contradiction. For every vertex a of the graph, denote by C_a the set of all vertices belonging to at least one circuit passing through a; then obviously

$$\left.\begin{array}{r} a \neq b \\ C_a \cap C_b \neq \emptyset \end{array}\right\} \Rightarrow C_a = C_b.$$

Thus the different sets of the form C_a form a partition of the set of vertices of G; and a set C_a will be called here a *strongly connected component* of the graph. If G is not strongly connected, it has several strongly connected components; as G is connected, there exist two disjoint strongly connected components joined by an arc (a,b). No circuit passes through (a,b) (for otherwise $C_a = C_b$), therefore a cocircuit passes through (a,b) (by the lemma on coloured arcs) which is impossible.

Proposition 2. *For a graph G with at least one arc, the following conditions are equivalent:*

(1) *G is a graph without circuits;*
(2) *A cocircuit passes through every arc.*

This is obvious.

We shall give here two very simple algorithms:

Algorithm to determine whether a graph is strongly connected.

We define an iterative procedure of labelling vertices as follows:

(1) label an arbitrary vertex a_1 with a plus and a minus sign;
(2) if a is labelled plus, label plus on all vertices b such that $(a,b) \in U$;
(3) if a is labelled minus, label minus on all vertices b such that $(b,a) \in U$.

If, finally, all the vertices are labelled both plus and minus, the graph is strongly connected. Otherwise, it is not strongly connected (notice that in this case the set of vertices labelled plus and minus form the strongly connected component containing the vertex a_1).

Algorithm to determine if a graph is without circuits.

We define an iterative procedure of labelling the vertices as follows:

(1) label every vertex a which has no successor;
(2) label every vertex a all of whose successors are labelled.

If, in this way, all vertices are labelled, the graph is without circuits. For, as a circuit allows us to define a path of infinite length, the necessary and sufficient condition that no circuit passes through a vertex a, is that all the paths leading from a are of finite length. Let $f(a)$ be the length of the longest path leading from a; $f(a)$ is defined step by step by the following rule:

(1) at every vertex a which has no successor we have $f(a) = 0$.
(2) if $f(b)$ is defined for all the successors b of a, we have

$$f(a) = \max\{f(b) \mid (a,b) \in U\} + 1.$$

At every vertex a which is labelled by this algorithm we may define a number $f(a) < \infty$, representing the length of the longest path leading from a.

Theorem 2. *If the graph G is without circuits it has a basis of $l(G)$ independent cocircuits.*

We may suppose that G is connected, for if it had connected components, $C_1, C_2, \ldots, C_p$, there would be at least

$$\sum_{i=1}^{p} (|C_i|-1) = n-p = l(G)$$

independent cocircuits and the theorem would be proved.

We have thus to show that there *exist* $l(G) = n-1$ *independent cocircuits*.

This result is true for graphs with 1 or 2 vertices, we shall suppose that it is true for graphs with $n-1$ vertices and show that it is still true for a graph G with n vertices.

In the graph G, there exists at least one vertex b such that the length of the longest path leading from b is $f(b) = 1$; there is also a vertex a without successors such that $(b,a) \in U$. Consider the graph G' obtained from G by deleting the arcs joining a and b and contracting these two vertices a and b into a single vertex, which is denoted by c ('shrinking' the set $\{a,b\}$).

The graph G' has no circuit since if such a circuit $\boldsymbol{\mu}'$ existed it would necessarily pass through c; moreover its length would be > 1. Let d be the successor of c on this circuit. In the graph G the cycle $\boldsymbol{\mu}$ which corresponds to $\boldsymbol{\mu}'$ must pass through both the vertices a and b (for G is without circuits), hence $(b,d) \in U$ and there would be a path of length > 1 from b to a which is impossible.

The graph G' which thus has no circuits, is connected and has $n-1$ vertices, therefore it contains $n-2$ independent cocircuits: $\boldsymbol{\omega}'(A_1')$, $\boldsymbol{\omega}'(A_2'), \ldots, \boldsymbol{\omega}'(A_{n-2}')$. To these there correspond the $n-2$ coboundaries in G: $\boldsymbol{\omega}(A_1)$, $\boldsymbol{\omega}(A_2), \ldots, \boldsymbol{\omega}(A_{n-2})$ which are necessarily cocircuits. As the vector $\boldsymbol{\omega}(A_i)$ has the same components as $\boldsymbol{\omega}'(A_i')$, the $\boldsymbol{\omega}(A_i)$ are linearly independent vectors. The vectors $\boldsymbol{\omega}(a)$, $\boldsymbol{\omega}(A_1)$, $\boldsymbol{\omega}(A_2), \ldots, \boldsymbol{\omega}(A_{n-2})$ are also linearly independent, for $\boldsymbol{\omega}(a)$ contains the arc (b,a) which none of the other cocircuits contain.

Hence we have obtained $n-1$ independent cocircuits.

Theorem 3. *If the graph G is strongly connected, it has a basis of $k(G)$ independent circuits.*

For, we shall show that every elementary cycle $\boldsymbol{\mu}$ is a linear combination of circuits.

Among the vertices contained in the cycle $\boldsymbol{\mu}$ we can distinguish a set S of vertices, each of which is such that one arc of $\boldsymbol{\mu}$ is incident to it and one arc of $\boldsymbol{\mu}$ is incident from it; a set S' of vertices, from which two arcs of $\boldsymbol{\mu}$ are incident, a set S'' of vertices to which two arcs of $\boldsymbol{\mu}$ are incident. The number of terminal vertices being equal to the number of initial vertices, we have $|S'| = |S''|$; let $a_1', a_2', \ldots, a_q'$ be the elements of S' and $a_1'', a_2'', \ldots, a_q''$ be those of S''.

On the cycle μ the elements of S' alternate with those of S'' and we can thus assume that after $a'_i \in S'$, the first vertex encountered which does not belong to S is $a''_i \in S''$; finally if μ^0 is a path which encounters the vertex a before the vertex b, let us denote by $\mu^0\,[a,b]$ the partial path from a to b. As the graph is strongly connected, there must be a circuit μ^i which passes through a'_{i+1} and a''_i and which uses the arcs of μ to go from a'_{i+1} to a''_i. The cycle μ is a linear combination of circuits, for we can write:

$$\begin{aligned}\mu &= \mu[a'_1, a''_1] - \mu^1[a'_2, a''_1] + \mu[a'_2, a''_2] + \dots \\ &= \mu[a'_1, a''_1] + \mu^1[a''_1, a'_2] + \mu[a'_2, a''_2] + \mu^2[a''_2, a'_3] + \dots - (\mu^1 + \mu^2 + \dots).\end{aligned}$$

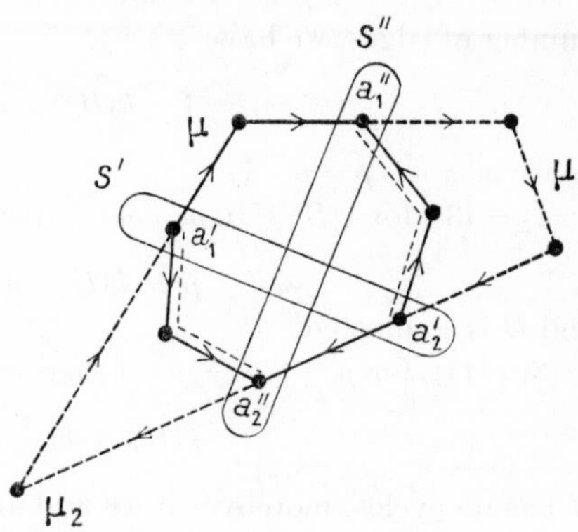

FIG. 7.2

Since

$$\mu[a'_1, a''_1] + \mu^1[a''_1, a'_2] + \mu[a'_2, a''_2] + \mu^2[a''_2, a'_3] + \dots$$

constitutes a circuit, we see clearly that every elementary cycle is a linear combination of circuits, and the same is true for any cycle by Property 1 on p. 120.

In $\mathbf{R}^m$, the circuits constitute a basis of the vector subspace generated by the cycles, and from Theorem 1 this basis is of dimension $k(G)$: the maximum number of independent circuits is thus $k(G)$.

7.4. TREES AND COTREES

A *tree* is defined as a connected graph with at least two vertices and no cycles; since a tree has no cycles, it has no multiple edges, because of this we may equally well speak of 'arcs' or 'edges'. A *forest* is a graph every connected component of which is a tree; in other words it is a graph without cycles and without isolated vertices.

Theorem 4. *Let $H = (X, U)$ be a graph of order $|X| = n \geqslant 2$; the following properties are equivalent for characterizing a tree:*

(1) *H is connected and without cycles;*
(2) *H is without cycles and has $n-1$ arcs;*
(3) *H is connected and has $n-1$ arcs;*

(4) *H is without cycles and by adding an arc, one and only one cycle is formed*;

(5) *H is connected and if we delete any one arc it is no longer connected*;

(6) *every pair of vertices is joined by one and only one chain.*

(1) ⇒ (2), for if p is the number of connected components, and m the number of edges, we have

$$p = 1, \quad k(H) = m - n + p = 0,$$

hence $m = n - p = n - 1$.

(2) ⇒ (3), for $k(H) = 0$, $m = n - 1$, hence

$$p = k(H) - m + n = 1,$$

and H is connected.

(3) ⇒ (4), for $p = 1$, $m = n - 1$, hence

$$k(H) = m - n + p = 0;$$

H has no cycles, moreover if we add an arc, $k(H)$ becomes equal to 1 and therefore exactly one cycle is formed.

(4) ⇒ (5), for if H is not connected, we cannot form a cycle by adding the arc (a,b) where a and b are two vertices which are in different components; therefore $p = 1$, $k(H) = 0$, hence $m = n - 1$. On the other hand, by deleting an arc we have

$$m' = n' - 2, \quad k(H') = 0;$$

hence

$$p' = k(H') - m' + n' = 2$$

and H' is no longer connected.

(5) ⇒ (6), since for two vertices, a and b say, there is a chain from one to the other (since H is connected) and there cannot be more than one such chain (for the deletion of an arc which belongs only to the second chain would not disconnect the graph).

(6) ⇒ (1), for if H had a cycle, at least one pair of vertices would be connected by two distinct chains.

Theorem 5. *A tree has at least two pendant vertices (a vertex which is the extremity of a single arc is called a pendant vertex).*

Let H be a tree with less than two pendant vertices. Consider a man who sets out to traverse the graph and who starts from any vertex (if there are no pendant vertices), or from the pendant vertex (if there is exactly one): if he does not use the same edge twice, he cannot go to the same vertex twice (since H is without cycles); on the other hand, if he arrives at a point a, he can always leave it by a new edge (for a is not the pendant vertex).

Thus he would travel indefinitely, which is impossible since the graph H is finite.

Theorem 6. *A graph $G = (X, U)$ has a partial graph which is a tree, if and only if G is connected.*

If G is not connected, none of its partial graphs is connected and therefore G has no partial graph which is a tree.

If G is connected, let us look for an arc which may be deleted without disconnecting the graph. If there is no such arc, G is a tree by virtue of property (5); and if there is such an arc, it is deleted and we look for a new one to delete, etc.,....

When no more arcs can be deleted, we shall have a tree in which the set of vertices is precisely X.

NOTE. This theorem gives a simple algorithm with which we may construct a tree H, of a connected graph G.

We could also construct the tree H as follows:

Let us consider any arc i_0 and find an arc i_1 which does not form a cycle with the arc i_0; then find an arc i_2 which does not form a cycle with $\{i_0, i_1\}$, etc. When the procedure cannot be continued any more, we have a partial graph H which is a tree, according to property (4) of Theorem 4.

Theorem 7. *Let G be a connected graph, H a partial graph which is a tree; if i is an arc of G not appearing in H, its adjunction to H determines a cycle μ^i because of property (4), and the different cycles μ^i form a basis of independent cycles.*

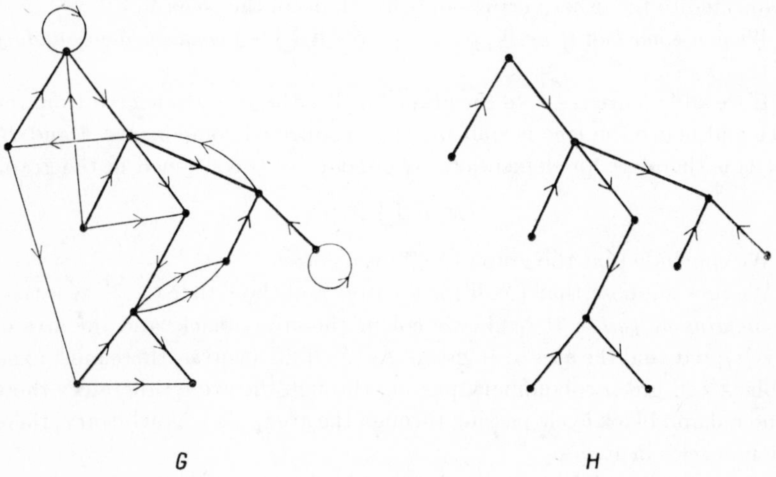

FIG. 7.3

These cycles μ^i are independent since every one of them contains an arc not contained in the others. On the other hand, the number of cycles μ^i formed is equal to the number of arcs of G less the number of arcs of H, thus

$$m-(n-1) = m-n+p = k(G).$$

According to Theorem 1, the μ^i form a basis of cycles.

NOTE. This theorem gives a simple algorithm for constructing a basis of cycles of a connected graph G; if G is not connected we treat each of its connected components separately.

Let us now consider a connected graph $G = (X, U)$, we have seen that a partial graph $H = (X, V)$ is a *tree* if it does not contain elementary cycles of G, but upon adding any arc of $U - V$ it does contain an elementary cycle of G. In the same way, we say that a partial graph (X, W) is a *cotree* if it does not contain any elementary coboundary of G, but upon adding any arc of $U - W$ it does contain an elementary coboundary of G.

Theorem 8. *Let $G(X, U)$ be a connected graph, and (X, V) and (X, W) be two partial graphs with*

$$V \cup W = U, \quad V \cap W = \emptyset;$$

the necessary and sufficient condition that (X, W) be a cotree is that (X, V) must be a tree.

We first suppose that (X, V) is a tree and show that (X, W) is a cotree.

We will show that (X, W) has no coboundaries of G.

No elementary coboundary $\omega(A)$ of G is contained in W, since A is connected to the other vertices of G by chains of the tree (X, V).

We now show that if $i_1 \in V$, the set of arcs $W \cup \{i_1\}$ contains a coboundary of G.

If we add an arc $i_1 \in V$ to the graph (X, W), the arc i_1 is deleted from the tree and hence the tree is split into two connected components A and B; $\omega(A)$ is therefore an elementary coboundary of G contained in the graph

$$(X, W \cup \{i_1\}).$$

We conclude that the graph (X, W) is a cotree.

We now suppose that (X, W) is a cotree and show that (X, V) is a tree. *V contains no cycles.* If $i_1 \in V$, we colour the arc i_1 black, and the arcs of $V - \{i_1\}$ red, and the arcs of W green. As (X, W) is a cotree, there must exist a black and green coboundary passing through the arc i_1; therefore there is no red and black cycle passing through the arc i_1. As i_1 is arbitrary, there are no cycles in V.

If $i_1 \in W$ the set $V \cup \{i_1\}$ contains a cycle. Let us colour the arc i_1 black, the arcs of V red, and the arcs of $W - \{i_1\}$ green. Since there is no black and green coboundary passing through the arc i_1, there is a black and red cycle passing through the arc i_1.

We have thus proved that (X, V) is a tree.

Theorem 9. *Let $F = (X, W)$ be a cotree of a connected graph $G = (X, U)$; if i is an arc not appearing in F, its adjunction to F forms a unique coboundary $\boldsymbol{\omega}^i$, and the different coboundaries $\boldsymbol{\omega}^i$ form a basis of independent coboundaries.*

If we delete the arc i of the tree $(X, U - W)$, two connected components A and B of the tree are formed and the required coboundary is uniquely determined and may be denoted by $\boldsymbol{\omega}(A)$.

The coboundaries $\boldsymbol{\omega}^i$ are independent, since each of them contains an arc not contained in the others. On the other hand, the number of coboundaries $\boldsymbol{\omega}^i$ is equal to the number of arcs of the tree $(X, U - W)$, that is to say, $n - 1 = l(G)$. According to Theorem 1, the $\boldsymbol{\omega}^i$ form a basis of coboundaries.

This theorem gives a simple algorithm for determining a basis of independent coboundaries.

A vertex a_1, from which every other vertex of the graph can be reached by a path starting from a_1 is called a *centre* of the graph. A centre does not always exist.

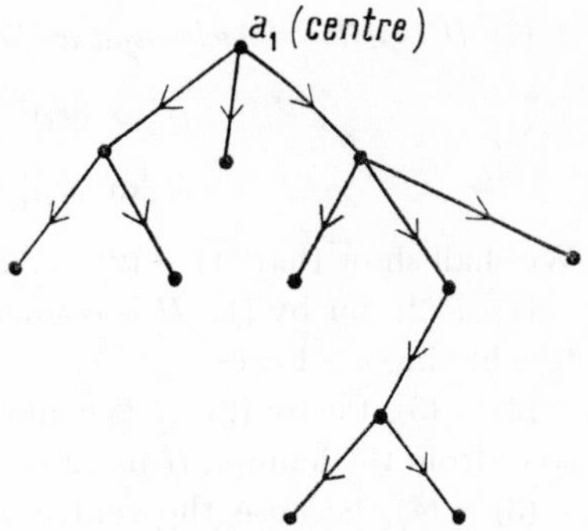

FIG. 7.4. Arborescence

A graph G is said to be *quasi strongly connected* if for every pair of vertices (a, b) there is a vertex z from which a path goes to a and a path goes to b. A strongly connected graph is therefore quasi strongly connected (since we can take $z = a$) but the converse is not true. A quasi strongly connected graph is connected.

Finally, a tree which has a centre is called an *arborescence*; for example, the genealogical tree of male descendants of King Henry IV is an arborescence whose centre is Henry IV.

Lemma. *The necessary and sufficient condition for a graph $G = (X, U)$ to have a centre is that it is quasi strongly connected.*

It is clear that if a graph has a centre, it is quasi strongly connected.

On the other hand, if a graph G is quasi strongly connected, consider the set of vertices $a_1, a_2, \ldots, a_n$; there is a vertex z_2 from which we can go to a_1 and to a_2; there is a vertex z_3 from which we can go to z_2 and to a_3, etc.; there is a vertex z_n from which we can go to z_{n-1} and a_n; this vertex z_n is therefore a centre of the graph G.

Theorem 10. *Let $H = (X, U)$ be a graph of order $|X| n > 1$; the following properties are equivalent for characterizing an arborescence:*

(1) *H is quasi strongly connected and without cycles;*
(2) *H is quasi strongly connected and has $n-1$ arcs;*
(3) *H is a tree having a centre a_1;*
(4) *there is a vertex a_1 which is joined to every other vertex by a single path (this path moreover starts from a_1);*
(5) *H is strongly connected, and it loses this property by the deletion of any one arc;*
(6) *H is connected and we have*

$$|\boldsymbol{\omega}^-(a_1)| = 0;$$
$$|\boldsymbol{\omega}^-(a_j)| = 1 \quad \textit{for } j \neq 1;$$

(7) *H is without cycles and we have*

$$|\boldsymbol{\omega}^-(a_1)| = 0$$
$$|\boldsymbol{\omega}^-(a_j)| = 1 \quad \textit{for } j \neq 1.$$

We shall show that (1) $\Rightarrow$ (2) $\Rightarrow \ldots \Rightarrow$ (7) $\Rightarrow$ (1).

(1) $\Rightarrow$ (2), for by (1), H is connected and without cycles, therefore it is a tree having $n-1$ arcs.

(2) $\Rightarrow$ (3), for by (2), H is connected and has $n-1$ arcs, therefore it is a tree; from the lemma, H has a centre a_1.

(3) $\Rightarrow$ (4), because the centre a_1 of the tree H possesses the required property.

(4) $\Rightarrow$ (5), for suppose that the graph is still quasi strongly connected even after the deletion of an arc (a, b); then there are two elementary paths

$$[z, c_1, c_2, \ldots, a] \quad \text{and} \quad [z, d_1, d_2, \ldots, b]$$

which do not use the arc (a, b); but then in the graph H there are two elementary paths directed from z to b. Therefore there are two elementary paths from a_1 to b, and this contradicts (4).

(5) $\Rightarrow$ (6); the graph H, being quasi strongly connected, is connected and has a centre a_1 (by the lemma); therefore we have

$$|\boldsymbol{\omega}^-(a_j)| \geqslant 1 \quad \text{for } j \neq 1.$$

On the other hand, if $|\boldsymbol{\omega}^-(a_j)| > 1$, there would be two distinct arcs (b, a_j) and (c, a_j) incident to a_j, and hence two distinct paths from a_1 to a_j; if the arc (b, a_j) is deleted the graph still has a_1 as centre and hence remains quasi strongly connected which contradicts (5). Hence

$$|\boldsymbol{\omega}^-(a_j)| = 1 \quad \text{for } j \neq 1.$$

Finally, there cannot be an arc incident to a_1, for the graph obtained after its deletion still has a_1 as its centre.

(6) $\Rightarrow$ (7), the number of arcs of H is

$$\sum_{j=1}^{n} |\omega^{-}(a_j)| = n-1.$$

H, being connected with $n-1$ arcs, is a tree and therefore has no cycles.

(7) $\Rightarrow$ (1); if we start from any vertex a_j, with $j \neq 1$, and traverse the graph H by following its arcs in the direction opposite to their orientation, we do not encounter the same vertex twice, for H is without cycles; if we arrive at a vertex a_k with $k \neq 1$ we can always leave it, for $|\omega^{-}(a_k)| = 1$; we are thus sure to reach eventually vertex a_1.

The vertex a_1 being thus a centre of the graph H, and hence the graph is quasi strongly connected.

Corollary. *A graph G has a partial graph which is an arborescence if and only if G is quasi strongly connected.*

If G is not quasi strongly connected, it cannot have an arborescence.

Conversely, if G is quasi strongly connected, we delete successively every arc whose deletion does not prevent the graph being quasi strongly connected; if such an arc does not exist, the graph is an arborescence by virtue of property (5).

7.5. PLANAR GRAPHS

A graph G is said to be *planar* if it can be represented on a plane in such a way that the vertices are all distinct points, the arcs are simple curves, and no two arcs meet except at their extremities. A diagram of G on a plane which conforms with these conditions is called a *topological planar graph* and will also be denoted by the same letter G; two topological planar graphs will not be regarded as distinct if they can be made to coincide with one another by elastic deformation of the plane.

EXAMPLE. *Problem of the three houses and the three public utilities.* There are three houses a, b, c each to be connected to the waterworks d, to the gas-works e, and to the electricity power station f. Can we represent (on a plane) the three houses, the three utilities, and their supply lines in such a way that no two supply lines cross one another except at their initial or terminal points? One finds by trial that eight lines can be laid but the ninth always crosses one of the first eight. (see Fig. 7.5) An explanation of this phenomenon will be given later.

Let G be a topological planar graph; a *face* of G is by definition a region of the plane bounded by arcs, and which contains neither vertices nor arcs in its interior; we shall denote faces by z, z',... and the set of faces by Z. The *contour* of a face z is the cycle formed by the arcs which *surround* z. The *frontier* of z is the set of arcs which *touch* the face z. The arcs of the contour belong to the frontier but the converse is not true: for instance, a pendant arc in the interior of a face belongs to the frontier but not to the contour. Two faces z and z' are said to be *adjacent* if their contours have at least one arc in common; two faces which only touch at one vertex are not adjacent.

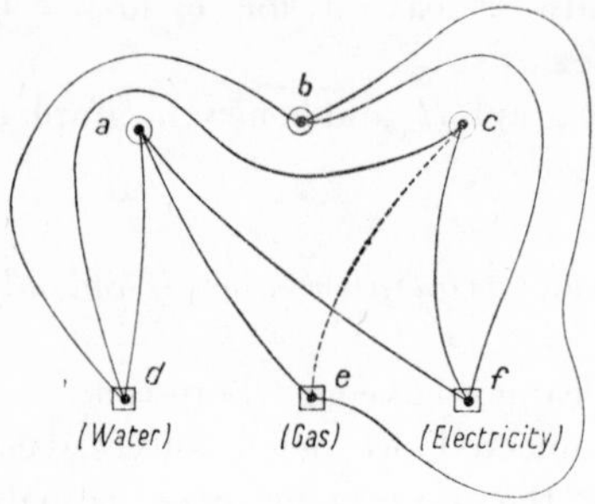

FIG. 7.5

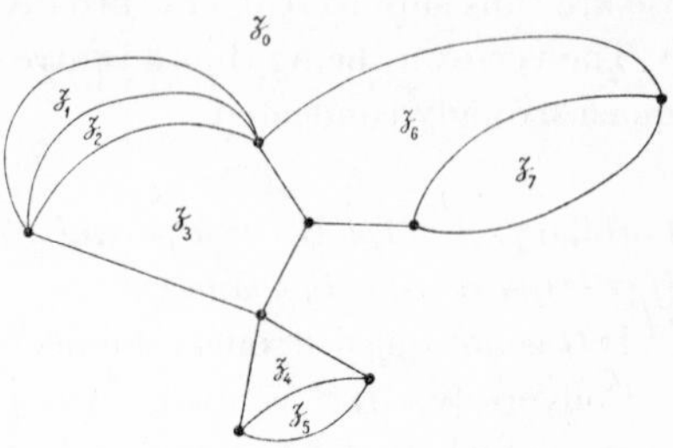

FIG. 7.6

EXAMPLE. A geographical map is a topological planar graph. If it has no islands, this graph has the property that each of its vertices is the extremity of at least three arcs. A face can be adjacent to the same face several times; notice that in Figure 7.6, z_3 is not adjacent to z_4 although these two faces have a vertex in common. Finally, we note that in every planar graph there is one and only one unbounded face which is called the *infinite face*, the other faces being the *finite faces* (here z_0 and $z_1, z_2, z_3, z_4, z_5, z_6, z_7$ respectively).

Theorem 11. *In a planar graph G, the contours of the finite faces form a fundamental basis of independent cycles.*

The theorem is true if G has only one finite face; assuming the theorem to be true for every graph of $k-1$ finite faces we show that it must be true for a topological planar graph G with k finite faces.

By deleting an arc which separates two distinct finite faces, we obtain a graph G' of $k-1$ finite faces, whose contours, by hypothesis, form a fundamental basis of independent cycles. In replacing the arc i we create a new finite face whose contour is a cycle independent of the preceding cycles (since it contains an arc not contained in the other cycles). As the addition of an arc increases the cyclomatic number by one at most, the finite faces of G must determine a fundamental basis of independent cycles.

Corollary 1 (*Euler's formula*). *If a connected planar graph has n vertices, m arcs and f faces, then*

$$n-m+f = 2.$$

For, the number of finite faces is equal to the cyclomatic number $k(G)$; hence

$$f = k(G)+1 = (m-n+1)+1 = m-n+2$$

which is the required result.

Corollary 2. *In every planar graph without multiple edges and without loops, there is a vertex which is the terminal of at most five arcs.*

In the corresponding topological planar graph, every face is bounded by at least three distinct arcs; consider the simple graph of incident faces and arcs,† the number of edges in this graph is $\leqslant 2m$ on the one hand and $\geqslant 3f$ on the other. Thus we have $f \leqslant 2m/3$. If every vertex were the terminal of at least six arcs, one would obtain in the same way $n \leqslant 2m/6$; therefore, by Euler's formula we would be able to write

$$2 = n-m+f \leqslant \frac{m}{3}-m+\frac{2m}{3} = 0,$$

which is false.

Euler's formula stated in Corollary 1 is useful in many circumstances.

EXAMPLE 1 (Euler). In a three-dimensional space, consider a convex polyhedron with n vertices, m edges and f faces. Clearly we can represent it on the surface of a sphere in such a way that no two edges cut one another except at their extremities; next, by making a stereographic projection of the surface from a centre in the middle of one of the faces, we can represent the polyhedron on a plane. As the resulting graph is planar, we obtain a fundamental relation concerning convex polyhedrons: $n-m+f = 2$.

EXAMPLE 2. Using Euler's formula, we shall show that the graph of the three houses and three public utilities is not planar. If it were planar, we would have

$$f = 2-n+m = 2-6+9 = 5.$$

The contour of each face must contain at least four arcs (for if a face had only three arcs it would be bordered by three vertices, two belonging to

† That is, the graph formed on sets X and Y of vertices, representing the faces and arcs, respectively, by drawing the arc (x, y) if and only if the face x touches the arc y.

the same category, house or utility, but two vertices of the same category cannot be adjacent). If we form the simple graph of incident faces and arcs, the number of edges is $\leqslant 2m$ on the one hand, $\geqslant 4f$ on the other hand; therefore

$$18 = 2m \geqslant 4f = 20,$$

which is false.

EXAMPLE 3. Similarly we shall show that the graph with five vertices, each pair of which is joined by one arc, is not planar. If this graph were planar, we would have

$$f = 2-n+m = 2-5+10 = 7.$$

The contour of each face contains at least three arcs. If we form the simple incidence graph of faces and arcs, the number of edges is $\leqslant 2m$, on the one hand, and $\geqslant 3f$ on the other; therefore

$$20 = 2m \geqslant 3f = 21,$$

which is false.

The graph of the houses and public utilities and the above graph of five vertices allow us to define a whole family of non-planar graphs: as we see in Figure 7.7 it is enough to place as many vertices as we like on each edge to define other non-planar graphs of Type 1 or Type 2. This remark has a converse, which can be stated in the form of a difficult theorem due to Kuratowski, as follows:

The necessary and sufficient condition for a graph G to be planar is that it should possess no partial subgraphs of Type 1 *or Type* 2.†

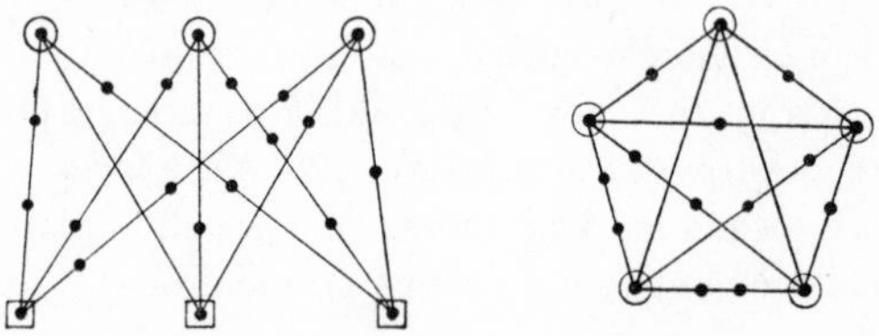

Type 1 Type 2

FIG. 7.7

Let us now consider an oriented connected and planar graph G, and associate with it a graph G^* in the following way: to every face z of G place in G^* a vertex z^* in the interior of z. To every arc i of G, separating the faces z_1 and z_2, we construct in G^* an arc i^* joining the vertices z_1^* and z_2^*, moreover, the arc i^* is oriented so that it makes an angle > 0 and $< 180°$ with

† For proof, cf. [2] p. 211.

the arc i. This construction is shown in Figure 7.8. The graph G^* is called the *dual graph* of G. It is also planar and connected. The dual of G^* is G.

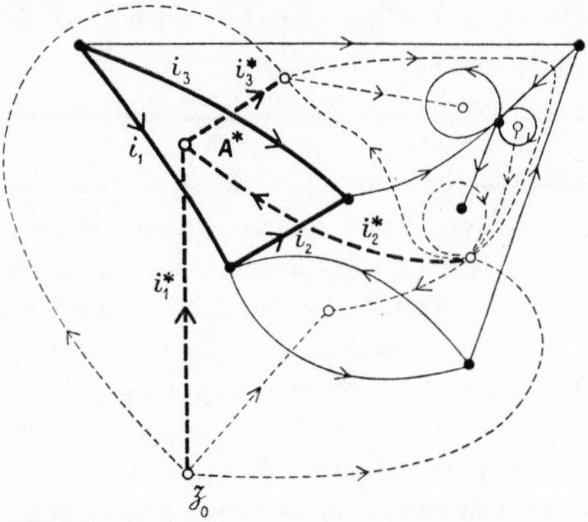

FIG. 7.8. Graph G in solid lines and its dual graph G^* in dotted lines

Theorem 12. *To every elementary cycle in G there corresponds an elementary coboundary in G^* and vice-versa; to every elementary circuit of G there corresponds an elementary cocircuit in G^* and vice-versa.*

Let $\boldsymbol{\mu} = (i_1, i_2, \ldots)$ be an elementary cycle in G and let A^* be the set of vertices of G^* which are inside the cycle. We have

$$\boldsymbol{\omega}(A^*) = \{i_1^*, i_2^*, \ldots\}.$$

Now, A^* is a connected subgraph of G^* (for we can always go from one face to another inside the cycle $\boldsymbol{\mu}$); for the same reason the complement $Z^* - A^*$ is also a connected subgraph of G^*. Therefore $\boldsymbol{\omega}(A^*)$ must be an elementary coboundary.

The other propositions may be proved in a similar way.

Corollary 1. *We have*

$$k(G^*) = l(G), \quad l(G^*) = k(G).$$

This follows from Theorem 12, but we can also deduce it from Euler's formula; we have:

$$k(G^*) = m - f + 1 = m - (2 + m - n) + 1 = n - 1 = l(G)$$

$$l(G^*) = f - 1 = m - n + 1 = l(G).$$

Corollary 2. *To every tree of G there corresponds a cotree of G^*, and vice-versa.*

In G, a tree H is characterized by the following property: it contains no cycles of G, but adding an arc creates one. In G^*, a cotree H^* has been defined by the property: it does not contain coboundaries of G^*, but adding an arc creates one. These two are thus corresponding concepts by duality.

NOTE. When the graph G is not planar it is still possible to represent it on a surface other than a plane such that no two arcs intersect. Remember that a surface is said to be *orientable* if it is possible to define a positive rotation at each of its points, all the rotations being consistent. An orientable surface is said to be of *genus* g if by elastic deformations it can be made to coincide with a sphere with g handles: thus the ordinary sphere is of genus 0, the torus of genus 1, the 'pretzel' of genus 2, etc. If we represent a given graph G on an orientable surface (of smallest possible genus), we may define in an exactly similar way its dual G^* and the correspondence between G and G^* is one–one. *Every coboundary of G is a cycle of G^*, but there exist $r(G)$ independent cycles of G which do not correspond to any coboundaries of G^*, $r(G)$ being an integer between* 0 *and* $2g$ (cf. Ghellinck [16]). Similarly a set of $f-1$ faces no longer forms a basis of fundamental cycles and we have the relation

$$k(G) = (f-1)+r(G); \quad 0 \leqslant r(G) \leqslant 2g.$$

MacLane [29] has shown that $k(G) = f-1$ if and only if the graph G is planar. More precisely *a necessary and sufficient condition for a graph G to be planar is that it contains a basis of cycles such that every arc appears twice* (*at most*) *in the chosen set of cycles.*

8. General study of flows and potential differences

8.1. FLOW AND POTENTIAL DIFFERENCE

From now on we shall consider as given once and for all a set **S** of real numbers, which may be either the set **R** of all real numbers or the set of all integers positive, negative and zero. The set **S** will thus have the following properties:

(1) $$s, t \in \mathbf{S} \Rightarrow \quad s+t \in \mathbf{S},$$

(2) $$0 \in \mathbf{S},$$

(3) $$s \in \mathbf{S} \Rightarrow -s \in \mathbf{S},$$

(4) $$s, t \in \mathbf{S} \Rightarrow \quad st \in \mathbf{S}.$$

In what follows, we shall use these axioms and we shall not specify whether **S** is the set of all real numbers or of all integers.†

Let G be a graph with its arcs numbered 1, 2,..., m; a *flow* is a vector

$$\boldsymbol{\varphi} = (\varphi_1, \varphi_2, \ldots, \varphi_m)$$

such that

(1) for every $i \leqslant m$, we have $\varphi_i \in \mathbf{S}$ and this number φ_i is called the *flow* in arc i;

† We could have defined **S** axiomatically by the properties (1), (2), (3), and (4), but this would hardly add anything to the generality of the definition. For let us show that a subset **S** of **R** satisfying (1), (2) and (3), or in other words a subgroup of the group of real numbers is necessarily either dense in **R** or is equal to $\{0\}$ or to

$$T_\alpha = \{\ldots, -2\alpha, -\alpha, 0, \alpha, 2\alpha, \ldots\}, \quad \text{with } \alpha \in \mathbf{R}.$$

If **S** has only one element we have $\mathbf{S} = \{0\}$ by virtue of (2). Otherwise it contains an element $k > 0$ by virtue of (3). Let us write

$$\alpha = \inf\{k | k \in \mathbf{S}, k > 0\}.$$

If $\alpha = 0$, it follows that **S** is everywhere dense; if $\alpha > 0$, we have $\mathbf{S} \supset T_\alpha$ by virtue of (1) and as **S** cannot contain a number λ such that

$$n\alpha < \lambda < (n+1)\alpha$$

we must have $\mathbf{S} = T_\alpha$.

(2) for every vertex a, the algebraic sum of flows in arcs directed into a is equal to the algebraic sum of flows in arcs out of a; in other words, we have:

$$\sum_{i \in \omega^-(a)} \varphi_i = \sum_{i \in \omega^+(a)} \varphi_i \quad (a \in X)$$

In what follows, we shall denote the set of all flows $\boldsymbol{\varphi}$ by Φ and the set of all flows $\boldsymbol{\varphi} \geqslant \mathbf{0}$ (that is, such that

$$\varphi_i \geqslant 0; \quad i = 1, 2, \ldots, m)$$

by Φ^+.

NOTE 1. We observe at once that *every linear combination of flows with its coefficients in* $\mathbf{S}$, *is still a flow*, indeed:

$$\boldsymbol{\varphi}^1, \boldsymbol{\varphi}^2 \in \Phi \Rightarrow \boldsymbol{\varphi}^1 + \boldsymbol{\varphi}^2 \in \Phi,$$

$$s \in \mathbf{S},\ \boldsymbol{\varphi} \in \Phi \Rightarrow s\boldsymbol{\varphi} \in \Phi.$$

In the case where $\mathbf{S} = \mathbf{R}$, it is clear that Φ is a *vector subspace* of $\mathbf{R}^m$.

NOTE 2. Every cycle is an element of Φ, and every circuit is an element of Φ^+.

EXAMPLE. If the graph is a diagram of an electric installation with generators and resistances, we can take $\mathbf{S} = \mathbf{R}$, and the flow $\boldsymbol{\varphi} \in \Phi$ will be the *intensity* of the current.

If the graph is a road map (symmetric graph) we can take for $\mathbf{S}$ the set of integers and the flow $\boldsymbol{\varphi} \in \Phi^+$ will be the traffic, φ_i indicating the number of vehicles travelling along the arc i in a unit of time in the direction of its orientation.

Theorem 1. *Let $G = (X, U)$ be a connected graph without multiple edges and $H = (X, V)$ a partial graph which is a tree. Let $1, 2, \ldots, k$ be the arcs of $U - V$ and $\boldsymbol{\mu}^1, \boldsymbol{\mu}^2, \ldots, \boldsymbol{\mu}^k$ the corresponding cycles (cf. Theorem 7, Chapter 7) with their closing arcs having a positive direction. A flow $\boldsymbol{\varphi} = (\varphi_1, \varphi_2, \ldots, \varphi_m)$ is uniquely defined by its values on the arcs of $U - V$ by the formula:*

$$\boldsymbol{\varphi} = \varphi_1 \boldsymbol{\mu}^1 + \varphi_2 \boldsymbol{\mu}^2 + \ldots + \varphi_k \boldsymbol{\mu}^k.$$

Let $\boldsymbol{\varphi}'$ be any other flow whose first k values are the same as those of $\boldsymbol{\varphi}$, the remaining components being arbitrary. It then follows that

$$\boldsymbol{\varphi}'' = \boldsymbol{\varphi}' - \varphi_1 \boldsymbol{\mu}^1 - \varphi_2 \boldsymbol{\mu}^2 - \ldots - \varphi_k \boldsymbol{\mu}^k$$

is a flow (according to Notes 1 and 2) and has zero values on the arcs outside the tree H.

The theorem amounts to proving that the flow $\boldsymbol{\varphi}''$ is necessarily zero on the tree $H = (X, U)$. Let $V \subset U$ be the set of arcs of H in which the flow is not zero; we shall now show that $V = \emptyset$, i.e. that every connected component C of the partial graph (X, V) reduces to a point. Otherwise, C would be a tree and would necessarily possess a pendant vertex a, according to Theorem 5, Chapter 7. If, for example, the pendant arc is directed towards a we have

$$0 \neq \sum_{i \in \omega^-(a)} \varphi'_i = \sum_{i \in \omega^+(a)} \varphi'_i = 0,$$

which is the contradiction we are looking for.

Corollary. *A necessary and sufficient condition for a vector* $\boldsymbol{\varphi}$ *to be a flow is that it be of the form*

$$\boldsymbol{\varphi} = s_1 \boldsymbol{\mu}^1 + s_2 \boldsymbol{\mu}^2 + \ldots + s_k \boldsymbol{\mu}^k$$

where $s_1, s_2, \ldots, s_k \in \mathrm{S}$ *and* $\boldsymbol{\mu}^1, \boldsymbol{\mu}^2, \ldots, \boldsymbol{\mu}^k$ *are elementary cycles.*

Since a cycle is a flow, every linear combination of cycles is a flow. The converse follows immediately from Theorem 1, for we can suppose that the graph G is connected (since we can treat every connected component separately).

Theorem 1 is important; it shows in particular that a cycle $\boldsymbol{\mu}$ is obtained by adding all the cycles $\boldsymbol{\mu}^i$ from which $\boldsymbol{\mu}$ takes a closing arc, preceded by a positive or negative sign, according as to whether the positive direction of $\boldsymbol{\mu}$ is or is not that of the arc i. When we want to determine a flow $(\varphi_1, \varphi_2, \ldots, \varphi_m)$ this theorem allows us to reduce the number of unknowns from m to $k(G) = m - n + 1$.

Theorem 2. *A necessary and sufficient condition for a vector* $\boldsymbol{\varphi}$ *to be a flow of* Φ^+ *is that it be of the form*

$$\boldsymbol{\varphi} = s_1 \boldsymbol{\mu}^1 + s_2 \boldsymbol{\mu}^2 + \ldots + s_k \boldsymbol{\mu}^k$$

where $s_1, s_2, \ldots, s_k \in \mathrm{S}$, $s_1, s_2, \ldots, s_k \geqslant 0$, *and where* $\boldsymbol{\mu}^1, \boldsymbol{\mu}^2, \ldots, \boldsymbol{\mu}^k$ *are circuits.*

It is obvious that a vector $\boldsymbol{\varphi}$ of the form indicated is a flow of Φ^+; conversely, let us consider a non-zero flow $\boldsymbol{\varphi} \in \Phi^+$ and let $\bar{G}$ be the graph obtained by deleting the arcs in which the flow is zero. $\bar{G}$ cannot have a cocircuit for otherwise the flow in these arcs would be zero, and these have already been deleted. Therefore it contains at least one circuit $\boldsymbol{\mu}^1$. Let $s_1 > 0$ be the smallest flow in the arcs of $\boldsymbol{\mu}^1$; the vector

$$\boldsymbol{\varphi}^1 = \boldsymbol{\varphi} - s_1 \boldsymbol{\mu}^1$$

is a flow of Φ^+ with more zero components than $\boldsymbol{\varphi}$. If $\boldsymbol{\varphi}^1$ is not zero, we repeat the operation, etc., finally we obtain a flow of the form

$$\boldsymbol{\varphi}^k = \boldsymbol{\varphi} - s_1 \boldsymbol{\mu}^1 - s_2 \boldsymbol{\mu}^2 - \ldots - s_k \boldsymbol{\mu}^k = \mathbf{0}$$

with $s_1, s_2, \ldots, s_k \in \mathbf{S}$, $s_1, s_2, \ldots, s_k \geqslant 0$, which is the required form.

A *potential difference* (or *tension*) is a vector $\boldsymbol{\theta} = (\theta_1, \theta_2, \ldots, \theta_m)$ of $\mathbf{S}^m$ such that for every elementary cycle $\boldsymbol{\mu}$,

$$\sum_{i \in \mu^+} \theta_i - \sum_{i \in \mu^-} \theta_i = 0$$

where μ^+ and μ^- denote, as usual, the arcs of the cycle oriented in a given sense and in the opposite sense respectively.

We denote the set of potential differences by Θ and the set of potential differences $\boldsymbol{\theta} \geqslant \mathbf{0}$ by Θ^+. It should be noted that:

$$\boldsymbol{\theta}^1, \boldsymbol{\theta}^2 \in \Theta \Rightarrow \boldsymbol{\theta}^1 + \boldsymbol{\theta}^2 \in \Theta$$

$$s \in \mathbf{S}, \boldsymbol{\theta} \in \Theta \Rightarrow s\boldsymbol{\theta} \in \Theta.$$

In the case where $\mathbf{S} = \mathbf{R}$ we see that Θ is a vector subspace of $\mathbf{R}^m$.

EXAMPLE. If the graph is a diagram of an electrical installation, the potential difference defines the voltages in the different branches. But we can give other examples from widely different fields. In experimental psychology, we can consider an individual's preferences for different objects in the following way: draw a graph with vertices representing the different objects, and if an individual prefers a to b, draw an arc directed from a to b. Assuming that *degrees of preference* are implicit in these relations we can associate a degree of preference $\theta_{ab} > 0$ with every arc (a, b). It is convenient to put

$$\theta_{ba} = -\theta_{ab};$$

and for a consistent individual, we have the equation due to Chasles:

$$\theta_{ab} + \theta_{bc} = \theta_{ac}.$$

We then have a potential difference on a complete graph (cf. [10]).

Theorem 3. *A vector* $\boldsymbol{\theta} = (\theta_1, \theta_2, \ldots, \theta_m)$ *is a potential difference if and only if there exists a function $t(a)$ defined on the set X of vertices and with values in* $\mathbf{S}$, *such that for every arc $i = (a, b)$ we have*:

$$\theta_i = t(b) - t(a).$$

The function $t(a)$ is defined as the *potential associated with* $\boldsymbol{\theta}$. Firstly, if $\boldsymbol{\theta}$ is a vector defined by a function $t(a)$ consider a cycle

$$\boldsymbol{\mu} = (i_1, i_2, \ldots, i_k)$$

which meets successively the vertices $a, b, c, \ldots, z$; we can write

$$\mu_{i_1}\theta_{i_1} = t(b) - t(a)$$

$$\mu_{i_2}\theta_{i_2} = t(c) - t(b)$$

$$\cdots\cdots \quad \cdots \quad \cdots$$

$$\mu_{i_k}\theta_{i_k} = t(a) - t(z).$$

Hence summing:

$$\sum_{i\in\mu^+}\theta_i - \sum_{i\in\mu^-}\theta_i = 0.$$

Secondly, if $\boldsymbol{\theta}$ is a potential difference, let us define the potentials $t(a)$ step by step.

Take an arbitrary vertex a_0 and assign the coefficient $t(a_0) = 0$ to it. If a has been labelled, and b has not yet been labelled, and if $i = (a,b)$ is an arc, we write

$$t(b) = t(a) + \theta_i.$$

Similarly if $i = (b,a)$ is an arc, we write

$$t(b) = t(a) - \theta_i.$$

We can thus define the potentials of all the vertices of the graph if it is connected (and if it is not connected we treat every connected component separately in the same way).

The potential assigned to a vertex a is uniquely defined; for otherwise there would exist two chains $\boldsymbol{\mu}^1$ and $\boldsymbol{\mu}^2$ going from a_0 to a with

$$\langle\boldsymbol{\mu}^1, \boldsymbol{\theta}\rangle \neq \langle\boldsymbol{\mu}^2, \boldsymbol{\theta}\rangle,$$

hence

$$\langle\boldsymbol{\mu}^1 - \boldsymbol{\mu}^2, \boldsymbol{\theta}\rangle \neq 0.$$

As $\boldsymbol{\mu}^1 - \boldsymbol{\mu}^2$ is a flow, it is, according to Theorem 1, a linear combination of elementary cycles and therefore there exists an elementary cycle $\boldsymbol{\mu}$, with $\langle\boldsymbol{\mu}, \boldsymbol{\theta}\rangle \neq 0$, which contradicts the definition of potential difference.

CONSEQUENCE. This theorem shows clearly that a coboundary $\boldsymbol{\omega}(A)$ is a potential difference, by taking

$$t(a) = \begin{cases} 0 & \text{if } a \in A \\ 1 & \text{if } a \notin A. \end{cases}$$

For we have

t (terminal vertex of the arc i) $-t$ (initial vertex of the arc i)

$$= \begin{Bmatrix} +1 & \text{if } i \in \omega^+(A) \\ -1 & \text{if } i \in \omega^-(A) \\ 0 & \text{if } i \notin \omega(A) \end{Bmatrix} = \omega_i(A)$$

Theorem 4. *Let $G = (X, U)$ be a connected graph and $H = (X, V)$ a partial graph which is a tree; let 1, 2,..., l be the arcs of this tree, $\boldsymbol{\omega}^1$, $\boldsymbol{\omega}^2, \ldots, \boldsymbol{\omega}^l$ the corresponding coboundaries (cf. Theorem 9, Chapter 7); a potential difference*

$$\boldsymbol{\theta} = (\theta_1, \theta_2, \ldots, \theta_m)$$

is uniquely defined by its values on the arcs of the tree by the formula:

$$\boldsymbol{\theta} = \theta_1 \boldsymbol{\omega}^1 + \theta_2 \boldsymbol{\omega}^2 + \ldots + \theta_l \boldsymbol{\omega}^l$$

For, the vector

$$\boldsymbol{\theta}' = \boldsymbol{\theta} - \theta_1 \boldsymbol{\omega}^1 - \theta_2 \boldsymbol{\omega}^2 - \ldots - \theta_l \boldsymbol{\omega}^l$$

is a potential difference which has zero values on the arcs of the tree (X, V); if $\boldsymbol{\theta}'$ is defined by a potential function $t'(a)$, we have:

$$t'(a_1) = t'(a_2) = \ldots = t'(a_n).$$

Consequently $\boldsymbol{\theta}' = \mathbf{0}$ and hence we have the stated formula.

Corollary. *A necessary and sufficient condition for a vector $\boldsymbol{\theta}$ to be a potential difference is that it be of the form*

$$\boldsymbol{\theta} = s_1 \boldsymbol{\omega}^1 + s_2 \boldsymbol{\omega}^2 + \ldots + s_k \boldsymbol{\omega}^k,$$

where $s_1, s_2, \ldots, s_k \in \mathbf{S}$, and $\boldsymbol{\omega}^1$, $\boldsymbol{\omega}^2, \ldots, \boldsymbol{\omega}^k$ are elementary coboundaries.

The condition is sufficient since every linear combination of coboundaries is a potential difference, and it is necessary because of Theorem 4.

Theorem 4 is important in solving the problem of determining a potential difference

$$\boldsymbol{\theta} = (\theta_1, \theta_2, \ldots, \theta_m),$$

for it allows us to reduce the number of unknowns from m to $l(G) = n-1$.

Theorem 5. *A necessary and sufficient condition that $\boldsymbol{\theta} \in \Theta^+$ is that it be of the form*

$$\boldsymbol{\theta} = s_1 \boldsymbol{\omega}^1 + s_2 \boldsymbol{\omega}^2 + \ldots + s_k \boldsymbol{\omega}^k,$$

where $s_1, s_2, \ldots, s_k \in \mathbf{S}$, $s_1, s_2, \ldots, s_k \geqslant 0$ and where $\boldsymbol{\omega}^1$, $\boldsymbol{\omega}^2, \ldots, \boldsymbol{\omega}^k$ are all elementary cocircuits.

It is clear that every linear combination of cocircuits with non-negative coefficients is a potential difference belonging to Θ^+.

Conversely, let us consider a potential difference $\boldsymbol{\theta} \neq \mathbf{0}$, $\boldsymbol{\theta} \in \Theta^+$ and show that there exists an elementary cocircuit $\boldsymbol{\omega}^1$ and an $s_1 > 0$ such that the vector

$$\boldsymbol{\theta} - s_1 \boldsymbol{\omega}^1$$

has more zero components than the vector $\boldsymbol{\theta}$.

Let arc 1 be such that

$$\theta_1 = \min \{\theta_i | \theta_i \neq 0, \quad 0 \leqslant i \leqslant m\}.$$

Let us put

$$\theta_1 = s_1 > 0.$$

We colour the arcs i with $\theta_i \neq 0$ black, and the arcs i with $\theta_i = 0$ red.

There cannot be a red and black elementary cycle with all black arcs in the same direction and passing through the arc 1; therefore, by the Lemma on coloured arcs, an elementary black coboundary $\boldsymbol{\omega}^1$ passes through the arc 1, with all black arcs oriented in the same direction. Hence, $\boldsymbol{\omega}^1$ is a cocircuit and the vector

$$\boldsymbol{\theta} - s_1 \boldsymbol{\omega}^1$$

has more zero components than the vector $\boldsymbol{\theta}$ which is also a potential difference in Θ^+.

If $\boldsymbol{\theta} - s_1 \boldsymbol{\omega}^1 \neq \mathbf{0}$, we repeat this procedure with the new potential difference. Eventually we will obtain a potential difference

$$\boldsymbol{\theta} - s_1 \boldsymbol{\omega}^1 - s_2 \boldsymbol{\omega}^2 - \ldots - s_k \boldsymbol{\omega}^k = \mathbf{0}.$$

Theorem 6. *A vector* $\boldsymbol{\varphi} \in \mathbf{S}^m$ *is a flow if and only if it is orthogonal to every vector in* Θ; *a vector* $\boldsymbol{\theta} \in \mathbf{S}^m$ *is a potential difference if and only if it is orthogonal to every vector in* Φ.

(In the case where $\mathbf{S} = \mathbf{R}$, this expresses the fact that Φ and Θ are two supplementary orthogonal subspaces of the vector space $\mathbf{R}^m$.)

Firstly, let us show that if $\boldsymbol{\varphi} \in \Phi$ and $\boldsymbol{\theta} \in \Theta$, then they are orthogonal vectors, that is,

$$\sum_{i=1}^{m} \varphi_i \theta_i = \langle \boldsymbol{\varphi}, \boldsymbol{\theta} \rangle = 0.$$

We have for every elementary cycle $\boldsymbol{\mu}$,

$$\langle \boldsymbol{\mu}, \boldsymbol{\theta} \rangle = 0.$$

From Theorem 1, $\boldsymbol{\varphi}$ is of the form

$$\boldsymbol{\varphi} = \sum_k s_k \boldsymbol{\mu}^k;$$

therefore,

$$\langle \boldsymbol{\varphi}, \boldsymbol{\theta} \rangle = \sum_k s_k \langle \boldsymbol{\mu}^k, \boldsymbol{\theta} \rangle = 0.$$

Secondly, let $\boldsymbol{\varphi}$ be a vector such that $\langle \boldsymbol{\varphi}, \boldsymbol{\theta} \rangle = 0$ for every $\boldsymbol{\theta} \in \Theta$; then it is a flow, for if we consider a vertex a of the graph and if we take $\boldsymbol{\theta} = \boldsymbol{\omega}(a)$, we have

$$\sum_{i \in \omega^+(a)} \varphi_i - \sum_{i \in \omega^-(a)} \varphi_i = \langle \boldsymbol{\omega}(a), \boldsymbol{\varphi} \rangle = 0.$$

Thirdly, let $\boldsymbol{\theta}$ be a vector such that $\langle \boldsymbol{\varphi}, \boldsymbol{\theta} \rangle = 0$ for every $\boldsymbol{\varphi} \in \Phi$; then it is a potential difference, for we have, for every elementary cycle $\boldsymbol{\mu}$, the relation

$$\langle \boldsymbol{\mu}, \boldsymbol{\theta} \rangle = 0.$$

Corollary. *When* $\mathbf{S} = \mathbf{R}$ *every vector*

$$\boldsymbol{\xi} = (\xi_1, \xi_2, \ldots, \xi_m) \in \mathbf{S}^m$$

can be written uniquely as

$$\boldsymbol{\xi} = \boldsymbol{\varphi} + \boldsymbol{\theta}, \quad \textit{with } \boldsymbol{\varphi} \in \Phi, \ \boldsymbol{\theta} \in \Theta.$$

This is a well-known property of supplementary orthogonal subspaces in a vector space.

It should be noted that the above property is no longer true if $\mathbf{S}$ is the set of all integers. (Since this set is not a 'field' but only a 'ring', there can be no question of vector space.) Let us consider, for example, the graph of Figure 8.1. The only cycle is $\boldsymbol{\mu} = (1,1,1,1)$ and a basis of coboundaries is

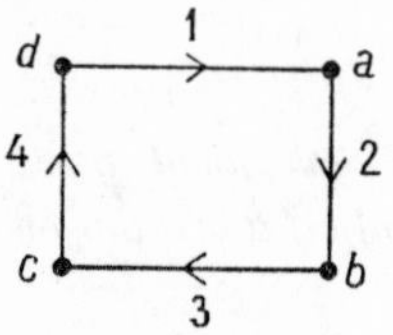

FIG. 8.1

$$\boldsymbol{\omega}(a) = (-1, +1, 0, 0), \quad \boldsymbol{\omega}(b) = (0, -1, +1, 0)$$

and

$$\boldsymbol{\omega}(c) = (0, 0, -1, +1).$$

If the corollary were true when $\mathbf{S}$ is the set of all integers, there would exist four integers, α, β, γ, δ such that:

$$(1,0,0,0) = \alpha(1,1,1,1) + \beta(-1, +1, 0, 0) + \gamma(0, -1, +1, 0) + \delta(0, 0, -1, +1).$$

The reader will verify at once that this equation requires the numbers α, β, γ, δ to be fractions.

8.2. MATRIX ANALYSIS OF FLOWS AND POTENTIAL DIFFERENCES

Consider a graph G, with vertices $a_1, a_2, \ldots, a_n$ and arcs $i = 1, 2, \ldots, m$. Let us write:

$$s_i^j = \begin{cases} +1 & \text{if the arc } i \in \omega^+(a_j) \\ -1 & \text{if the arc } i \in \omega^-(a_j) \\ \;\;0 & \text{if the arc } i \notin \omega(a_j). \end{cases}$$

The matrix $S = ((s_i^j))$ of n rows and m columns is called the (*vertex-arc*) *incidence matrix* of the graph G.

Consider the following graph:

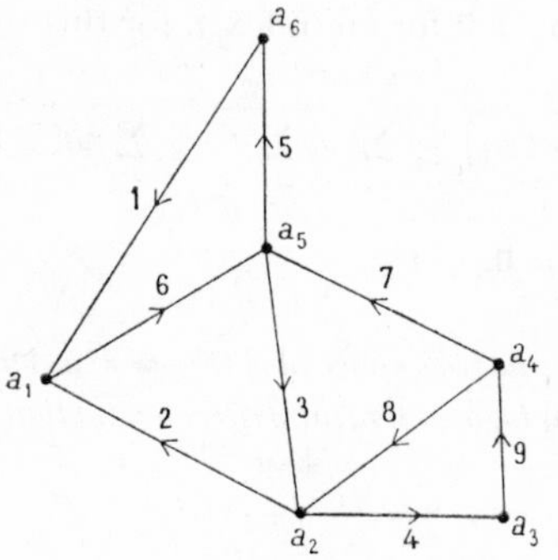

FIG. 8.2

We can easily form the incidence matrix S and obtain

$$S = \overbrace{\begin{bmatrix} -1 & -1 & 0 & 0 & 0 & +1 & 0 & 0 & 0 \\ 0 & +1 & -1 & +1 & 0 & 0 & 0 & -1 & 0 \\ 0 & 0 & 0 & -1 & 0 & 0 & 0 & 0 & +1 \\ 0 & 0 & 0 & 0 & 0 & 0 & +1 & +1 & -1 \\ 0 & 0 & +1 & 0 & +1 & -1 & -1 & 0 & 0 \\ +1 & 0 & 0 & 0 & -1 & 0 & 0 & 0 & 0 \end{bmatrix}}^{\text{arcs: } 1\;2\;3\;4\;5\;6\;7\;8\;9} \left.\begin{matrix} a_1 \\ a_2 \\ a_3 \\ a_4 \\ a_5 \\ a_6 \end{matrix}\right\} \text{vertices}$$

Notice that in column i there is exactly one $+1$ and one -1 and all other entries zero (except if the arc i is a loop, in which case all the coefficients are zero). An incidence matrix enables us to state a number of propositions in a convenient manner.

Proposition 1. *A necessary and sufficient condition that a vector*

$$\boldsymbol{\varphi} = (\varphi_1, \varphi_2, \ldots, \varphi_m)$$

be a flow is that $S\boldsymbol{\varphi} = \mathbf{0}$.

This is immediate, for we express the fact that φ is a flow by the relations:

$$\sum_{i \in \omega^+(a_j)} \varphi_i - \sum_{i \in \omega^-(a_j)} \varphi_i = \sum_i s_i^j \varphi_i = 0 \quad (j = 1, 2, \ldots, n).$$

Proposition 2. *A necessary and sufficient condition that* $\boldsymbol{\varphi}$ *be a flow is that* $S\boldsymbol{\varphi} \geqslant \mathbf{0}$.

For $S\boldsymbol{\varphi} = \mathbf{0}$ implies $S\boldsymbol{\varphi} \geqslant \mathbf{0}$; conversely, suppose that $S\boldsymbol{\varphi} \geqslant \mathbf{0}$, that is:

$$\langle \mathbf{s}^j, \boldsymbol{\varphi} \rangle \geqslant 0 \quad (j = 1, 2, \ldots, n).$$

We cannot have $\langle \mathbf{s}^j, \boldsymbol{\varphi} \rangle > 0$ for an index j, for this would mean

$$0 < \sum_j \left(\sum_i s_i^j \varphi_i \right) = \sum_i \varphi_i \sum_j s_i^j = \sum_i \varphi_i(-1+1) = 0;$$

therefore we have $S\boldsymbol{\varphi} = \mathbf{0}$.

Proposition 3. *Let* S^* *be the transpose of* S $(s^{*i}_j = s^j_i)$. *A necessary and sufficient condition that a vector* $\boldsymbol{\theta}$ *be a potential difference is that for some vector*

$$\mathbf{t} = (t_1, t_2, \ldots, t_n),$$

we have

$$\boldsymbol{\theta} = -S^* \mathbf{t}.$$

If the potential difference $\boldsymbol{\theta}$ has a potential-function t, we have

$$\boldsymbol{\theta}_i = t(b) - t(a)$$

were $i = (a, b) \in U$; hence,

$$\boldsymbol{\theta}_i = -\sum_{j=1}^{n} s_i^j t_j.$$

Let $\mathbf{c}_1 = (c_1^1, c_1^2, \ldots, c_1^m), \ldots, \mathbf{c}_k = (c_k^1, c_k^2, \ldots, c_k^m)$ be the vectors of a fundamental basis of cycles of the connected graph G, obtained from a tree H (whose arcs are $k+1, k+2, \ldots, m$) by adding separately the arcs 1, 2, ..., k. Let us form the matrix:

$$C = \begin{bmatrix} c_1^1 & c_2^1 & \cdots & c_k^1 \\ c_1^2 & c_2^2 & \cdots & c_k^2 \\ \vdots & \vdots & & \vdots \\ c_1^m & c_2^m & & c_k^m \end{bmatrix}$$

We say that C is a *fundamental matrix* of the graph G. For instance, take the accompanying figure and form a basis of cycles from the tree in thick lines. We then have:

$$C = \begin{bmatrix} +1 & 0 & 0 & 0 \\ 0 & +1 & 0 & 0 \\ 0 & 0 & +1 & 0 \\ 0 & 0 & 0 & +1 \\ +1 & 0 & 0 & 0 \\ +1 & +1 & 0 & 0 \\ 0 & -1 & +1 & 0 \\ 0 & +1 & -1 & +1 \\ 0 & 0 & 0 & +1 \end{bmatrix} = \begin{bmatrix} & \mathbf{I} & & \\ c_1^{k+1} & c_2^{k+1} & c_3^{k+1} & c_4^{k+1} \\ \cdots & \cdots & \cdots & \cdots \\ \cdots & \cdots & \cdots & \cdots \\ c_1^m & c_2^m & c_3^m & c_4^m \end{bmatrix}$$

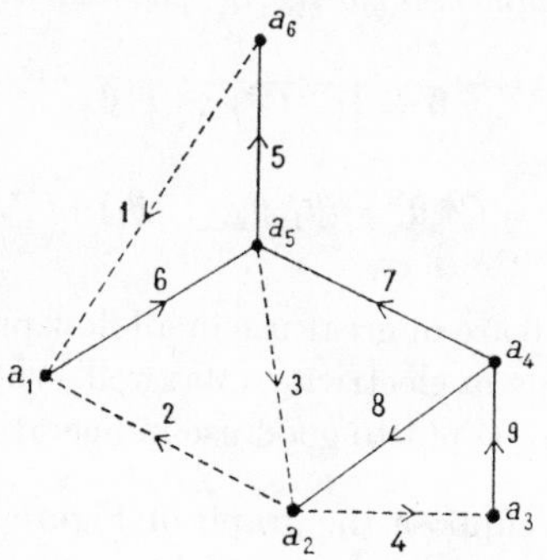

FIG. 8.2a

Notice that if a given fundamental matrix is formed from a tree it may be split up into a square unit matrix I and a rectangular matrix $\bar{C}$, this is sometimes written $C = I \otimes \bar{C}$.

Proposition 4. *The necessary and sufficient condition for a vector*

$$\boldsymbol{\theta} = (\theta_1, \theta_2, \ldots, \theta_m)$$

to be a potential difference is that $C^*\boldsymbol{\theta} = \mathbf{0}$.

For, $C^*\boldsymbol{\theta} = \mathbf{0}$ means that

$$\langle \mathbf{c}_i, \boldsymbol{\theta} \rangle = 0 \quad (i = 1, 2, \ldots, k),$$

which is equivalent to

$$\langle \boldsymbol{\mu}, \boldsymbol{\theta} \rangle = 0 \quad \text{for every cycle } \boldsymbol{\mu}.$$

Proposition 5. *In a flow problem on a graph G, if we take* $\varphi_1, \varphi_2, \ldots, \varphi_k$ *as the independent variables, and write*

$$\bar{\boldsymbol{\varphi}} = (\varphi_1, \varphi_2, \ldots, \varphi_k),$$

then the flow $\boldsymbol{\varphi}$ *is determined by the formula* $\boldsymbol{\varphi} = C\bar{\boldsymbol{\varphi}}$.

For, we have seen that the flow $\boldsymbol{\varphi}$ is completely determined by its values on a cotree; then according to Theorem 1 we have:

$$\boldsymbol{\varphi} = \varphi_1 \mathbf{c}_1 + \varphi_2 \mathbf{c}_2 + \ldots + \varphi_k \mathbf{c}_k.$$

Therefore

$$\boldsymbol{\varphi} = C\bar{\boldsymbol{\varphi}}.$$

Proposition 6. *In the problem of potential difference on a graph G, if we take* $\theta_{k+1}, \theta_{k+2}, \ldots, \theta_m$ *to be independent variables and write*

$$\bar{\boldsymbol{\theta}} = (\theta_{k+1}, \theta_{k+2}, \ldots, \theta_m);$$

if $C = I \otimes \bar{C}$ *is the fundamental matrix, the potential difference* $\boldsymbol{\theta}$ *is determined by the formula:*

$$\boldsymbol{\theta} = [(-\bar{C}^*) \otimes I]\bar{\boldsymbol{\theta}}.$$

For

$$\mathbf{0} = C^* \boldsymbol{\theta} = (\theta_1, \theta_2, \ldots, \theta_k) + \bar{C}^* \bar{\boldsymbol{\theta}};$$

hence the formula.

Propositions 5 and 6 are of great use in all flow problems. They are used in well-known methods in electricity (Maxwell's rules, G. Kron's method, etc.) but they can also be put to good use in operational research.

EXAMPLE. Let us suppose the graph of Figure 8.2 is a road map; we wish to determine the number of vehicles on each of these roads. This is a flow problem with $k(G) = m - n + 1 = 9 - 6 + 1 = 4$ suitably chosen independent variables. Suppose it is known that $\varphi_2 = 5$, $\varphi_3 = 5$, $\varphi_5 = -3$ and suppose $\varphi_9 = 2\varphi_6$. The system is thus completely determined. Let us form a tree by deleting the maximum number of arcs i for which φ_i is known. We shall delete, for instance, the arcs 1, 2, 3, and 4 putting $\varphi_1 = x$, $\varphi_2 = 5$, $\varphi_3 = 5$, $\varphi_5 = y$.

Then the flow φ is given by:

$$\boldsymbol{\varphi} = \begin{bmatrix} +1 & 0 & 0 & 0 \\ 0 & +1 & 0 & 0 \\ 0 & 0 & +1 & 0 \\ 0 & 0 & 0 & +1 \\ +1 & 0 & 0 & 0 \\ +1 & +1 & 0 & 0 \\ 0 & -1 & +1 & 0 \\ 0 & +1 & -1 & +1 \\ 0 & 0 & 0 & +1 \end{bmatrix} \times \begin{bmatrix} x \\ 5 \\ 5 \\ y \end{bmatrix} = \begin{bmatrix} \varphi_1 = x \\ \varphi_2 = 5 \\ \varphi_3 = 5 \\ \varphi_4 = y \\ \varphi_5 = x \\ \varphi_6 = x+5 \\ \varphi_7 = 0 \\ \varphi_8 = y \\ \varphi_9 = y \end{bmatrix}$$

$\varphi_5 = -3$ gives $x = -3$, and $\varphi_9 = 2\varphi_6$ gives $y = 4$. The required flow is therefore finally

$$\boldsymbol{\varphi} = (-3, 5, 5, 4, -3, 2, 0, 4, 4)$$

A *cyclomatic matrix* of a graph G is defined as a matrix of m rows whose column vectors are flows (which generate a space of $k(G)$ dimensions); a *cocyclomatic matrix* of a graph G is a matrix of m columns whose vectors are potential differences (which generate a space of $l(G)$ dimensions).

A fundamental matrix C is one particular kind of cyclomatic matrix and the incidence matrix S is a cocyclomatic matrix, since the row-vectors of S are successively $\boldsymbol{\omega}(a_1)$, $\boldsymbol{\omega}(a_2), \ldots, \boldsymbol{\omega}(a_n)$, and since every coboundary can be expressed as a linear function of $\boldsymbol{\omega}(a_i)$ by the formula

$$\boldsymbol{\omega}(A) = \sum_{a \in A} \boldsymbol{\omega}(a).$$

Cyclomatic and cocyclomatic matrices can be more elegantly studied using the duality principle already described and the properties of the incidence matrix S and the fundamental matrix C will be derived again as special cases.

Proposition 7. *Let C be a cyclomatic matrix; a matrix S of m columns and of rank $l(G)$ is cocyclomatic if and only if $SC = 0$.*

In the matrix product SC, the coefficient in the ith row of the jth column is the scalar product $\langle \mathbf{s}^i, \mathbf{c}_j \rangle$; as the $\mathbf{c}_j$ generate the space of flows Φ, the scalar product is zero if and only if $\mathbf{s}^i$ are coboundaries.

Proposition 8. *Let S be a cocyclomatic matrix; a matrix C of m rows and of rank $k(G)$ is cyclomatic if and only if $SC = 0$.*

Same proof.

Proposition 9. *Let S be a cocyclomatic matrix of a connected graph G. A set of $l(G)$ column vectors forms a basis of the vector subspace generated by all the column vectors $\mathbf{s}_1, \mathbf{s}_2, \ldots, \mathbf{s}_m$, if and only if these $l(G)$ vectors correspond to arcs forming a partial graph which is a tree of G.*

Notice first that the dimension of this subspace is equal to $l(G)$ since S is of rank $l(G)$.

Consider a basis of column vectors $\mathbf{s}_{i_1}, \mathbf{s}_{i_2}, \ldots, \mathbf{s}_{i_l}$ and let V be the set of arcs $i_1, i_2, \ldots, i_l$; let us show that (X, V) is a partial graph which is a tree. (X, V) cannot have a cycle $\boldsymbol{\mu}$, for if it did there would be a linear relation between the vectors of the basis; namely

$$\sum_{i \in \mu^+} \mathbf{s}_i - \sum_{i \in \mu^-} \mathbf{s}_i = S\boldsymbol{\mu} = \mathbf{0}.$$

Furthermore, (X, V) contains $l(G) = n-1$ arcs; it is therefore a tree by Property (2) of Theorem 4, Chapter 7.

Conversely, consider the column vectors whose indices correspond to a tree (X, V): these form a vector basis, for if $k \notin V$ this arc forms a cycle $\boldsymbol{\mu}$ with the arcs of V and we can write:

$$\mathbf{s}_k = -\sum_{\substack{i \in \mu^+ \\ i \neq k}} \mathbf{s}_i + \sum_{i \in \mu^-} \mathbf{s}_i.$$

Proposition 10. *Let C be a cyclomatrix of a connected graph G. A set of $k(G)$ row vectors forms a basis of the vector subspace generated by all the row vectors $\mathbf{c}^1, \mathbf{c}^2, \ldots, \mathbf{c}^m$ if and only if these $k(G)$ vectors correspond to arcs which form a cotree of G.*

Note first that the dimension of the subspace is equal to $k(G)$.

Consider a basis of row vectors and let W be the set of corresponding arcs. (X, W) cannot have a coboundary $\boldsymbol{\omega}$ of G, for if it did, there would be a linear relation between the vectors of the basis; namely

$$\sum_{i \in \omega^+} \mathbf{c}^i - \sum_{i \in \omega^-} \mathbf{c}^i = \mathbf{0}.$$

Furthermore (X, W) contains $k(G) = m-n+1$ arcs; the partial graph formed by those arcs not belonging to W is therefore connected with $n-1$ arcs, thus it is a tree and (X, W) is a cotree.

Conversely, consider the row vectors whose corresponding arcs belong to a cotree (X, W); these form a vector basis, for if $k \notin W$, this arc, with the arcs of W, forms a coboundary $\boldsymbol{\omega}$ and we can write

$$\mathbf{c}^k = -\sum_{\substack{i \in \omega^+ \\ i \neq k}} \mathbf{c}^i + \sum_{i \in \omega^-} \mathbf{c}^i.$$

These various propositions will be little used here but they enable us to simplify certain useful algorithms.

8.3. THE TRANSPORTATION PROBLEM

We shall now consider a graph G with arcs numbered $i = 1, 2, \ldots, m$.

Transportation problem. *Suppose that with every arc i of the graph, there is associated an interval $[b_i, c_i]$ and also a convex function f_i defined on this interval; find a flow*

$$\boldsymbol{\varphi} = (\varphi_1, \varphi_2, \ldots, \varphi_m)$$

such that

(1) $$b_i \leqslant \varphi_i \leqslant c_i \quad (i = 1, 2, \ldots, m)$$

and (2) $$F(\boldsymbol{\varphi}) = \sum_{i=1}^{m} f_i(\varphi_i) \quad \textit{is minimized.}$$

Problem of potential. *Suppose that with every arc i of the graph, there is associated an interval* $[k_i, l_i]$ *and also a convex function* h_i *defined on this interval; find a potential difference*

$$\boldsymbol{\theta} = (\theta_1, \theta_2, \ldots, \theta_m)$$

such that

(1) $$k_i \leqslant \theta_i \leqslant l_i \quad (i = 1, 2, \ldots, m)$$

and (2) $$H(\boldsymbol{\theta}) = \sum_{i=1}^{m} h_i(\theta_i) \quad \textit{is minimized.}$$

When it was realized that the transportation problem is of fundamental importance in operational research, there was much discussion about its origins. It has been variously attributed to Hitchcock [20] who, in 1941, treated it for simple graphs; to T. C. Koopmans [26] who independently studied it for a problem of maritime transport; and to Kantorovitch [25] who studied the continuous case; in fact Monge [32] had already studied it in 1781 using purely geometrical procedures.

Here we give two existence theorems (the proofs, which are interesting in themselves, are taken from [17]).

Potential difference existence theorem. *For given numbers* k_i *and* l_i, *when* $k_i \leqslant l_i$ *(for* $i = 1, 2, \ldots, m$*), a necessary and sufficient condition for the existence of a potential difference* $\boldsymbol{\theta}$ *such that* $k_i \leqslant \theta_i \leqslant l_i$ *is that for every elementary cycle* $\boldsymbol{\mu}$

$$\begin{cases} \sum_{i \in \mu^-} l_i \geqslant \sum_{i \in \mu^+} k_i, \\ \sum_{i \in \mu^+} l_i \geqslant \sum_{i \in \mu^-} k_i. \end{cases}$$

The condition is necessary; for if such a potential difference $\boldsymbol{\theta}$ exists, we have:

$$0 = \langle \boldsymbol{\mu}, \boldsymbol{\theta} \rangle = \langle \boldsymbol{\mu}^+, \boldsymbol{\theta} \rangle - \langle \boldsymbol{\mu}^-, \boldsymbol{\theta} \rangle \geqslant \sum_{i \in \mu^+} k_i - \sum_{i \in \mu^-} l_i.$$

By reversing the sense of orientation, we obtain the second inequality. *The condition is sufficient;* for, let us consider the intervals

$$X_i = [k_i, l_i] = \{x | x \in \mathbf{S}, x \geqslant k_i, x \leqslant l_i\}.$$

Here we shall use the concepts of the *vector sum* of two sets A and B, defined as

$$A + B = \{a + b | a \in A, b \in B\}.$$

The conditions of the theorem can be written

$$0 \in \sum_{i \in \mu^+} X_i - \sum_{i \in \mu^-} X_i \tag{1}$$

since the expression on the right-hand side defines the interval

$$\left[\sum_{i \in \mu^+} k_i - \sum_{i \in \mu^-} l_i, \quad \sum_{i \in \mu^+} l_i - \sum_{i \in \mu^-} k_i\right].$$

We shall show that condition (1) implies the existence of a potential difference $\boldsymbol{\theta}$ such that $k_i \leqslant \theta_i \leqslant l_i$. This is true for a graph with one arc; we shall suppose that it is true for every graph with $m-1$ arcs, and show that it holds for a graph G with m arcs with intervals $X_1, X_2, \ldots, X_m$ subject to condition (1).

Let k be an arc of G such that $|X_k| > 1$, and let us show that condition (1) is still true even if we replace X_k by a set $X'_k = \{x_k\}$, where x_k is a suitably chosen element of X_k. It is enough to repeat this transformation on every arc i for which $|X_i| > 1$, to obtain a vector

$$\mathbf{x} = (x_1, x_2, \ldots, x_m)$$

satisfying (1); that is,

$$0 = \sum_{i \in \mu^+} x_i - \sum_{i \in \mu^-} x_i$$

for every elementary cycle $\boldsymbol{\mu}$.

In other words, this vector $\mathbf{x}$ is a potential difference compatible with the inequalities, therefore this will prove the theorem.

It remains to demonstrate the existence of a number $x_k \in X_k$, such that

$$x_k \in \sum_{i \in \mu^+} X_i - \sum_{\substack{i \in \mu^- \\ i \neq k}} X_i = A_k(\boldsymbol{\mu})$$

for every elementary cycle $\boldsymbol{\mu}$ with $k \in \boldsymbol{\mu}^-$.

By induction, there exists a suitable potential difference $\bar{\boldsymbol{\theta}}$ for the graph $\bar{G}$ obtained from G by deleting the arc k or, equivalently, by replacing X_k by $\bar{X}_k = [-\infty, +\infty]$.

Therefore for every cycle $\boldsymbol{\mu}$ not containing the arc k, we have

$$\bar{\theta}_k \in A_k(\boldsymbol{\mu}).$$

Thus

$$\bigcap_{\mu / k \in \mu^-} A_k(\mu) \neq \emptyset.$$

The sets $A_k(\boldsymbol{\mu})$ are intervals and by virtue of (1) they intersect all the intervals X_k. But every finite family of pairwise intersecting intervals has a non-empty intersection, that is:

$$X_k \cap \bigcap_{\mu / k \in \mu^-} A_k(\boldsymbol{\mu}) \neq \emptyset.$$

This guarantees the existence of the required point and completes the proof of the theorem.

Corollary 1 ([38]). *A potential difference* $\boldsymbol{\theta}$ *such that* $\theta_i \geqslant k_i$ *(for all i) exists if and only if, for every circuit* $\boldsymbol{\mu}$

$$\sum_{i \in \mu} k_i \leqslant 0.$$

This follows by taking $l_i = +\infty$ for every i.

Corollary 2. *A potential difference* $\boldsymbol{\theta}$ *such that* $\theta_i \leqslant l_i$ *(for all i) exists if and only if, for every circuit* $\boldsymbol{\mu}$

$$\sum_{i \in \mu} l_i \geqslant 0.$$

Corollary 3. *A vector*

$$\mathbf{y} = (y_1, y_2, \ldots, y_m)$$

is a sub-tension (or sub-potential difference) if there exists a potential difference $\boldsymbol{\theta}$ *with* $y_i \leqslant \theta_i$ *for every i. A necessary and sufficient condition for a vector* $\mathbf{y}$ *to be a sub-tension is that*

$$\langle \boldsymbol{\varphi}, \mathbf{y} \rangle \leqslant 0 \quad \text{for every } \boldsymbol{\varphi} \in \Phi^+.$$

Moreover, a sub-tension $\mathbf{y}$ *and a flow* $\boldsymbol{\varphi} \in \Phi^+$ *satisfy* $\langle \boldsymbol{\varphi}, \mathbf{y} \rangle = 0$ *if and only if* $\mathbf{y}$ *is a potential difference on the partial graph generated by the arcs i for which* $\varphi_i > 0$.

If $\mathbf{y}$ satisfies the given inequality, we can write, taking a circuit $\boldsymbol{\mu}$ for $\boldsymbol{\varphi}$,

$$\langle \boldsymbol{\mu}, \mathbf{y} \rangle = \sum_{i \in \mu} y_i \leqslant 0;$$

as this is true for every circuit $\boldsymbol{\mu}$ by Corollary 1, $\mathbf{y}$ must be a sub-tension.

Conversely, let $\mathbf{y}$ be a sub-tension; if $\boldsymbol{\varphi} \in \Phi^+$ we have

$$\langle \boldsymbol{\varphi}, \mathbf{y} \rangle = \sum_{i=1}^{m} \varphi_i y_i \leqslant \sum_{i=1}^{m} \varphi_i \theta_i = 0.$$

Then the inequality becomes an equality if and only if,

$$\varphi_i > 0 \Rightarrow y_i = \theta_i.$$

We thus see that if $\langle \boldsymbol{\varphi}, \mathbf{y} \rangle = 0$, $\mathbf{y}$ is a potential difference on the partial graph generated by the arcs i with $\varphi_i > 0$ (since we then have $y_i = \theta_i$ on these arcs). Finally if $\mathbf{y}$ is a potential difference on the partial graph generated by the arcs i with $\varphi_i > 0$, we have

$$\sum_{\varphi > 0} y_i \varphi_i = 0.$$

Hence

$$\langle \boldsymbol{\varphi}, \mathbf{y} \rangle = \sum_{\varphi_i > 0} y_i \varphi_i + \sum_{\varphi_i = 0} y_i \varphi_i = 0.$$

Existence theorem for a flow (Hoffman, [21]). *Given numbers b_i and c_i with $b_i \leqslant c_i$ (for $i = 1, 2, \ldots, m$), a necessary and sufficient condition for the existence of a flow $\boldsymbol{\varphi}$ such that $b_i \leqslant \varphi_i \leqslant c_i$ is that for every elementary coboundary $\boldsymbol{\omega}$*

$$\begin{cases} \sum_{i \in \omega^-} c_i \geqslant \sum_{i \in \omega^+} b_i, \\ \sum_{i \in \omega^+} c_i \geqslant \sum_{i \in \omega^-} b_i. \end{cases}$$

The condition is necessary; for if such a flow $\boldsymbol{\varphi}$ exists, then:

$$0 = \langle \boldsymbol{\varphi}, \boldsymbol{\omega} \rangle = \langle \boldsymbol{\varphi}, \boldsymbol{\omega}^+ \rangle - \langle \boldsymbol{\varphi}, \boldsymbol{\omega}^- \rangle \geqslant \sum_{i \in \omega^+} b_i - \sum_{i \in \omega^-} c_i.$$

By reversing the sense of direction in ω, we similarly get

$$0 \geqslant \sum_{i \in \omega^-} b_i - \sum_{i \in \omega^+} c_i.$$

The condition is sufficient; by considering the intervals $X_i = [b_i, c_i]$ the conditions of the theorem can be written

$$0 \in \sum_{i \in \omega^+} X_i - \sum_{i \in \omega^-} X_i. \tag{1}$$

It is true that (1) implies the existence of a flow $\boldsymbol{\varphi}$ with $b_i \leqslant \varphi_i \leqslant c_i$ whenever the graph has one vertex. We shall suppose that it is true for every graph with $n-1$ vertices and show that it holds for a graph G with n vertices and with the intervals $X_1, X_2, \ldots, X_m$ satisfying condition (1).

Let k be an arc with $|X_k| > 1$, and let us show that condition (1) still holds even after X_k is replaced by $X'_k = \{x_k\}$ where x_k is a suitably chosen element of X_k; that is, there exists a number $x_k \in X_k$ such that

$$x_k \in \sum_{i \in \omega^+} X_i - \sum_{\substack{i \in \omega^- \\ i \neq k}} X_i$$

for every $\boldsymbol{\omega}$ not containing k.

By induction, there exists a suitable flow $\overline{\boldsymbol{\varphi}}$ for the graph $\overline{G}$ obtained from G by identifying the two extremities of arc k, or equivalently by replacing X_k by

$$\overline{X}_k = [-\infty, +\infty].$$

Then for every coboundary $\boldsymbol{\omega}$ not containing k, we have

$$\bar{\varphi}_k = \sum_{i \in \omega^+} \bar{\varphi}_i - \sum_{\substack{i \in \omega^- \\ i \neq k}} \bar{\varphi}_i \in \sum_{i \in \omega^+} X_i - \sum_{\substack{i \in \omega^- \\ i \neq k}} X_i.$$

The sets on the right-hand side are intervals which intersect one another and from (1), all of these intervals intersect X_k. Therefore,

$$X_k \cap \bigcap_{\omega/k \in \omega^-} \left[\sum_{i \in \omega^+} X_i - \sum_{\substack{i \in \omega^- \\ i \neq k}} X_i \right] \neq \emptyset.$$

This guarantees the existence of x_k and completes the proof of the theorem.

Corollary 1. *A flow* $\boldsymbol{\varphi}$ *such that* $\varphi_i \geqslant b_i$ *exists if and only if, for every cocircuit* $\boldsymbol{\omega}$, *we have*

$$\sum_{i \in \omega} b_i \leqslant 0.$$

This follows upon taking $c_i = +\infty$ for every i.

Corollary 2. *A flow* $\boldsymbol{\varphi}$ *such that* $\varphi_i \leqslant c_i$ *exists if and only if, for every cocircuit* $\boldsymbol{\omega}$, *we have*

$$\sum_{i \in \omega} c_i \geqslant 0.$$

Corollary 3. *A vector*

$$\mathbf{x} = (x_1, x_2, \ldots, x_m)$$

is called a sub-flow if there exists a flow $\boldsymbol{\varphi}$ *with* $x_i \leqslant \varphi_i$ *for every* i; *a necessary and sufficient condition for a vector* $\mathbf{x}$ *to be a sub-flow is that*

$$\langle \mathbf{x}, \boldsymbol{\theta} \rangle \leqslant 0$$

for every $\boldsymbol{\theta} \in \Theta^+$.

Moreover, a sub-flow $\mathbf{x}$ *and a potential difference* $\boldsymbol{\theta} \in \Theta^+$ *satisfy* $\langle \mathbf{x}, \boldsymbol{\theta} \rangle = 0$ *if and only if* $\mathbf{x}$ *is a flow for the graph obtained by identifying the extremities of each arc* k *such that* $\theta_k = 0$.

If $\mathbf{x}$ satisfies the inequality, we can write for any cocircuit $\boldsymbol{\omega}$, using Corollary 1;

$$\sum_{i \in \omega} x_i = \langle \mathbf{x}, \boldsymbol{\omega} \rangle \leqslant 0,$$

therefore $\mathbf{x}$ is a sub-flow.

Conversely, let $\mathbf{x}$ be a sub-flow; if $\boldsymbol{\theta} \in \Theta^+$, then

$$\langle \boldsymbol{\theta}, \mathbf{x} \rangle = \sum_{i=1}^{m} \theta_i x_i \leqslant \sum_{i=1}^{m} \theta_i \varphi_i = 0.$$

Furthermore, the inequality becomes an equality if and only if

$$\theta_i > 0 \Rightarrow x_i = \varphi_i;$$

we thus see that if $\langle \boldsymbol{\theta}, \mathbf{x} \rangle = 0$, $\mathbf{x}$ is a flow on the smaller graph.

Finally, if $\mathbf{x}$ is a flow on this smaller graph, then since $\boldsymbol{\theta}$ is a potential difference on the original graph, we have

$$\sum_{\theta_i > 0} x_i \theta_i = 0;$$

hence

$$\langle \mathbf{x}, \boldsymbol{\theta} \rangle = \sum_{\theta_i > 0} x_i \theta_i + \sum_{\theta_i = 0} x_i \theta_i = 0.$$

8.4. NEW FORMULATION OF THE TRANSPORTATION PROBLEM

The transportation problem and the problem of potential can be compared to two other problems which we now define.

Here we shall say that a set $\mathscr{C} \subset \mathbf{R}^2$ is an *increasing curve* if:

(1) *the projections*

$$\mathrm{proj}_x \mathscr{C} = \{x | \text{there exists a } y \text{ with } (x,y) \in \mathscr{C}\}$$

and

$$\mathrm{proj}_y \mathscr{C} = \{y | \text{there exists an } x \text{ with } (x,y) \in \mathscr{C}\}$$

are intervals; and

(2) *if* (x,y) *and* (x',y') *are two points of* $\mathscr{C}$ *then either* $x \leqslant x'$, $y \leqslant y'$ *or* $x \geqslant x'$, $y \geqslant y'$ (in other words $\mathscr{C}$ is a totally ordered set by the natural order relation).

EXAMPLE. Consider a numerical function $f(x)$ defined on an interval $[b,c]$ of the straight line $\mathbf{R}$. Let $f(x)$ be a convex function, that is

$$\left.\begin{aligned} x, y &\in [b,c] \\ p, q &\geqslant 0 \\ p+q &= 1 \end{aligned}\right\} \Rightarrow f(px+qy) \leqslant pf(x)+qf(y).$$

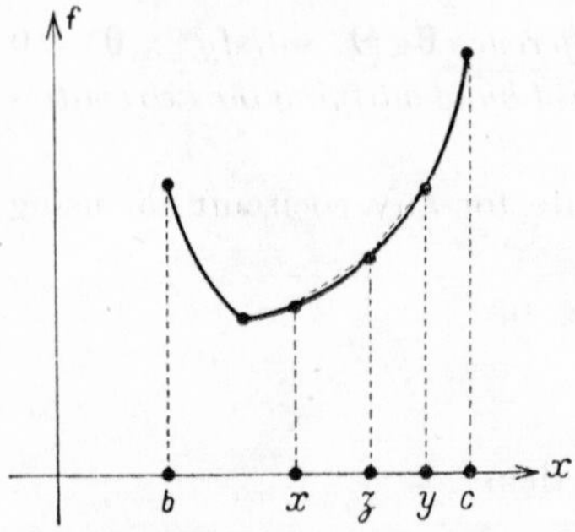

FIG. 8.3

Let us consider three points x, z and y in that order in the interval $[b,c]$; it follows at once that

$$\frac{f(y)-f(z)}{y-z} \geqslant \frac{f(x)-f(z)}{x-z}.$$

When y tends to z, the left-hand side decreases and therefore tends to a limit $f'_+(z)$, called the *derivative from the right*. Similarly as x tends to z the right-hand side increases and hence tends to a limit $f'_-(z)$ called the *derivative from the left*. Clearly,

$$f'_-(z) \leqslant f'_+(z).$$

With every number $x_0 \in [b,c]$ let us associate the set

$$\mathscr{C}_{x_0} = \{(x, y) | x = x_0, y \in \mathbf{R}, f'_-(x_0) \leqslant y \leqslant f'_+(x_0)\};$$

let us also write

$$\mathscr{C}_b = \{(x, y) | x = b, y \in \mathbf{R}, -\infty \leqslant y \leqslant f'_+(b)\},$$
$$\mathscr{C}_c = \{(x, y) | x = c, y \in \mathbf{R}, f'_-(c) \leqslant y \leqslant +\infty\}.$$

It follows that *the set* $\mathscr{C}$ *where*

$$\mathscr{C} = \bigcup_{x \in [b,c]} \mathscr{C}_x$$

is an increasing curve in the plane, we have

$$\text{proj}_x \mathscr{C} = [b, c],$$
$$\text{proj}_y \mathscr{C} = [-\infty, +\infty].$$

Moreover, if (x,y) and (x',y') are two points of $\mathscr{C}$ then

$$x < x' \Rightarrow f'_+(x) \leqslant f'_-(x') \Rightarrow y \leqslant y'.$$

Consequently, either

$$x \leqslant x', \quad y \leqslant y' \quad \text{or} \quad x \geqslant x', y \geqslant y'.$$

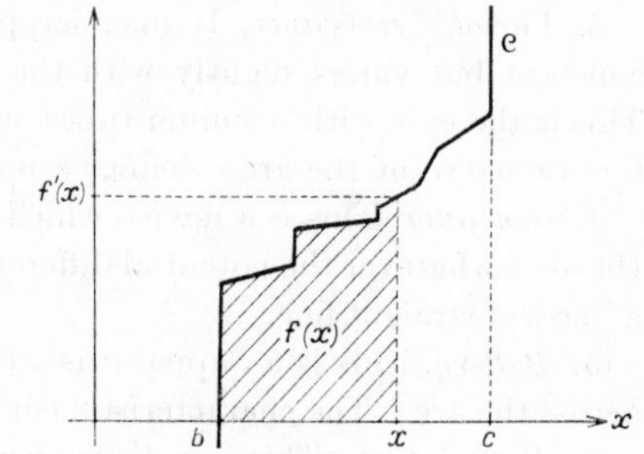

Fig. 8.4

It should be noticed that just as every convex function f allows us to define an increasing curve $\mathscr{C}$, so every increasing curve $\mathscr{C}$ allows us to define a convex function (except for an additive constant) by the Riemann integral along the curve $\mathscr{C}$.

Finally, if f is a function defined in $\mathbf{S}$ with values in $\mathbf{S}$ notice that $\mathscr{C}$ is a curve of $\mathbf{S}^2$: this is true if $\mathbf{S}$ is the set of real numbers, and it is also true if $\mathbf{S}$ is the set of all integers.

Consider a graph G and with every arc i associate an increasing curve $\mathscr{C}_i$; we shall say that a vector

$$\mathbf{y} = (y_1, y_2, \ldots, y_m)$$

is an *image across the curves* $\mathscr{C}_i$ of a vector

$$\mathbf{x} = (x_1, x_2, \ldots, x_m)$$

if

$$(x_i, y_i) \in \mathscr{C}_i \quad (i = 1, 2, \ldots, m).$$

It is, of course, possible for a vector $\mathbf{x}$ to have several images. We now consider the fundamental problem of finding a flow which has a potential difference as one of its images. This problem is well known in hydraulics and electric networks. An electric network is a graph formed by terminals (vertices) and branches (arcs), the orientation of the arcs being arbitrary.

In each arc i there can be different types of electrical equipment, amongst which the principal ones are:

1. *Perfect conductor.* Such an arc is characterized by zero potential difference; we can thus associate with it the characteristic curve $\mathscr{C}_i$ whose equation is $\theta_i = 0$.

2. *Ordinary resistance.* A resistance is a metal tube defined by the coefficient $k_i > 0$ such that for the flow φ_i and potential difference θ_i, $\theta_i = k_i \varphi_i$. The characteristic curve of the arc i is a straight line passing through the origin.

3. *Variable resistance.* It may happen that the coefficient k_i is not a constant but varies slightly with the flow, φ_i, which passes through it. This is the case with selenium tubes, copper oxide tubes, etc. The characteristic curve of the arc i defines a monotonic curve through the origin.

4. *Generator.* This is a device which maintains a constant flow through the arc i whatever the potential difference. The characteristic curve is then a vertical straight line.

5. *Battery.* This is an apparatus which maintains a constant potential across the arc i. The characteristic curve is then a horizontal line.

6. *Perfect diode.* This is a device which allows no current to pass if the potential difference $\theta_i \leqslant 0$ and which acts as a perfect conductor if $\theta_i > 0$. The characteristic curve of the arc i is formed by two segments.

In all the cases mentioned above the characteristic curve $\mathscr{C}_i$ is an *increasing curve* in $\mathbf{R}^2$. The fundamental problem of electric currents is as follows: given a set of arcs I and the values of the current $\boldsymbol{\varphi}$ on the arcs of I, to determine the flow φ_i in every arc $i \notin I$. This therefore is the problem of finding a flow which has a potential difference as one of its images; for every arc i for which the flow φ_i is given, we write

$$b_i = c_i = \varphi_i.$$

The fact that the new fundamental problem and the transportation problem are identical was noticed by Maxwell in 1873 in the case

$$b_i = -\infty, \quad c_i = +\infty \quad \text{and} \quad f_i(x) = \tfrac{1}{2} k_i x^2,$$

(which corresponds to electric circuits with resistances and sources of potential difference only). More recently this identity has been established by T. Sunaga and M. Iri [23] in the case

$$b_i = 0, \quad c_i > 0, \quad f_i(x) = l_i x$$

(which corresponds to a classical problem in operational research). We now prove that this is a very general property.

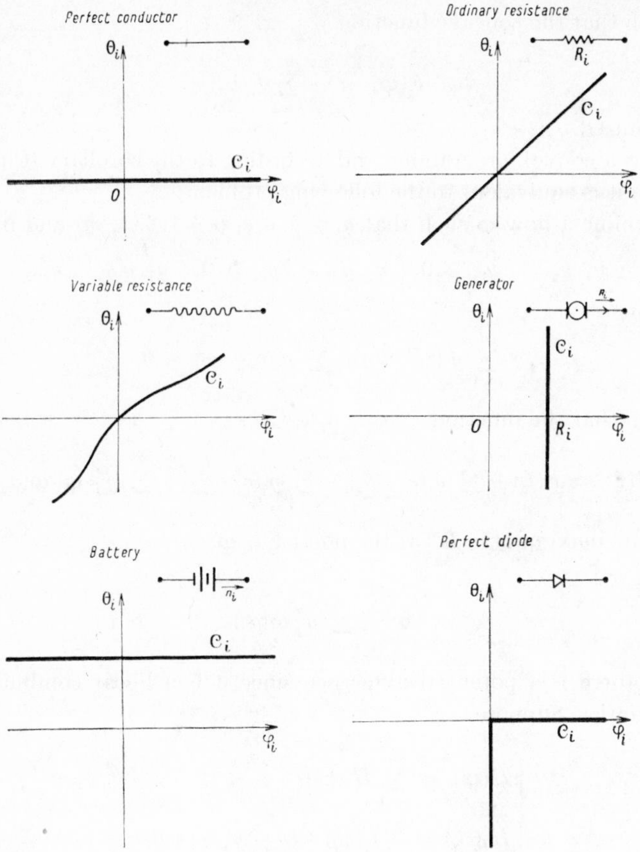

FIG. 8.5

Theorem 7 ([3], [7]). *Consider the transportation problem with convex functions $f_i(x)$ in the intervals $[b_i, c_i]$, and with corresponding increasing curves $\mathscr{C}_i$. Every flow* $\boldsymbol{\varphi}$ *which has a potential difference across the curves $\mathscr{C}_i$ for its image, is a solution of the transportation problem and vice versa.*

The transportation problem can be written as follows: find a vector

$$\boldsymbol{\varphi} = (\varphi_1, \varphi_2, \ldots, \varphi_m)$$

such that

$$\varphi_i - b_i \geqslant 0 \quad (i = 1, 2, \ldots, m),$$

$$c_i - \varphi_i \geqslant 0 \quad (i = 1, 2, \ldots, m),$$

$$\langle \boldsymbol{\varphi}, \boldsymbol{\omega}(a_j) \rangle = 0 \quad (j = 1, 2, \ldots, n),$$

and such that the concave function

$$F(\boldsymbol{\varphi}) = -\sum_{i=1}^{m} f_i(\varphi_i)$$

is maximized.

This is a convex programme and according to the corollary (Chapter 4, page 83) it is equivalent to the following problem:

Determine a flow $\boldsymbol{\varphi}$ such that $b_i \leqslant \varphi_i \leqslant c_i$ $(i = 1,2,\ldots,m)$ and numbers

$$y_1, y_2, \ldots, y_m \geqslant 0, \quad y'_1, y'_2, \ldots, y'_m \geqslant 0, \quad y''_1, y''_2, \ldots, y''_n,$$

such that

$$\sum_{i=1}^{m} y_i(\varphi_i - b_i) + \sum_{i=1}^{m} y'_i(c_i - \varphi_i) = 0, \tag{1}$$

and such that the function

$$H(\boldsymbol{\xi}) = F(\boldsymbol{\xi}) + \sum_{i=1}^{m} y_i(\xi_i - b_i) + \sum_{i=1}^{m} y'_i(c_i - \xi_i) + \sum_{j=1}^{n} y''_j \langle \boldsymbol{\varphi}, \boldsymbol{\omega}(a_j) \rangle$$

attains its maximum in $\mathbf{R}^m$ at the point $\boldsymbol{\xi} = \boldsymbol{\varphi}$.

Let

$$\boldsymbol{\theta} = \sum_{j=1}^{n} y''_j \boldsymbol{\omega}(a_j),$$

this vector $\boldsymbol{\theta}$ is a potential difference since it is a linear combination of coboundaries. Suppose

$$\begin{cases} H(\boldsymbol{\varphi}) = \sum_{i=1}^{m} H_i(\varphi_i); \\ H_i(\varphi_i) = -f_i(\varphi_i) + (y_i - y'_i)\,\varphi_i + \theta_i\,\varphi_i. \end{cases}$$

Notice that $H(\boldsymbol{\xi}) \leqslant H(\boldsymbol{\varphi})$ for every $\boldsymbol{\xi} \in \mathbf{R}^m$, if and only if for any i

$$H_i(\xi_i) \leqslant H_i(\varphi_i) \quad \text{for every } \xi_i \in \mathbf{R}.$$

This shows that the concave function $H_i(\xi_i)$ attains its maximum at a point $\xi_i = \varphi_i$, i.e. at the point φ_i such that

$$H'_{i+}(\varphi_i) \leqslant 0 \leqslant H'_{i-}(\varphi_i).$$

Therefore

$$f'_{i-}(\varphi_i) \leqslant y_i - y'_i + \theta_i \leqslant f'_{i+}(\varphi_i).$$

If $b_i < \varphi_i < c_i$, then $y'_i = 0 = y_i$, by (1), and the condition

$$f'_{i-}(\varphi_i) \leqslant \theta_i \leqslant f'_{i+}(\varphi_i)$$

follows.

If $\varphi_i = b_i < c_i$ then $y'_i = 0$ by (1), and hence

$$f'_{i+}(\varphi_i) \geqslant \theta_i + y_i \geqslant \theta_i.$$

If $\varphi_i = c_i > b_i$ then $y_i = 0$ by (1) and hence

$$f'_{i-}(\varphi_i) \leqslant \theta_i - y'_i \leqslant \theta_i.$$

If $\varphi_i = b_i = c_i$, θ_i is arbitrary (for we may then suppose

$$f'_{i-}(b_i) = -\infty, \quad f'_{i+}(b_i) = +\infty).$$

In all cases, we have:

$$(\varphi_i, \theta_i) \in \mathscr{C}_i,$$

which proves the equivalence of the two problems.

Theorem 8. *Consider the problem of potential with the convex functions $h_i(x)$ in an interval $[k_i, l_i]$, with which the curves $\mathscr{C}'_i$ are associated (as on p. 161). Every potential difference which has a flow as its image across the curves $\mathscr{C}'_i$ is a solution of the problem of potential and vice versa.*

The problem of potential consists in finding a vector

$$\boldsymbol{\theta} = (\theta_1, \theta_2, \dots, \theta_m)$$

such that

$$\theta_i - k_i \geqslant 0 \quad (i = 1, 2, \dots, m),$$

$$l_i - \theta_i \geqslant 0 \quad (i = 1, 2, \dots, m),$$

$$\langle \boldsymbol{\mu}^j, \boldsymbol{\theta} \rangle = 0 \quad (j = 1, 2, \dots, k),$$

(where $\boldsymbol{\mu}^1, \boldsymbol{\mu}^2, \dots, \boldsymbol{\mu}^k$ form a cycle-basis) and such that

$$H(\boldsymbol{\theta}) = -\sum_{i=1}^{m} h_i(\theta_i)$$

is maximized. We have seen (Chapter 4, Section 4.2) that this programme is equivalent to the following problem: determine a potential difference $\boldsymbol{\theta}$ satisfying $k_i \leqslant \theta_i \leqslant l_i$ (for $i = 1, 2, \dots, m$) and numbers

$$y_1, y_2, \dots, y_m \geqslant 0, \quad y'_1, y'_2, \dots, y'_m \geqslant 0, \quad y''_1, y''_2, \dots, y''_k,$$

such that

$$\sum_{i=1}^{m} y_i(\theta_i - k_i) + \sum_{i=1}^{m} y'_i(l_i - \theta_i) = 0 \tag{1}$$

and such that the function

$$H(\boldsymbol{\xi}) + \sum_{i=1}^{m} y_i(\xi_i - k_i) + \sum_{i=1}^{m} y'_i(l_i - \xi_i) + \sum_{j=1}^{k} y''_j \langle \mu^j, \theta \rangle$$

attains its maximum in $\mathbf{R}^m$ at the point $\boldsymbol{\xi} = \boldsymbol{\theta}$. Let

$$\boldsymbol{\varphi} = \sum_{j=1}^{k} y''_j \boldsymbol{\mu}^j.$$

This vector $\boldsymbol{\varphi}$ is clearly a flow, and we see, as before, that the last condition can be written:

$$h'_{i-}(\theta_i) \leqslant y_i - y'_i + \varphi_i \leqslant h'_{i+}(\theta_i).$$

To show that $(\theta_i, \varphi_i) \in \mathscr{C}'_i$, it is enough to interchange the roles of $\boldsymbol{\varphi}$ and $\boldsymbol{\theta}$ in the proof of Theorem 7.

Theorem 9. *Let G be a graph with an increasing curve $\mathscr{C}_i$ associated with every arc i. Let $\boldsymbol{\varphi}$ and $\boldsymbol{\varphi}'$ be two flows whose images are the potential differences $\boldsymbol{\theta}$ and $\boldsymbol{\theta}'$; for every arc i either $\varphi_i = \varphi'_i$ or $\theta_i = \theta'_i$.*

Suppose that this is not true for an arc $i = 1$; then

$$\varphi_1 \neq \varphi'_1, \quad \theta_1 \neq \theta'_1,$$

where we may assume that $\varphi_1 < \varphi'_1$. Since $\mathscr{C}_1$ is an increasing curve $\theta_1 \leqslant \theta'_1$, hence $\theta_1 < \theta'_1$.

For every arc i such that $\varphi_i \neq \varphi'_i$, by changing its orientation if necessary it may be assumed that $\varphi_i < \varphi'_i$. We now apply the Lemma on coloured arcs by colouring black all the arcs i with $\varphi_i < \varphi'_i$, and colouring green all the arcs i with $\varphi_i = \varphi'_i$.

CASE 1. There is a black and green coboundary $\boldsymbol{\omega}$, passing through the arc $i = 1$, with all black arcs oriented in the same direction; then

$$\sum_{i \in \omega^+} (\varphi_i - \varphi'_i) = \langle \boldsymbol{\varphi} - \boldsymbol{\varphi}', \boldsymbol{\omega} \rangle = 0,$$

since for every i, $\varphi_i \leqslant \varphi'_i$, and since $\varphi_1 < \varphi'_1$, we have an impossibility.

CASE 2. There is a black cycle $\boldsymbol{\mu}$ passing through the arc $i = 1$ with all black arcs oriented in the same direction; then

$$\sum_{i \in \mu} (\theta_i - \theta'_i) = \langle \boldsymbol{\mu}, \boldsymbol{\theta} - \boldsymbol{\theta}' \rangle = 0,$$

since $\theta_i \leqslant \theta'_i$ for every arc $i \in \boldsymbol{\mu}$ (i being black, we have $\varphi_i < \varphi'_i$); since $\theta_1 < \theta'_1$ we have an impossibility in this case also.

This proves the theorem.

Uniqueness theorem for a flow. *If for every arc i belonging to a certain cotree (X, W) the curve $\mathscr{C}_i$ does not contain horizontal segments, then there is at most one flow which has a potential difference as its image.*

Consider two flows $\boldsymbol{\varphi}$ and $\boldsymbol{\varphi}'$ whose images are respectively the potential differences $\boldsymbol{\theta}$ and $\boldsymbol{\theta}'$. For every arc $i \in W$ either $\varphi_i = \varphi'_i$ or $\theta_i = \theta'_i$, which implies $\varphi_i = \varphi'_i$ (since the curve $\mathscr{C}_i$ does not contain horizontal segments). The flow is entirely determined by its values on a cotree (Theorem 1); therefore $\boldsymbol{\varphi} = \boldsymbol{\varphi}'$.

Corollary. *If, in a transportation problem the functions f_i are strictly convex for every arc i of a cotree, the solution* $\boldsymbol{\varphi}$ *(if it exists) is unique.*

This follows from Theorem 7.

Uniqueness theorem for a potential difference. *If for every arc i of a tree* (X, V) *the curve* $\mathscr{C}_i$ *does not contain vertical segments there exists at most one potential difference which can be the image of a flow.*

Consider two flows $\boldsymbol{\varphi}$ and $\boldsymbol{\varphi}'$, whose respective images are the potential differences $\boldsymbol{\theta}$ and $\boldsymbol{\theta}'$. For every arc $i \in V$, either $\theta_i = \theta_i'$ or $\varphi_i = \varphi_i'$, which implies $\theta_i = \theta_i'$. A potential difference is completely determined by its values on a tree (Theorem 4), so $\boldsymbol{\theta} = \boldsymbol{\theta}'$.

Corollary. *If in a problem of potential the functions h_i are strictly convex for every arc i of a tree H, the solution* $\boldsymbol{\theta}$ *(if it exists) is unique.*

This follows from Theorem 8.

These uniqueness theorems contain Duffin's [9] theorem on the uniqueness of an electric current as a special case.

8.5. THE FUNDAMENTAL DUALITY THEOREM

It has been shown that to every convex function $f(x)$ defined in an interval $[b,c]$ we can assign an increasing curve $\mathscr{C}$.

Conversely, considering an increasing curve $\mathscr{C}$ we associate with every $x \in [b,c]$ a number $y(x)$ such that

$$(x, y(x)) \in \mathscr{C}.$$

Take a point $(x_0, y_0) \in \mathscr{C}$ and form the Riemann integral:

$$f(x) = \int_{x_0}^{x} y(x)\, dx = \lim \sum_{k=1}^{m} y(x_k)\,(x_{k+1} - x_k).$$

This Riemann integral always exists (for the function $y(x)$ is monotonic); the function $f(x)$ thus defined is convex, and represents the algebraic sum of areas bounded by axes of coordinates, the two verticals at the abscissae x_0 and x and the curve $\mathscr{C}$ (with the usual rules for signs). The correspondence is therefore one–one between the convex functions $f(x)$ (defined except for a positive constant) and the curves $\mathscr{C}$.

Lemma. *Let $f(x)$ be a convex function defined in the interval $[b,c]$ and let $\mathscr{C}$ be the corresponding increasing curve. There exists a convex function $h(y)$ such that for every point $(x,y) \in \mathscr{C}$, we have*

$$f(x) + h(y) = xy.$$

The functions $f(x)$ and $h(y)$ are said to be conjugate.

Let us construct the curve $\mathscr{C}$ corresponding to the function $f(x)$ and let us take two points (x_0, y_0) and (x, y) on $\mathscr{C}$; let $\bar{f}(x)$ denote the line integral along $\mathscr{C}$ from (x_0, y_0) to (x, y); the mirror image $\mathscr{C}'$ of $\mathscr{C}$ in the main diagonal is also an increasing curve and therefore defines a convex function $\bar{h}(y)$, the line integral along $\mathscr{C}'$ from (y_0, x_0) to (y, x).

Consider the set of points of subdivision of $\mathscr{C}$ $(x_1, y_1), (x_2, y_2), \ldots, (x_k, y_k)$, with:

$$x_0 \leqslant x_1 \leqslant \ldots \leqslant x_k = x,$$

$$y_0 \leqslant y_1 \leqslant \ldots \leqslant y_k = y.$$

Then

$$\sum_{j=1}^{k} y_j(x_j - x_{j-1}) + \sum_{j=1}^{k} x_{j-1}(y_j - y_{j-1}) = xy - x_0 y_0;$$

on taking the points of subdivision closer and closer we have in the limit

$$\int_{x_0}^{x} y\,dx + \int_{y_0}^{y} x\,dy = xy - x_0 y_0,$$

hence

$$\bar{f}(x) + \bar{h}(y) = xy - x_0 y_0.$$

As $f(x) = \bar{f}(x) + K$ we may write

$$f(x) + [\bar{h}(y) - K + x_0 y_0] = xy.$$

The function inside the square brackets is the *conjugate* $h(y)$ of $f(x)$.

NOTE. It must be remembered that a convex function is always given with an interval of definition $[b, c]$ which may be finite or infinite. Its conjugate $h(y)$ is only defined on a well-determined interval $[k, l]$. If $c < +\infty$ then necessarily $l = +\infty$; if $b > -\infty$ then necessarily $k = -\infty$; but if $c = +\infty$ or $b = -\infty$ the interval of definition of the function $h(y)$ can be a half-line or even a finite segment.

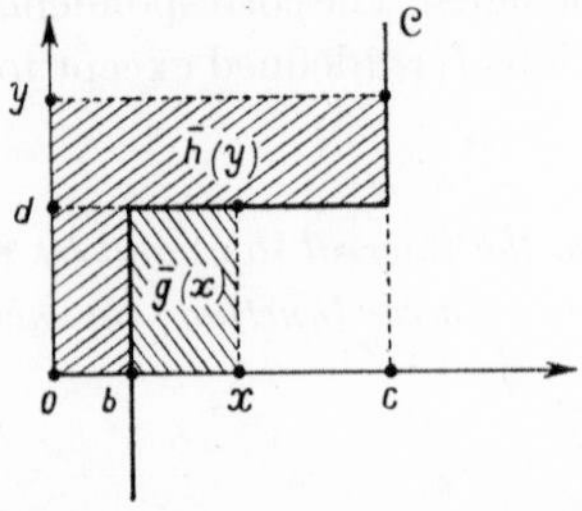

FIG. 8.6

Finally, notice that the *concave* functions $f(x)$ and $h(y)$ are said to be *conjugate* if the convex functions $-f(x)$ and $-h(-y)$ are conjugate. We come back to the definitions of Part I, page 94).

EXAMPLE. Consider the function $g(x) = dx$, defined in an interval $[b, c]$ with $0 \leqslant b < c < +\infty$. Let us find its conjugate function $h(y)$.

Construct the curve $\mathscr{C}$ and take $x_0 = b$,

$y_0 = 0$; the functions $\bar{g}(x)$ and $\bar{h}(y)$ represent the areas marked in Figure 8.6, and we have

$$\bar{h}(y) = \begin{cases} by & \text{if } y \leqslant d, \\ cy - d(c-b) & \text{if } y > d. \end{cases}$$

We deduce that

$$h(y) = \begin{cases} by - bd & \text{if } y \leqslant d, \\ cy - cd & \text{if } y > d. \end{cases}$$

Duality theorem. *Consider the transportation problem with convex functions $f_i(x)$ and the problem of potential with convex functions $h_i(y)$; if for every i the convex functions $f_i(x)$ and $h_i(y)$ are conjugates (bearing in mind their intervals of definition) then*

$$\min_{\varphi} F(\boldsymbol{\varphi}) + \min_{\theta} H(\boldsymbol{\theta}) = 0.$$

Let $\overline{\boldsymbol{\varphi}}$ be a flow such that:

$$F(\overline{\boldsymbol{\varphi}}) = \min_{\varphi} F(\boldsymbol{\varphi}).$$

As $\overline{\boldsymbol{\varphi}}$ is a solution of the transportation problem, by Theorem 7 a potential difference $\overline{\boldsymbol{\theta}}$ exists such that:

$$(\bar{\varphi}_i, \bar{\theta}_i) \in \mathscr{C}_i \quad (i = 1, 2, \ldots, m).$$

Consequently

$$f_i(\bar{\varphi}_i) + h_i(\bar{\theta}_i) = \bar{\varphi}_i \bar{\theta}_i.$$

Hence, by adding,

$$F(\overline{\boldsymbol{\varphi}}) + H(\overline{\boldsymbol{\theta}}) = \langle \overline{\boldsymbol{\varphi}}, \overline{\boldsymbol{\theta}} \rangle = 0.$$

Furthermore, $\overline{\boldsymbol{\theta}}$ is an image potential difference of a flow $\overline{\boldsymbol{\varphi}}$, therefore by Theorem 8 it is a solution to the problem of potential with respect to the functions h_i; hence

$$\min_{\varphi} F(\boldsymbol{\varphi}) + \min_{\theta} H(\boldsymbol{\theta}) = 0.$$

NOTE. This result gives a simple criterion for determining whether a flow $\overline{\boldsymbol{\varphi}}$ is a solution of the transportation problem. For, if we can find a potential difference $\overline{\boldsymbol{\theta}}$ such that $F(\overline{\boldsymbol{\varphi}}) + H(\overline{\boldsymbol{\theta}}) = 0$, we can be certain that $F(\overline{\boldsymbol{\varphi}})$ is minimized (and that $H(\overline{\boldsymbol{\theta}})$ is minimized).

This remark will be used often in the following chapter.

9. Flow algorithms

9.1. THE PATH PROBLEM

By the path problem, we shall mean the following:

Given a graph G and two vertices $\bar{a}$ and $\bar{b}$, find a path from $\bar{a}$ to $\bar{b}$.

We shall see later that this problem is a particular case of the problem of potential; it is met frequently in this form as will be seen in the following examples:

EXAMPLE 1. All one-person games (the ring-puzzle, the fifteen puzzle, solitaire, etc....) reduce to *step-wise procedures*: given a state $\bar{a}$ we try to reach a state $\bar{b}$ by successive stages. A well-known example is the maze:

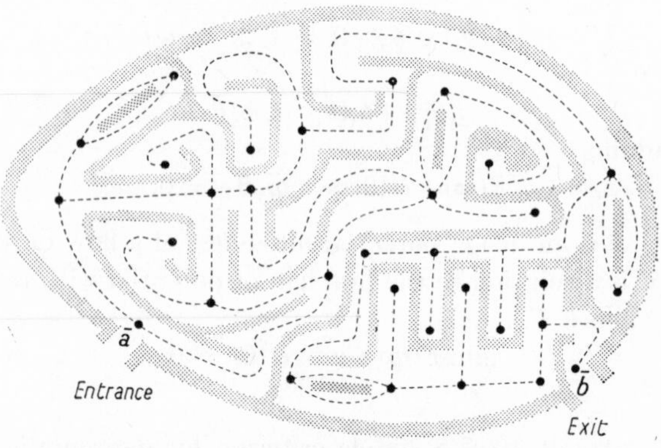

FIG. 9.1

An individual at $\bar{a}$ tries to get out of the maze by following the paths in Figure 9.1; this is equivalent to solving Problem 1 for the graph corresponding to the maze, where $\bar{X}$ is the set of junctions and where two oppositely oriented arcs represent the passages between two junctions. It will be noted that this graph is planar.

EXAMPLE 2. *The problem of the wolf, the cabbage and the goat.* A wolf, a cabbage and a goat are on one bank of a river. A ferryman wants to take them across the river to the opposite bank. Because his boat is too small, he can only take one at a time. Obviously, neither the wolf and the goat, nor the goat and the cabbage can be left alone together unguarded. How would the ferryman take them across?

This well-known problem can be easily solved mentally because of the small number of stages to be considered; nevertheless, it is a typical example of the path problem. Draw a graph with the different possible stages as vertices and look for a path going from stage $\bar{a}$ (at which the cabbage C, the ferryman F, the goat G, and the wolf W are all on one bank) to stage $\bar{b}$ (at which that bank is empty). The arrows in Figure 9.2 indicate such a path.

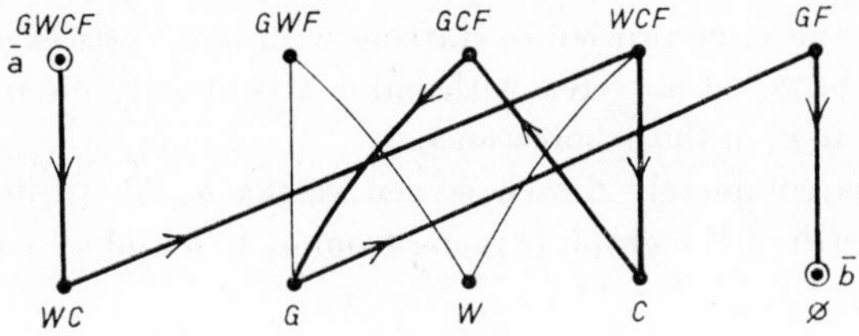

FIG. 9.2

In a more complicated case a systematic algorithm would have been necessary and several have been proposed.

EXAMPLE 3. Consider an electric network with nodes and branches, where some branches contain diodes (which allow current to pass in one direction only) and switches.

We wish to determine all possible combinations of switches which allow current to pass from node $\bar{a}$ to node $\bar{b}$.

Form a graph of this electric network where a branch without a diode is represented by two arcs of opposite orientations, and a branch with a diode by an arc oriented in the appropriate direction and where all the switches on a branch are assumed to be off. The problem is to find *all* elementary paths from vertex $\bar{a}$ to vertex $\bar{b}$.†

General algorithm.

Let G be a graph with vertices $a_1 = \bar{a}, a_2, \ldots, a_n = \bar{b}$. A general procedure for determining all the solutions to the path problem has been described by Riguet [36] as follows:

† An analytic method using Boolean variables may be used; cf. for example F. Hohn, 'Some mathematical aspects of switching', *Amer. Math. Monthly* **62**, 75, 1955. The algorithm in [36] uses the Boolean method and the graphic method simultaneously.

Starting from the vertex $\bar{a} = a_1$ as centre, construct step by step an arborescence H', whose other vertices are denoted by $a'_2, a''_2, \ldots, a'_3, a''_3, \ldots$; the vertices $a'_i, a''_i, \ldots$ of the aborescence will all correspond to the vertex a_i of the initial graph G and every path of the arborescence H' will correspond to an elementary path of G.

1. Begin by drawing the vertex a'_1 representing the vertex a_1;
2. If $(a_1, a_{i_1}), (a_1, a_{i_2}), \ldots$, are the arcs of G issuing from a_1, draw the vertices $a'_{i_1}, a'_{i_2}, \ldots$ and the arcs $(a'_1, a'_{i_1}), (a'_1, a'_{i_2}), \ldots$;
3. For every vertex a'_i draw the arcs $(a'_i, a'_{j_1}), (a'_i, a'_{j_2}), \ldots$, corresponding to the arcs issuing from a_i in the graph G, to two distinct arcs (a_{i_1}, a_j) and (a_{i_2}, a_j) of G, there will correspond two distinct vertices a'_j and a''_j of the arborescence.
4. Repeat the same procedure starting with new vertices a'_j but do not draw an arc (a'_j, a'_k) if a vertex with index k is already on any particular path from a'_1 to a'_j in the arborescence.

After H' is completely drawn, every vertex $b', b'', \ldots$, determines an elementary path of the graph G going from a_1 to b and all paths are thus obtained.

EXAMPLE. For the wolf, cabbage and goat problem, the graph has the following arborescence H':

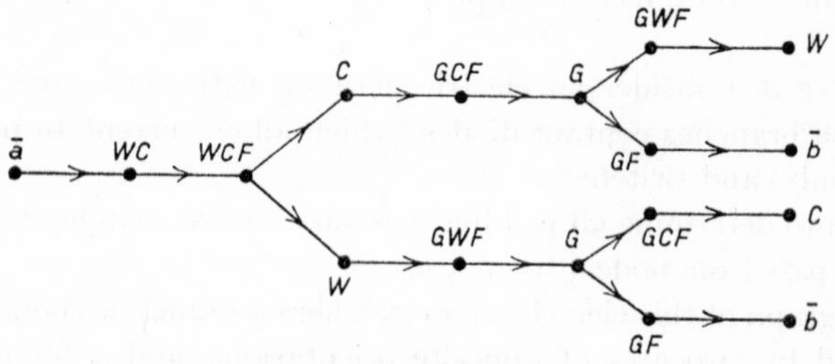

FIG. 9.3

In G there are thus two solutions for a path going from $\bar{a}$ to $\bar{b}$ (this can be seen at once because of the simple structure of the graph).

Trémaux's algorithm.

If it is required to find only a path from $\bar{a}$ to $\bar{b}$, it is enough to observe the following procedure:

1. Leaving $\bar{a}$, we move along any path as far as possible, always labelling with a cross each arc as it is traversed, and not using it again (at least in the direction of its orientation).

2. If a dead-end is reached, return in the opposite direction putting a second cross on the arc.

3. If an unused arc leads to a vertex which has already been explored, return as if it were a dead-end.

4. If we return to a_i, we leave it again by an arc not yet traversed, if such an arc exists; if not, we go back by the arc labelled with a cross by which we reached a_i for the first time; the procedure stops when vertex b is reached or when we cannot proceed further.

Before proving the effectiveness of this algorithm we prove a lemma.

Lemma. *If Trémaux's rule is followed, all arcs traversed will have been used in both directions.*

For, suppose we mark with a thick line every arc which has been traversed and on arriving at a vertex already explored by an arc which has not yet been traversed, suppose that we detach this arc from its terminal vertex before returning (rule 3). Thus one forms an aborescence by virtue of property 6 of Theorem 10 (Chapter 7), and one has successively explored all the branches by following only rules 1, 2, and 4. Consequently all the arcs marked with a thick line would have been followed in reverse.

PROOF. We now show that if there exists a path

$$\mu = [\bar{a}, a_2, \ldots, a_n]$$

going from $\bar{a}$ to a_n, then one is bound to get to the vertex a_n; for, suppose that a_n is not reached and that Trémaux's rule cannot be followed; let a_k be the last vertex in the path μ which has been reached, then $a_k \neq a_n$. Let (a, a_k) be the arc which has led us to a_k for the first time. The arc (a, a_k) has not been retraced either by virtue of rule 2 (for a_k is not a dead-end), or by virtue of rule 3 (for this arc has led us to a_k for the first time), or by virtue of rule 4 (for there is still an unused direction). This contradicts the lemma.

EXAMPLE. Consider the following problem.

On the chess-board of Figure 9.4, certain squares are cross-hatched while the others are white. A knight is placed on square $g1$. Is it possible for the knight to reach square $b1$ without using any of the cross-hatched squares? The reader may see that it is a path problem in the auxiliary graph G given in Figure 9.5. This is a symmetric graph: every edge such as $[g1, h3]$ in fact represents two arcs of opposite orientation: $(g1, h3)$ and $(h3, g1)$. Applying Trémaux's algorithm, if arc $(g1, h3)$ is traversed it is useless to follow with the arc $(h3, g1)$, which is a dead-end (the vertex $g1$ being already used).

The procedure then gives:

*g*1, *h*3, *f*2, *d*1, *e*3, *g*2, *e*1, (retrace *g*2), (retrace *e*3), *g*4, *f*6, *e*8, *g*7, *e*6, *f*8, *g*6, *e*7, *c*6, *b*4, *a*2, (retrace *b*4), *a*6, *b*8, *c*6, (retrace *b*8), (retrace *a*6), (retrace *b*4), (retrace *c*6), *a*5, *b*3, *d*2, *b*1.

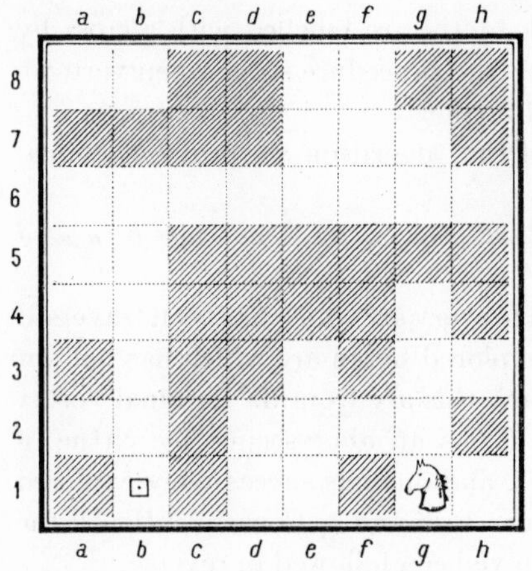

FIG. 9.4

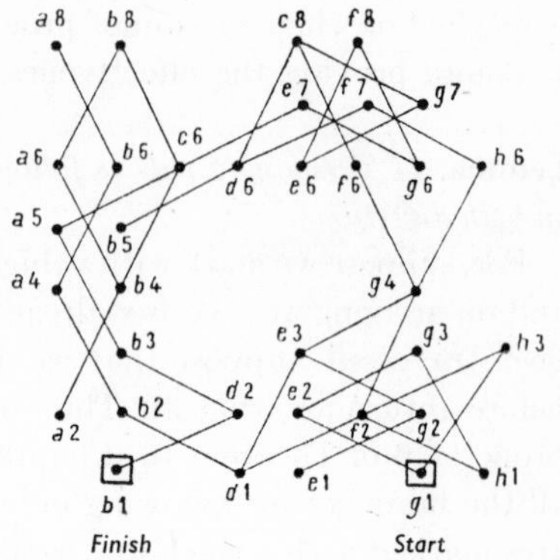

FIG. 9.5

Algorithm in the case of a planar graph.

In the case of the maze, where the graph G is planar and remains planar after joining the arc $(\bar{a}, \bar{b})$, it is enough to observe the following rule: *at crossroads, always choose the extreme right-hand path.*

This algorithm always gets us out of the maze without using the same edge twice; furthermore it means the traveller who has lost his way has no need to mark his path with crosses as in Trémaux's algorithm.

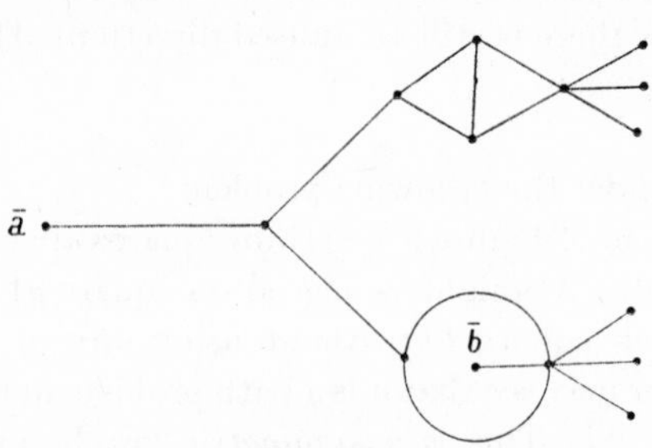

FIG. 9.6

Notice that the rule is invalid if the points $\bar{a}$ and $\bar{b}$ cannot be joined by a continuous line without cutting the other edges. For example, this rule yields no path from $\bar{a}$ to $\bar{b}$ in the maze of Figure 9.6.

Analogous algorithm in the case of a symmetric graph.

In the case of a symmetric graph, a useful algorithm consists in representing the arcs by pieces of string with knots at the position of the vertices. If $\bar{a}$ and $\bar{b}$ represent the start and finish, stretch the system holding $\bar{a}$ and $\bar{b}$. The pieces of string which are taut between $\bar{a}$ and $\bar{b}$ give the required path.

9.2. THE PROBLEM OF THE SHORTEST PATH

The *shortest path problem* is the following:

In a given graph G, associate with each arc i a number $l_i \geqslant 0$ which will be called the 'length' of the arc i. Find a path μ from a vertex $\bar{a}$ to a vertex $\bar{b}$ such that the total length

$$\sum_{i \in \mu} l$$

is as small as possible.

EXAMPLE. We may consider a geographical map and look for the shortest route from place $\bar{a}$ to place $\bar{b}$. Draw the graph with two arcs of opposite orientation representing each road between two places. The problem of the shortest path is treated by letting l_i be the length of the road corresponding to the arc i.

We can also look for the quickest or most economical journey.

Algorithm

The problem of the shortest path has been solved by a number of authors in similar ways: the most rapid algorithm appears to be that proposed by G. Dantzig [6], as follows:

Considering the vertex of departure, $\bar{a} = a_1$ in the graph, and $\bar{b} = a_n$, the vertex of arrival, determine for all vertices a_j of the graph, the length $t(a_j)$ of the shortest path from $\bar{a} = a_1$ to a_j.

The step-wise procedure is:

1. To begin with suppose $t(a_1) = 0$. This function t is therefore defined on the set $A_1 = \{a_1\}$.

2. At the kth stage, suppose we have defined the function t on a set A_k of k vertices; we associate with every vertex $a_j \in A_k$, a vertex $b_j \notin A_k$ such that the distance $l(a_j, b_j)$ is a minimum. We will find a vertex $a_q \in A_k$ such that

$$t(a_q) + l(a_q, b_q) = \min \{t(a_j) + l(a_j, b_j)\},$$

we then write

$$A_{k+1} = A_k \cup \{b_q\},$$
$$t(b_q) = t(a_q) + l(a_q, b_q).$$

We will show that $t(b_q)$ represents the length of the shortest path b_q and that the shortest path going to b_q passes through a_q. It must be that $t(a_j)$ is the length of the shortest path from $\bar{a} = a_1$ to a_j (for every $a_j \in A_k$), since every path which leaves A_k has length $\geqslant t(a_q) + l(a_q, b_q) = t(b_q)$, and to go to b_q we are bound to leave A_k since $a_1 \in A_k$.

Notice that whenever $t(b_q)$ has been determined for a vertex b_q, all the arcs incident to b_q may be deleted.

NOTE. After finding b_j, which is associated with $a_j \in A_k$, to determine the $(k+1)$th vertex, k comparisons only are necessary. The maximum number of comparisons for a graph G of n vertices is

$$1+2+\ldots+(n-1) = \tfrac{1}{2}n(n-1).$$

In determining the length of the shortest path from $\bar{a}$ to $\bar{b}$ we could also work backwards, as it were, from $\bar{b}$ and determine some of the numbers $t'(b_i)$, the length of the shortest path from b_i to $\bar{b}$. If both procedures were carried out simultaneously, the length of the shortest path from $\bar{a}$ to $\bar{b}$ would be found as soon as there was a vertex c for which both $t(c)$ and $t'(c)$ were known. The number of comparisons to determine the length of the shortest path from $\bar{a}$ to $\bar{b}$ by this means could not be more than

$$2\left(1+2+\ldots+\left[\frac{n}{2}\right]\right) \approx \frac{1}{2}\frac{n(n+2)}{2}.$$

This therefore is a still more economical procedure.

EXAMPLE. As an example of the application of the theory, consider the graph of Figure 9.7.

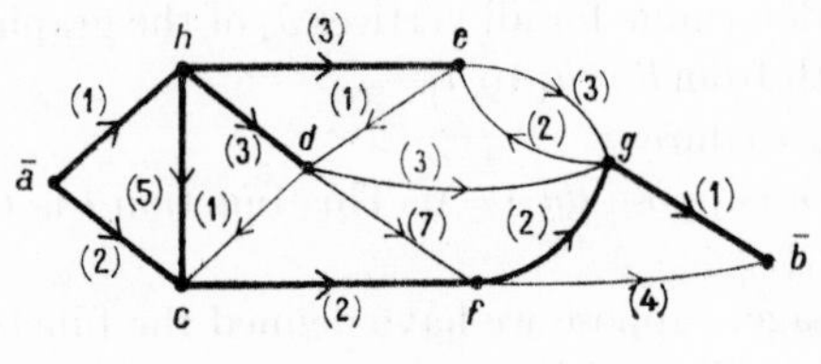

FIG. 9.7

The number on an arc i is l_i.

1. $t(\bar{a}) = 0$; compare $\bar{a}h$ $(0+1)$ and $\bar{a}c$ $(0+2)$. So choose $\bar{a}h$.
2. $t(h) = 1$; compare he $(1+3)$, hd $(1+3)$ and $\bar{a}c$ $(0+2)$. Choose $\bar{a}c$.
3. $t(c) = 2$; compare he $(1+3)$, hd $(1+3)$ and cf $(2+2)$. Choose he, hd, cf.
4. $t(e) = t(d) = t(f) = 4$; compare eg $(4+3)$, dg $(4+3)$, and fg $(4+2)$.

Choose fg.

5. $t(g) = 6$; compare $g\bar{b}$ $(6+1)$ and $f\bar{b}$ $(4+4)$. Choose $g\bar{b}$.
6. $t(\bar{b}) = 7$.

The shortest path from $\bar{a}$ to $\bar{b}$ is therefore $\bar{a}cfg\bar{b}$.

9.3. THE PROBLEM OF THE SHORTEST SPANNING TREE

A variation of the preceding problem which frequently arises can be formulated as follows:

Consider a connected graph $G = (X, U)$, and to every edge $u \in U$ assign a number $l(u) \geqslant 0$ which is called its *length. It is required to find a tree* $H = (X, V)$, *in* G *whose length*

$$\sum_{u \in V} l(u)$$

is as short as possible.

This is the *problem of the shortest spanning tree.*

EXAMPLE. Let us, for example, determine the smallest length of pipeline, necessary to connect n given towns. In problems of telecommunication, the junctions of several pipelines are important, since these can only be situated in a town. These towns are then the vertices of the graph, and $l(a, b)$ is the distance separating the towns a and b. The network of pipelines must be a connected graph and since it is of minimum length, it cannot have cycles. It is therefore a tree. Here we are looking for the shortest possible spanning tree of the complete graph of n vertices.

First we establish a lemma.

Lemma. *If* $G = (X, U)$ *is a complete graph and if the lengths* $l(u)$ *assigned to the edges are all different, the problem has a unique solution* (X, V); *the set*

$$V = \{v_1, v_2, \ldots, v_{n-1}\}$$

is obtained in the following way: v_1 *is the shortest edge;* v_2 *is the shortest edge such that* $v_2 \neq v_1$ *and* $\{v_1, v_2\}$ *does not contain any cycles;* v_3 *is the shortest edge such that* $v_3 \neq v_1$, $v_3 \neq v_2$ *and* $\{v_1, v_2, v_3\}$ *does not contain any cycles, etc....*

Let the edges $v_1, v_2, \ldots, v_k$ be as described above and suppose that no edge can be added to

$$V_k = \{v_1, v_2, \ldots, v_k\}$$

without creating cycles. The characterizing property (4), (p. 130) of trees, shows that the graph (X, V_k) is a tree and property (2) shows that $k = n-1$.

Let (X, V) be a tree for which

$$\sum_{u \in V} l(u)$$

is a minimum; we show that $V = V_{n-1}$.

If

$$V \neq V_{n-1} = \{v_1, \ldots, v_{n-1}\},$$

let v_k be the first of the edges $v_1, v_2, \ldots$ which is not in V.

Then by the characterizing property (4), there is one and only one cycle in $V \bigcup \{v_k\}$; and this cycle contains an edge $u_0 \notin V_{n-1}$. If we write

$$W = (V \bigcup \{v_k\}) - \{u_0\},$$

the graph (X, W) is without cycles and contains $n-1$ edges. Therefore it is a tree (by property (2)).

$V_{k-1} \bigcup \{u_0\}$ is without cycles because it is contained in V, therefore $l(u_0) > l(v_k)$; the tree (X, W), which is obtained from the tree (X, V) by changing u_0 into v_k has therefore a total length less than that of (X, V); but as (X, V) is a tree of shortest length, this gives a contradiction.

Algorithm for determining the shortest spanning tree (Kruskal [28])

Proceed by stages, each time choosing the shortest edge which does not form a cycle with the edges already chosen.

In this way we arrive at a set $V_{n-1} = \{v_1, \ldots, v_{n-1}\}$ of $n-1$ edges, and the graph (X, V_{n-1}) is a tree of minimum total length.

It may be arranged so that all the edges have different lengths; if, for example

$$l(u_1) = l(u_2) = l(u_3),$$

we make the alterations:

$$l(u_1) \to l'(u_1) = l(u_1) + \epsilon,$$

$$l(u_2) \to l'(u_2) = l(u_2) + 2\epsilon,$$

$$l(u_3) \to l'(u_3) = l(u_3) + 3\epsilon,$$

taking ϵ small enough so that there is no inversion in the size of these edges relative to the other edges.

In the same way we can arrange for the graph to be complete, by adding edges w_k as required, of length sufficient to satisfy

$$l(w_k) > \sum_{u \in U} l(u).$$

In the new graph, there is one and only one tree $H = (X, V_{n-1})$ of minimum total length. If the graph is connected V_{n-1} does not contain any edge w_k because w_k is too long.

H is therefore a spanning tree of *G* with minimum total length.

Notice that if all the edges are of different lengths, the tree *H* is unique. Also notice that we could have proceeded in a dual fashion by eliminating step by step the longest edge whose deletion does not disconnect the graph.

Another algorithm for the shortest spanning tree problem (Sollin [39])

When the graph has a large number of edges, the preceding procedure is long and tedious, for it requires many comparisons to find a 'shortest edge' and for every comparison it must be verified that no cycles are being formed. The following algorithm is much quicker. We assume that the graph is connected and to simplify the explanation, we suppose that no two edges are of same length. Draw the shortest spanning tree by stages.

FIRST STAGE. Join every vertex to its nearest neighbour.

This operation in practice requires very few comparisons and can be carried out by different draughtsmen each working on a particular region of the graph.

SECOND STAGE. Let G^1 be the graph obtained from G, by considering every connected component drawn at the first stage as if it were a single vertex but keeping all edges joining these different components (this is 'shrinking' these connected components). Repeat, joining every new vertex to its nearest neighbour.

THIRD STAGE. Shrink the connected components drawn in the second stage, and repeat the same operation, etc.

Stop 'shrinking' when a single point is reached. The edges traced at different stages constitute the shortest spanning tree.

(1) We first show that the edges traced at different stages determine a tree. *The partial graph determined by these edges is connected.* This follows from the fact that *G* was connected; each vertex at each stage has a unique nearest neighbour. *The partial graph determined by these edges contains no cycles.* For if a cycle is drawn at the first stage, for example, orient each edge of this cycle from the vertex to its nearest neighbour. The arcs on the cycle cannot all go in the same direction since if they did the lengths of the arcs would continuously decrease. But if they are not all in the same direction there will be a vertex from which two arcs issue, this contradicts the fact that the nearest neighbour of this vertex is unique.

(2) We now show that this tree is of minimum length. If (X, V) is a shortest spanning tree, *all edges traced in the first stage belong to* V; if not,

let (a,b) be the edge such that b is the nearest vertex to a and which is not in V. This edge with V forms a cycle $abc_1c_2\dots c_ka$, and

$$l(a,b) < l(c_k,a);$$

therefore the tree obtained by replacing (c_k,a) in V by the edge (a,b) is of smaller length than the tree (X,V), which is a contradiction.

In the same way all *edges drawn at the kth stage* are contained in V.

By (1) the number of edges drawn is $n-1 = |V|$, these edges are all the edges of V.

9.4. THE GENERALIZED PROBLEM OF THE SHORTEST PATH

Here we consider the problem of the shortest path but without the restriction assumed in section 9.2 that all $l_i \geqslant 0$. It is obvious that Dantzig's algorithm is inapplicable.

The length of a path μ is a number, positive or negative, defined by

$$\sum_{i\in\mu} l_i,$$

and we look for the coefficients $t(a_j)$ representing 'the minimum time to arrive' at a_j.

Suppose we eliminate, in the graph, each vertex which is not a descendent of $\bar{a}$ (i.e. which cannot be reached by a path coming from $\bar{a}$). Similarly, eliminate each vertex which is not an ascendent of $\bar{b}$ (i.e., which is not the start of a path going to $\bar{b}$). Finally, suppose there is no circuit left whose length is strictly negative, for then the shortest path could be of length $-\infty$.

General algorithm

An easy mechanical procedure for graphs with many vertices can be described as follows:

Write $t(\bar{a}) = 0$ and following paths that issue from $\bar{a}$, determine the coefficients $t(a_i)$, which represent the time taken to arrive at a_i, but not necessarily the minimum time.

The paths followed to determine these coefficients form an arborescence with centre at $\bar{a}$, they are coloured provisionally.

Now decrease the coefficients $t(a_i)$ until they represent the minimum times of arrival. We look for an arc (a_i,a_j), if it exists in the graph, of length $l(a_i,a_j)$ such that

$$t(a_j)-t(a_i) > l(a_i,a_j).$$

If such an arc does exist, replace $t(a_j)$ by

$$t'(a_j) = t(a_i)+l(a_i, a_j) < t(a_j).$$

Then colour the arc (a_i, a_j) and remove the colour from the arc entering into a_j.

The quantity $t(a)$ is decreased by $t(a_j)-t'(a_j)$ whenever a is a descendent vertex of a_j of the arborescence.

Repeat this process until it is not possible to decrease any $t(a_j)$.

Now we show that $t(a_j)$ is the *length of the shortest path from $\bar{a}$ to a_j.*

First let us establish a lemma:

Lemma. *At every stage, the coloured arcs form an arborescence with centre $\bar{a} = a_1$ and for every arc (a_i, a_j) of this arborescence:*

$$t(a_j)-t(a_i) = l(a_i, a_j).$$

At the outset, the proposition is true; assume that it is true at the kth stage and we shall show that the lemma holds also at the $(k+1)$th stage. For, there exists a coloured arc and one only, entering into a_j (for all $j \neq 1$). Furthermore, suppose while colouring the arc (a_i, a_j) we form a coloured cycle

$$\mu = [a_j, c_1, c_2, \ldots, c_k, a_i, a_j].$$

This cycle is necessarily a circuit (for otherwise, it would have two coloured arcs entering the same vertex); and

$$\sum_{i\in\mu} l_i = [t(c_1)-t(a_j)]+[t(c_2)-t(c_1)]+\ldots+[t(a_i)-t(c_k)]+l(a_i, a_j)$$

$$= t(a_i)-t(a_j)+l(a_i, a_j) < 0.$$

This is impossible, for we have supposed that there are no circuits of negative length.

Therefore the coloured partial graph at the $(k+1)$th stage is without cycles; furthermore, only one arc enters into a_j for $j \neq 1$, and no arc enters into a_1. The coloured graph is therefore an arborescence: (Theorem 10, Chapter 7, property (7)).

PROOF OF THE GENERAL ALGORITHM. The coloured arcs form an arborescence with centre $\bar{a}$. There exists only one coloured path from $\bar{a}$ to $\bar{b}$, the length of which, from the lemma, is equal to $t(\bar{b})$. We shall show that this is *a path of minimum length from $\bar{a}$ to $\bar{b}$.*

Let

$$\mu = [\bar{a}, a_2, \ldots, a_{k-1}, \bar{b}]$$

be any path of the graph G between $\bar{a}$ and $\bar{b}$ and $l(\boldsymbol{\mu})$ its length; we have

$$l(\bar{a}, a_2) \geqslant t(a_2) - 0,$$

$$l(a_3, a_2) \geqslant t(a_3) - t(a_2),$$

$$\dots\dots\dots\dots$$

$$l(a_{k-1}, \bar{b}) \geqslant t(\bar{b}) - t(a_{k-1}).$$

Adding term by term, we obtain

$$l(\boldsymbol{\mu}) \geqslant t(\bar{b}).$$

The coloured path is of length $t(\bar{b})$. Therefore it is of minimum length.

The reader may use the graph of Figure 9.7 as an exercise.†

9.5. THE PROBLEM OF MAXIMUM POTENTIAL DIFFERENCE

Consider a graph G with vertices $a_1, a_2, \ldots, a_n, \bar{a}, \bar{b}$, and arcs $1, 2, \ldots, m$. The arc $(\bar{b}, \bar{a})$ which plays a special role here will be denoted by $i = 1$. For every $i \neq 1$, numbers k_i and l_i are given with $k_i \leqslant l_i$. The problem is the following:

Find in G a potential difference

$$\boldsymbol{\theta} = (\theta_1, \theta_2, \ldots, \theta_m)$$

such that

(1) $$k_i \leqslant \theta_i \leqslant l_i \quad (i \neq 1)$$

(2) θ_1 *is maximized.*

We can suppose that there is only one arc joining two vertices in the same direction, for if two arcs i and j exist, they may be replaced by a single arc with the interval

$$[k_i, l_i] \cap [k_j, l_j].$$

We can also suppose that two vertices are joined only in one direction, for if two arcs i and j are joined in both directions, they may be replaced by a single arc oriented in the same direction as i with the interval

$$[k_i, l_i] \cap [-l_j, -k_j].$$

The problem of maximum potential difference appears in various forms of scheduling problems in operational research.

† Here the graph does not contain circuits of strictly negative length, but if, because of errors, or contradictory requirements, such parasitic circuits were to exist, the algorithm could be followed indefinitely. B. Roy has given algorithms which are less general, but which do not present this difficulty ([38] p. 68 and 100).

EXAMPLE [38]. The construction of a large factory or a liner, calls for a number of different operations which will be denoted by $a_1, a_2, \ldots, a_n$. To begin a particular operation a_j, it is often necessary that operation a_i should have reached a certain stage; let k_{ij} be the time to be allotted to operation a_i before work on operation a_j can be begun.

On the other hand, an operation a_i cannot be started before a certain fixed time k'_i and it has to be finished in a given time k''_i. With these constraints, let us determine when each operation is to start so that the construction will be finished in the minimum possible time.

Consider a graph G where the operations a_i are represented by the vertices, and where (a_i, a_j) is an arc if operation a_j necessarily follows operation a_i. We add a 'source' $\bar{a}$ and draw the arcs $(\bar{a}, a_i)$ corresponding to different operations a_i which cannot be started before some fixed time. Add finally a 'sink' $\bar{b}$ and draw the arcs $(a_i, \bar{b})$ for $i = 1, 2, \ldots, n$.

Denote by $t(a_i)$, the moment when operation $\bar{a}_i$ is started and suppose

$$t(\bar{a}) = 0$$
$$t(\bar{b}) = \max_i \{t(a_i) + k''_i\}.$$

Then

$$\begin{aligned} t(a_i) &= t(a_i) - t(\bar{a}) \geqslant k'_i && \text{if } (\bar{a}, a_i) \in U, \\ t(a_j) - t(a_i) &\geqslant k_{ij} && \text{if } (a_i, a_j) \in U, \\ t(\bar{b}) - t(a_i) &\geqslant k''_i && \text{for } (a_i, \bar{b}) \in U; \end{aligned}$$

for $(a, b) \in U$, the quantities

$$\theta(a, b) = t(b) - t(a)$$

define a potential difference and we want to minimize $t(\bar{b})$, that is, maximize the potential difference $t(\bar{a}) - t(\bar{b})$ of the arc $(\bar{b}, \bar{a})$. We find the problem of maximum potential difference again, with

$$l_2 = l_3 = \ldots = l_m = +\infty.$$

B. Roy ([38]) studied this problem, as well as various questions of optimality and periodicity which can occur in practice.

Algorithm

An easy way to solve this problem is to reduce it to the case where all coefficients k_i are equal to $-\infty$; if the potential difference θ_i satisfies $k_i \leqslant \theta_i \leqslant l_i$ and if $k_i \neq -\infty$, it is sufficient to replace the arc i by two arcs of opposite orientations, i and j, with the constraints

$$\theta_i \leqslant l_i$$
$$\theta_j = -\theta_i \leqslant k_i = l_j.$$

If we write

$$\theta(a, b) = t(b) - t(a),$$

we recognize the problem of finding coefficients $t(a)$ such that

$$\begin{cases} t(b) - t(a) \leqslant l(a, b) \\ t(\bar{a}) = 0 \\ t(\bar{b}) \text{ is minimized.} \end{cases}$$

If $l(a, b)$ is interpreted as the length of the arc (a, b) and $t(a)$ as the minimum time to arrive at a point a, we have the generalized problem of the shortest path, which we solve as in Section 9.4.

9.6. THE PROBLEM OF MAXIMUM FLOW

A *transportation network* is here defined as a graph G with vertices $a_1, a_2, \ldots, a_n, \bar{a}, \bar{b}$ and arcs $1, 2, \ldots, m$ such that:

1. $(\bar{b}, \bar{a})$ is an arc denoted by $i = 1$, this arc, which plays an important role is called the *return arc*.
2. The vertex $\bar{b}$, called the *sink*, has only the arc 1 in $\boldsymbol{\omega}^+(\bar{b})$; the arcs in $\boldsymbol{\omega}^-(\bar{b})$ are called the *sink arcs*.
3. The vertex $\bar{a}$, called the *source*, has only the arc 1 in $\boldsymbol{\omega}^-(\bar{a})$; the arcs in $\boldsymbol{\omega}^+(\bar{a})$ are called the *source arcs*.
4. To every arc $i \neq 1$, there is associated a number $c_i \geqslant 0$ called the *capacity* of the arc i.

The problem of maximum flow is the following: *Find in the transportation network G, a flow*

$$\boldsymbol{\varphi} = (\varphi_1, \varphi_2, \ldots, \varphi_m),$$

such that

$$(1) \qquad 0 \leqslant \varphi_i \leqslant c_i \quad (i \neq 1)$$

$$(2) \qquad \varphi_1 \textit{ is maximized.}$$

Such a flow is often called the maximum flow and φ is its *value*.

Notice that we can assume that no two arcs i and j join two vertices in the same direction, for we would then replace them by a single arc of capacity $c_i + c_j$. To simplify the explanation suppose the domain of values **S** is the set of integers: in what follows, φ_i and c_i are non-negative integers.

EXAMPLE 1. *The end-of-term dance.* In an American co-educational college there are as many boys as girls; every girl has m boy-friends and every boy has m girl-friends. Is it possible at the same time for each girl to dance with one of her boy-friends?

Transportation network theory shows that the answer is 'yes'. To find a solution of this problem draw a transportation network in which the vertices $a_1, a_2, \ldots, a_n$ represent the girls, the vertices $a'_1, a'_2, \ldots, a'_n$ represent the boys, and in which is drawn an arc (a_i, a'_j) of capacity 1 whenever a'_j is a boy-friend of the girl a_i; join the source $\bar{a}$ to every vertex a_i by an arc of capacity $c(\bar{a}, a_i) = 1$ and join every vertex a'_j to the sink $\bar{b}$ by an arc of capacity $c(a'_j, \bar{b}) = 1$.

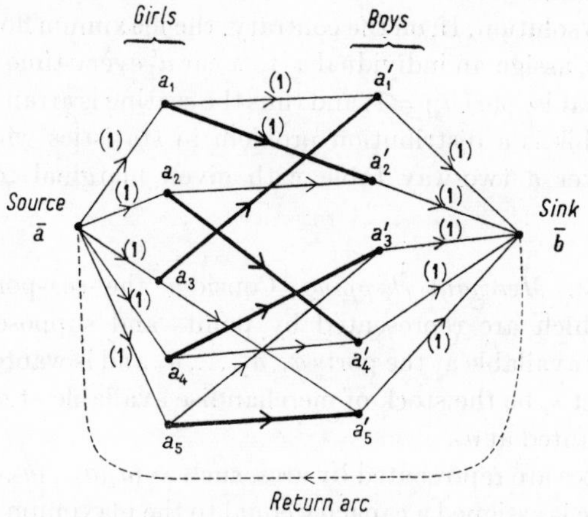

FIG. 9.8. The thick lines represent the saturated intermediate arcs in the problem of college girls and boys

A maximum flow of integral values will saturate a certain number of arcs (a_i, a'_j), and each time this happens girl a_i is to dance with boy a'_j. Conversely to every assignment of the maximum number of girls there corresponds a maximum flow.

EXAMPLE 2. *The family excursion.* A certain number of families, denoted by $a_1, a_2, \ldots, a_p$ want to go for an outing in cars $a'_1, \ldots, a'_q$. Knowing the number, s_i, in the family a_i and d_j the number of seats in car a'_j, and supposing, naturally, that

$$\sum_{j=1}^{q} d_j \geqslant \sum_{i=1}^{p} s_i,$$

is it possible to arrange the seating so that no two members of the same family are in the same car?

We draw the graph with the vertices $a_1, a_2, \ldots, a_p, a'_1, \ldots, a'_q$, to which we add the source $\bar{a}$ and the sink $\bar{b}$.

For each a_i and a'_j, we draw the arc (a_i, a'_j) to which is assigned the capacity

$$c(a_i, a'_j) = 1.$$

For each $i \leqslant p$, draw the arc, $(\bar{a}, a_i)$ to which is assigned the capacity

$$c(\bar{a}, a_i) = s_i;$$

for each $j \leqslant q$, draw the arc $(a'_j, \bar{b})$ to which is assigned the capacity

$$c(a'_j, \bar{b}) = d_j.$$

Let $\boldsymbol{\varphi}$ be a maximum flow. If the source arcs are not saturated then the problem has no solution. If, on the contrary, the maximum flow $\boldsymbol{\varphi}$ saturates the source arcs, assign an individual a_i to a car a'_j every time the arc (a_i, a'_j) is saturated (that is, $\varphi(a_i, a'_j) = 1$) and thus the seating is arranged as desired.

Note that this is a distribution problem in statistics which has to be solved whenever a two-way table with given marginal totals is to be constructed.

EXAMPLE 3. *Merchant shipping.* Consider the sea-ports $a_1, a_2, \ldots, a'_{k+1}, \ldots, a'_n$ which are represented by points and suppose that certain merchandise is available at the ports $a_1, a_2, \ldots, a_k$ and is wanted at the ports $a'_{k+1}, \ldots, a'_n$. Let s_i be the stock of merchandise available at a_i and let d_j be the amount wanted at a'_j.

The sea routes are represented by arcs, such as (a_i, a_k), (a_i, a'_j), (a'_j, a'_l) and to each of these is assigned a capacity equal to the maximum total quantity of merchandise which can be transported on that route. Is it possible to satisfy all the demands? How are the journeys to be organized? Draw a source $\bar{a}$, joined to the ports a_i with $i \leqslant k$, by arcs of capacity

$$c(\bar{a}, a_i) = s_i;$$

then draw the sink $\bar{b}$ joined to the ports a'_j by arcs of capacity

$$c(a'_j, \bar{b}) = d_j.$$

If $\boldsymbol{\varphi}$ is a maximum flow, it will show, for every arc, the quantity of merchandise to be exported so as best to satisfy the demand.

EXAMPLE 4. *The Battle of the Marne.* From the different towns $a_1, a_2, \ldots, a_n$, buses leave to go to a single destination b. If there is a direct road from town a_i to town a_j, we are given the number, c_{ij}, of buses which can leave a_i for a_j in a unit of time, and the time, t_{ij}, required for the journey. Given the number, s_i, of vehicles available at a_i at the start, and the number c_i of vehicles that can be parked at a_i, we want to organize the traffic routes so that in a given interval of time T, the number of vehicles arriving at b will be as large as possible. This type of problem has been studied by R. Fulkerson under the name of 'dynamic flow problems'. This can be reduced to a single maximum flow problem, by drawing in space-time the vertices $a_i(t)$, where $i = 1, 2, \ldots, n$ and $t = 0, 1, \ldots, T$. Join the vertex $a_i(t)$ to the vertex $a_i(t+1)$ by an arc of capacity c_i; if there is a route from a_i to a_j, draw the arc from $a_i(t)$ to $a_j(t+t_{ij})$ with capacity c_{ij}

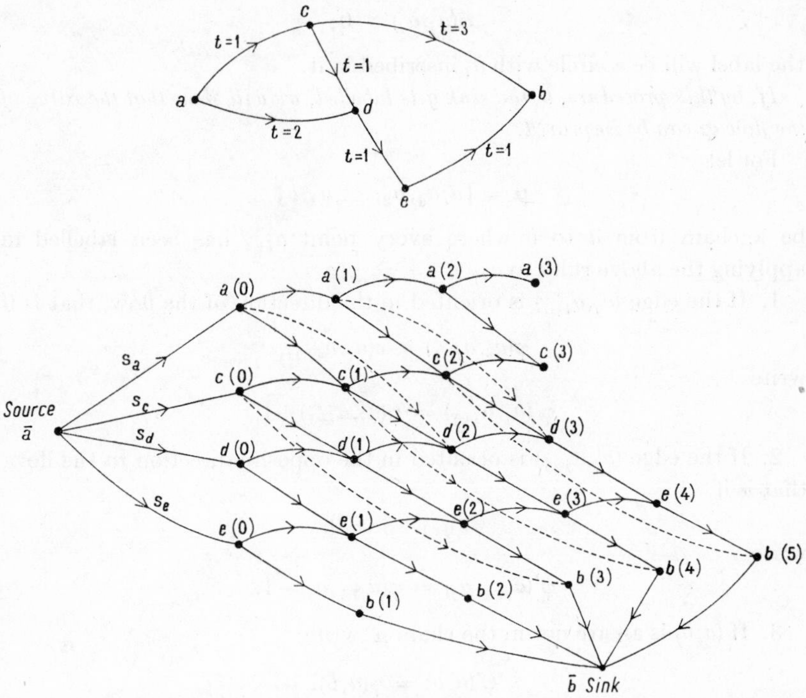

FIG. 9.9

and add the source $\bar{a}$, and the sink $\bar{b}$; in arcs $(\bar{a}, a_i(0))$ the capacity is s_i and in arcs $(b(t), \bar{b})$ the capacity is ∞. The maximum flow determines the optimum traffic routes.

General algorithm (Ford and Fulkerson)

Suppose we want a maximum flow with integer values. Start with any flow $\boldsymbol{\varphi}$, such that $0 \leqslant \varphi_i \leqslant c_i$ for $i \neq 1$, and improve its value by an iterative procedure.

Label the vertices of the graph, step by step, using the following rules.

1. Label the vertex $\bar{a}$.

2. If a_i is a labelled vertex and a_j is not labelled and if (a_i, a_j) is an arc, label the vertex a_j whenever

$$\varphi(a_i, a_j) < c(a_i, a_j);$$

the label for the vertex a_j may be, for example, a circle with a_i inside it.

3. If a_i is a labelled vertex and a_j is not yet labelled and if (a_j, a_i) is an arc, we then label the vertex a_j whenever

$$\varphi(a_j, a_i) > 0;$$

the label will be a circle with a_i inscribed in it.

If, by this procedure, $\bar{b}$, the sink gets labelled, we will show that the value of the flow $\boldsymbol{\varphi}$ can be improved.

For let

$$\boldsymbol{\mu} = [\bar{a}, a_1, a_2, \ldots, a_k, \bar{b}]$$

be a chain from $\bar{a}$ to $\bar{b}$ where every point a_{i+1} has been labelled in applying the above rules to a_i.

1. If the edge (a_i, a_{i+1}) is oriented in the direction of the flow, that is if

$$\varphi(a_i, a_{i+1}) < c(a_i, a_{i+1}),$$

write

$$\varphi'(a_i, a_{i+1}) = \varphi(a_i, a_{i+1}) + 1.$$

2. If the edge (a_j, a_{j+1}) is oriented in the opposite direction to the flow, that is if

$$\varphi(a_{j+1}, a_j) > 0,$$

write

$$\varphi'(a_{j+1}, a_j) = \varphi(a_{j+1}, a_j) - 1.$$

3. If (a,b) is an arc not in the chain μ, write

$$\varphi'(a,b) = \varphi(a,b).$$

It is obvious that φ' is also a flow and that

$$\varphi_1' = \varphi_1 + 1.$$

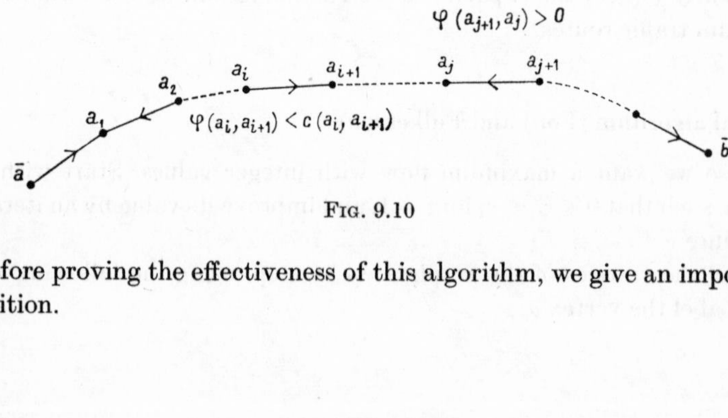

FIG. 9.10

Before proving the effectiveness of this algorithm, we give an important definition.

If, in the transport network G, A is a set of vertices such that $\bar{a} \notin A$, $\bar{b} \in A$, then the set of arcs $\boldsymbol{\omega}^-(A)$ is said to be a *cut*. The *capacity* of the cut is

$$c_A = \sum_{i \in \omega^-(A)} c_i.$$

Lemma 1. *If a set A defines a cut and if* $\boldsymbol{\varphi}$ *is a flow compatible with the capacities then*

$$\varphi_1 \leqslant c_A.$$

If a set A such that $\bar{a} \notin A$ *and* $\bar{b} \in A$ *and a flow* $\boldsymbol{\varphi}$ *satisfies* $\varphi_i = c_A$, *then* $\boldsymbol{\varphi}$ *is a maximum flow and A defines a cut of minimum capacity.*

The formula is obvious, for:

$$\varphi_1 \leqslant \sum_{i \in \omega^+(A)} \varphi_i = \sum_{i \in \omega^-(A)} \varphi_i \leqslant \sum_{i \in \omega^-(A)} c_i = c_A.$$

If, with the given procedure, $\bar{b}$ the sink does not get labelled, we will show that the flow $\boldsymbol{\varphi}$ is a maximum.

Let A be the set of vertices which have not been labelled in the above procedure; $\bar{a} \notin A$, $\bar{b} \in A$, and we can write

$$\varphi_1 = \sum_{i \in \omega^-(A)} \varphi_i - \sum_{\substack{i \neq 1 \\ i \in \omega^+(A)}} \varphi_i = \sum_{i \in \omega^-(A)} c_i - 0 = c_A.$$

Therefore by Lemma 1, the flow $\boldsymbol{\varphi}$ is a maximum.

NOTE 1. We have thus proved that in a graph G

$$\max \varphi_1 = \min c_A.$$

Hence we obtain the result:

Theorem (Ford and Fulkerson). *In a transportation network with capacities* c_i *the maximum value of a flow is equal to the minimum capacity of a cut.*

NOTE 2. With the above algorithm, we start with any flow $\boldsymbol{\varphi}$, compatible with the capacities, for example $\boldsymbol{\varphi} = \mathbf{0}$. Nevertheless the computations can be considerably shortened if the flow $\boldsymbol{\varphi}$, has a high value to begin with. An arc i is said to be *saturated* if $\varphi_i = c_i$ and a flow $\boldsymbol{\varphi}$ is said to be *complete* if every path from $\bar{a}$ to $\bar{b}$ contains at least one saturated arc. It is easy enough to construct a complete flow. Starting with any flow $\boldsymbol{\varphi}$, colour the unsaturated arcs, and in the partial graph determined by the coloured arcs find a path $\boldsymbol{\mu}$ from $\bar{a}$ to $\bar{b}$; Trémaux's algorithm (Section 9.1), for instance, may be used to find $\boldsymbol{\mu}$.

Put

$$\varphi_i' = \varphi_i + 1 \quad \text{if } i \in \boldsymbol{\mu} \text{ or } i = 1,$$

$$\varphi_i' = \varphi_i \quad \text{if } i \notin \boldsymbol{\mu} \text{ and } i \neq 1.$$

The flow $\boldsymbol{\varphi}'$ has a greater value than that of the flow $\boldsymbol{\varphi}$ and we can repeat the procedure till the flow is complete.

EXAMPLE. Consider the transportation network of Figure 9.11.

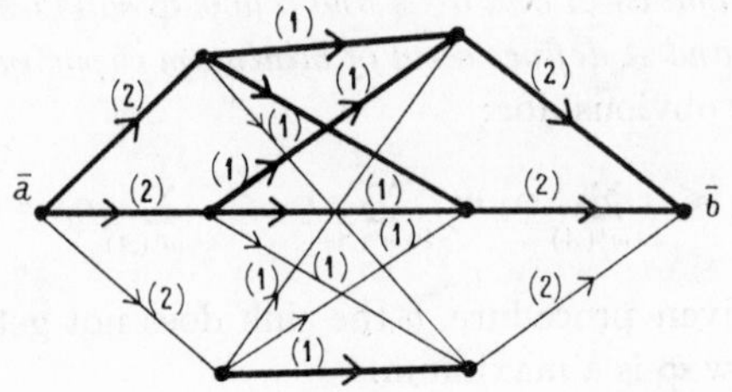

FIG. 9.11

The arc of return $(\bar{b}, \bar{a})$ is omitted to simplify the figure. The capacities are 2 for the source and sink arcs, and 1 for the intermediary arcs. A complete flow is easily obtained and the saturated arcs of the flow are indicated in the figure by thick lines. The value of the flow is $\varphi_1 = 5$. However this flow is not a maximum and using the Ford and Fulkerson procedure one finds that the value of the maximum flow is 6.

Note that for a network of this type the maximum flow may be obtained directly by the following rule: increase the value of the flow step by step by directing one unit of flow at a time to the vertex for which the current value of

$$\sum_{u \in U_x^+} (c(u) - \varphi(u))$$

is greatest. As soon as the flow is complete, the maximum is reached. But this phenomenon is not true in general, it only holds for the particular type of network being considered here.

Algorithm for a planar graph

If the graph G is planar, proceed as follows.

1. Draw the arc $(\bar{b}, \bar{a})$ horizontally, the vertex $\bar{a}$ is on the left, and $\bar{b}$ on the right. Draw the graph above the arc $(\bar{b}, \bar{a})$ in such a way that no two arcs cut one another except at their vertices. On this planar topological graph, an upper path from $\bar{a}$ to $\bar{b}$ can be determined by always taking an

arc to the extreme left (except that we must retrace our steps if we get to a dead-end).

2. Considering the upper path $\boldsymbol{\mu}^1$ directed from $\bar{a}$ to $\bar{b}$, subtract from the capacities of all its arcs the quantity

$$\epsilon_1 = \min_{i \in \mu^1} c_i$$

and delete the arcs of zero capacity.

3. With this new network determine, in the same way, an upper path $\boldsymbol{\mu}^2$ and subtract from the capacities of its arcs the quantity

$$\epsilon_2 = \min_{i \in \mu^2} c_i.$$

4. Repeat this procedure till there is no path from $\bar{a}$ to $\bar{b}$. The required flow is obtained by directing along each path $\boldsymbol{\mu}^k$ an amount equal to ϵ_k.

To show that this algorithm is effective we establish a lemma.

Lemma 2. *Let A be a set of vertices such that $\bar{a} \notin A$, $\bar{b} \in A$ and $\boldsymbol{\omega}^-(A)$ is a minimum cut; the upper path $\boldsymbol{\mu}^1$ meets the cut $\boldsymbol{\omega}^-(A)$ exactly once.*

It is clear that the path $\boldsymbol{\mu}^1$ meets the cut $\boldsymbol{\omega}^-(A)$ at least once. Suppose it meets $\boldsymbol{\omega}^-(A)$ in two arcs, for example i and j (successively in that order).

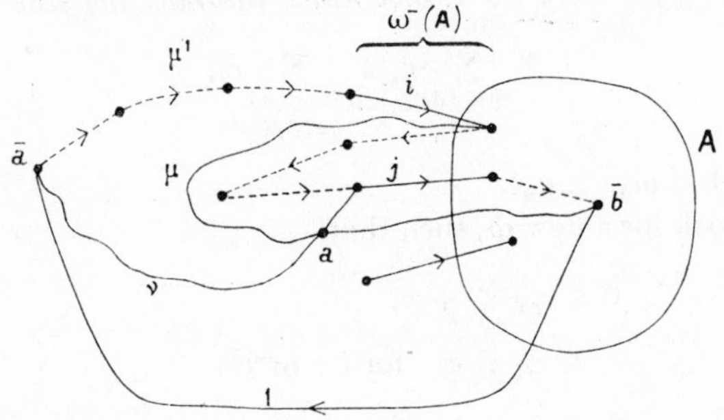

Fig. 9.12

We will show that there is a path $\boldsymbol{\mu}$ from $\bar{a}$ to $\bar{b}$ which meets $\boldsymbol{\omega}^-(A)$ only in i. Colour the arc i red, the other arcs of $\boldsymbol{\omega}^-(A)$ green and all other arcs black. Since $\boldsymbol{\omega}^-(A)$ is a minimum cut, there is no green and black coboundary through arc 1, all of whose black arcs are oriented in the same direction. Therefore, from the Lemma on coloured arcs, there is a red and black cycle through 1, all of whose black arcs are oriented in the same direction. It may be easily verified that this cycle is a circuit through i, from which we obtain the required path $\boldsymbol{\mu}$.

Similarly there exists a path $\boldsymbol{\nu}$ from $\bar{a}$ to $\bar{b}$ which meets $\boldsymbol{\omega}^-(A)$ only in j.

As $\boldsymbol{\mu}^1$ is the upper path, the second part of $\boldsymbol{\mu}$ (after the arc i) and the first part of $\boldsymbol{\nu}$ (before the arc j) meet at a common vertex a, which is impossible as it would mean $a \in A$, and $a \notin A$. This suffices to prove the lemma.

We now show that *the flow* $\boldsymbol{\varphi}$ *obtained by the above algorithm is maximal.* Let A_0 be the set of vertices that cannot be reached by any path from $\bar{a}$ when the above procedure has been carried out as long as possible.

$$\bar{a} \notin A_0, \quad \bar{b} \in A_0,$$

$\boldsymbol{\omega}^-(A_0)$ is therefore a cut; let $\boldsymbol{\omega}^-(A)$ be a minimum cut contained in $\boldsymbol{\omega}^-(A_0)$. By Lemma 2, the procedure at the kth stage decreases the capacity of the cut $\boldsymbol{\omega}^-(A)$ by exactly ϵ_k and we end with a zero capacity. Therefore

$$\varphi_1 = \sum_k \epsilon_k = \sum_{i \in \omega^-(A)} c_i = c_A.$$

From Lemma 1, this shows that $\boldsymbol{\varphi}$ is a maximum flow.

There are other results yet to be described. The general existence theorem for a flow (Chapter 8, Section 8.3) has a number of corollaries appropriate to particular types of transportation networks.

Theorem (Gale [19]). *Let G be a transportation network with capacities $c_i \geqslant 0$. A necessary and sufficient condition for the existence of a flow* $\boldsymbol{\varphi}$ *such that $0 \leqslant \varphi_i \leqslant c_i$, for every $i \neq 1$, and which saturates the sink arcs is that*

$$\sum_{i \in \omega^-(A)} c_i \geqslant \sum_{\substack{i \in \omega^+(A) \\ i \in \omega^-(\bar{b})}} c_i,$$

for every set $A \subset \{a_1, \ldots, a_n\}$.

First, we look for a flow $\boldsymbol{\varphi}$, such that

$$0 \leqslant \varphi_1 \leqslant +\infty,$$

$$c_i \leqslant \varphi_i \leqslant c_i \quad \text{for } i \in \boldsymbol{\omega}^-(\bar{b})$$

$$0 \leqslant \varphi_i \leqslant c_i \quad \text{for } i \neq 1, i \notin \boldsymbol{\omega}^-(b).$$

From Hoffman's theorem (page 158), a necessary and sufficient condition for its existence is that for every set

$$A \subset \{a_1, a_2, \ldots, a_n, \bar{a}, \bar{b}\}$$

we have

$$\sum_{i \in \omega(A)} c_i \geqslant \sum_{i \in \omega^+(A)} b_i.$$

If $\bar{a} \in A$, $\bar{b} \notin A$, then this condition is always satisfied (for the expression on the left-hand side is equal to $+\infty$). If $\bar{b} \in A$, the condition is always satisfied (for the expression on the right-hand side is equal to 0).

If $\bar{a} \notin A$, $\bar{b} \notin A$, the condition can be written as

$$\sum_{i \in \omega^-(A)} c_i \geqslant \sum_{i \in \omega^+(A)} b_i = \sum_{\substack{i \in \omega^+(A) \\ i \in \omega^-(\bar{b})}} c_i + 0.$$

Corollary. *In a transportation network G, denote by Z the set of vertices* a_i *joined to the sink* $\bar{b}$. *For every* $z \in Z$, *the demand* $d(z)$ *is defined by*

$$d(z) = c(z, \bar{b});$$

for all $A \subset Z$, *the demand* $d(A)$ *is defined as*

$$d(A) = \sum_{z \in A} d(z).$$

For $A \subset Z$, $F(A)$ *denotes the total quantity of flow that can enter into A. The necessary and sufficient condition for the existence of a flow in G which saturates the sink arcs is that*

$$F(A) \geqslant d(A)$$

for every set $A \subset Z$.

(This is deduced at once from Gale's theorem and Ford and Fulkerson's theorem.)

This corollary has numerous applications in algebra, in the theory of graphs, and in many entertaining combinatorial problems. Some of these are published in [2], and the reader can find others as exercises at the end of this book.

9.7. THE GENERALIZED PROBLEM OF MAXIMUM FLOW

Consider a graph G, in which the vertices are $a_1, a_2, \ldots, a_n, \bar{a}, \bar{b}$ and the arcs are $1, 2, \ldots, m$; the arc $1 = (\bar{b}, \bar{a})$ is called the *arc of return* as before, and for every arc $i \neq 1$ there are given two numbers b_i and c_i with $-\infty \leqslant b_i \leqslant c_i \leqslant +\infty$.

We are now concerned with the following problem: *Find in the graph G, a flow*

$$\boldsymbol{\varphi} = (\varphi_1, \varphi_2, \ldots, \varphi_m)$$

such that

(1) $$b_i \leqslant \varphi_i \leqslant c_i,$$

(2) φ_1 *is maximized.*

The graph G with the intervals $[b_i, c_i]$ is still called a *transportation network*. Notice that it can always be assumed that there are no multiple edges; if two arcs i and j join the same vertices in the same direction, replace them by a single arc with the interval $[b_i+b_j, c_i+c_j]$; if two arcs i and j

join the same vertices in opposite directions, replace them by a single arc in the direction of i and with the interval $[b_i - c_j, c_i - b_j]$.

EXAMPLE. *The problem of representatives.* In a community X of individuals there are a certain number of clubs $C_1, C_2, \ldots, C_q$ (which are not necessarily disjoint subsets of X) and a certain number of political parties $P_1, P_2, \ldots, P_r$ (which are disjoint subsets of X). Every club choses from its members a representative with special powers, and an individual can represent only one club (even if he belongs to several). The problem is to choose a system of distinct representatives

$$E = \{e_1, e_2, \ldots, e_q\},$$

so that the number of representatives belonging to each party P_j, satisfies

$$b_j \leqslant |E \cap P_j| \leqslant c_j.$$

We reduce this problem to a flow problem by constructing a graph with the vertices $a_1, a_2, \ldots, a_n$ representing the individuals, with the vertices $C_1, C_2, \ldots, C_q$ representing the clubs, $P_1, P_2, \ldots, P_r$ representing the political parties and finally with a source $\bar{a}$ and a sink $\bar{b}$.

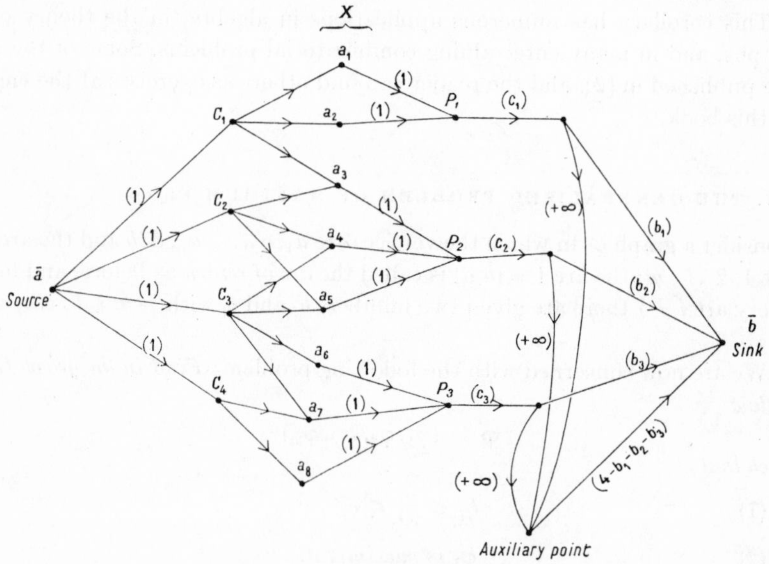

FIG. 9.13

Draw the arcs $(\bar{a}, C_i)$ with the interval $[1, 1]$; the arcs (C_i, a_j) whenever a_j belongs to the club C_i; the arcs (a_j, P_i) if the individual a_j belongs to the political party P_i; and the arcs $(P_i, \bar{b})$ with an interval $[b_i, c_i]$.

If a compatible flow exists, it will define a system of distinct representatives E, and vice versa.

The solution to this problem is found very quickly by applying Ford and Fulkerson's algorithm to the classical transportation network with the intervals $[0, c_i]$; more precisely, every solution is given by the following transportation network in Fig. 9.13.

It is left to the reader to verify that every maximum flow, if it saturates the sink arcs, gives a system of distinct representatives.

Algorithm to obtain a flow compatible with given intervals.

We propose, here, to construct a flow $\boldsymbol{\varphi}$ in the transportation network G, such that

$$b_i \leqslant \varphi_i \leqslant c_i \quad (i = 2, 3, \ldots, m).$$

We reduce this to a classical maximum flow problem in a graph G' with the intervals $[0, c_i']$. The graph G' is formed by the vertices and the arcs of G and by putting:

$$c_1' = +\infty$$

$$c_i' = c_i - b_i \quad \text{if } i = 2, 3, \ldots, m.$$

Add a source $\bar{a}$ and a sink $\bar{\bar{b}}$, which are joined to the vertices of G as follows:

If the arc $i = (a_k, a_l)$ is such that $b_i \geqslant 0$, draw an arc $(a_k, \bar{\bar{b}})$ of capacity

$$c'(a_k, \bar{\bar{b}}) = b_i$$

and an arc $(\bar{a}, a_l)$ of capacity

$$c'(\bar{\bar{a}}, a_l) = b_i.$$

If the arc $j = (a_p, a_q)$ is such that $b_j < 0$, draw an arc $(\bar{\bar{a}}, a_p)$ of capacity

$$c'(\bar{\bar{a}}, a_p) = -b_j$$

and an arc $(a_q, \bar{b})$ of capacity

$$c'(a_q, \bar{\bar{b}}) = -b_j.$$

We will show that with a flow $\boldsymbol{\varphi}'$ which saturates the sink arcs in G', there can be associated a compatible flow $\boldsymbol{\varphi}$ in G. Write

$$\varphi_i = \varphi_i' + b_i \quad (i = 2, 3, \ldots, m)$$

$$\varphi_1 = \varphi_1'.$$

Since

$$0 \leqslant \varphi_i' \leqslant c_i - b_i \quad (i = 2, 3, \ldots, m),$$

we have

$$b_i \leqslant \varphi_i \leqslant c_i \quad (i = 2, 3, \ldots, m).$$

Furthermore, since $\boldsymbol{\varphi}'$ is a flow in G', we may write for every coboundary $\boldsymbol{\omega}(a)$ in G,

$$\sum_{i \in \omega^+(a)} \varphi_i - \sum_{i \in \omega^-(a)} \varphi_i =$$

$$\sum_{\substack{i \in \omega^+(a)\\ b_i \geqslant 0}} (\varphi_i' + b_i) + \sum_{\substack{j \in \omega^+(a)\\ b_j < 0}} (\varphi_j' + b_j) - \sum_{\substack{i \in \omega^-(a)\\ b_i \geqslant 0}} (\varphi_i' + b_i) - \sum_{\substack{j \in \omega^-(a)\\ b_j < 0}} (\varphi_j' + b_j) = 0.$$

Therefore $\boldsymbol{\varphi}$ is a flow with the required properties.

Conversely, we see in the same way that every compatible flow $\boldsymbol{\varphi}$ in G is associated with a flow $\boldsymbol{\varphi}'$ in G' which saturates the sink arcs in G. The

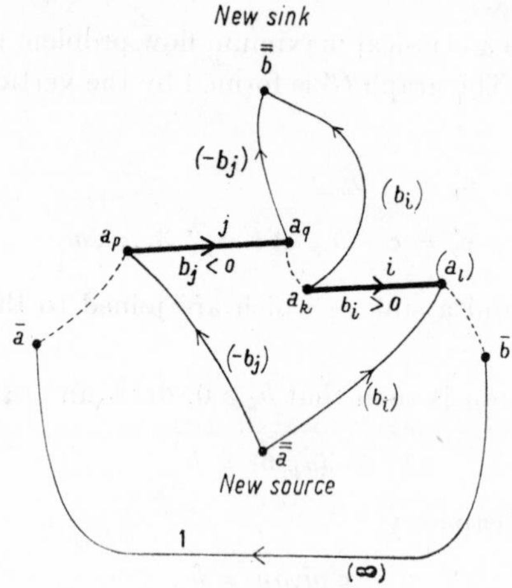

FIG. 9.14

problem with respect to G may thus be solved by applying the Ford and Fulkerson algorithm in the transportation network G'.

Algorithm for obtaining a maximum flow

Let G be a transportation network and construct, as before, a flow $\boldsymbol{\varphi}$ such that

$$b_i \leqslant \varphi_i \leqslant c_i \quad (i = 2, 3, \ldots, m).$$

Increase its value step by step until the flow is a maximum. The procedure is exactly the same as that of Ford and Fulkerson.

1. Label the source $\bar{a}$.

2. If a_j is a labelled vertex and a_k is not labelled, and if (a_j, a_k) is an arc, label the vertex a_k whenever

$$\varphi(a_j, a_k) < c(a_j, a_k).$$

3. If a_j is a labelled vertex and a_k is not labelled, and if (a_k, a_j) is an arc, then label the vertex a_k whenever

$$\varphi(a_k, a_j) > b(a_k, a_j).$$

If, following this procedure, the sink $\bar{b}$ is labelled, the flow can be increased as in Ford and Fulkerson's algorithm. If, with the flow $\boldsymbol{\varphi}$, $\bar{b}$ is not labelled, then let A be the set of vertices which cannot be labelled. Then $\bar{a} \notin A$, $\bar{b} \in A$, and the value of the flow $\boldsymbol{\varphi}$ is

$$\varphi_1 = \sum_{i \in \omega^-(A)} \varphi_i - \sum_{\substack{i \in \omega^+(A) \\ i \neq 1}} \varphi_i = \sum_{i \in \omega^-(A)} c_i - \sum_{\substack{i \in \omega^+(A) \\ i \neq 1}} b_i.$$

As the value of the flow never exceeds

$$\sum_{i \in \omega^-(A)} c_i - \sum_{\substack{i \in \omega^+(A) \\ i \neq 1}} b_i,$$

the flow $\boldsymbol{\varphi}$ must be a maximum.

From this we deduce the following result.

Proposition. *If in a transportation network, there is a flow* $\boldsymbol{\varphi}$ *with* $b_i \leqslant \varphi_i \leqslant c_i$ *for every* $i \neq 1$, *the value of such a flow is*

$$\varphi_1 = \min_{\substack{\bar{a} \notin A \\ \bar{b} \in A}} \left\{ \sum_{i \in \omega^-(A)} c_i - \sum_{\substack{i \in \omega^+(A) \\ i \neq 1}} b_i \right\}.$$

9.8. THE TRANSHIPMENT PROBLEM

Consider a transportation network G, with vertices $a_1, a_2, \ldots, a_n, \bar{a}, \bar{b}$, and arcs $1, 2, \ldots, m$; $(\bar{b}, \bar{a})$ is the arc of return, denoted by $i = 1$; and there is no arc $i \neq 1$ incident to $\bar{a}$, and no arc $i \neq 1$ incident from $\bar{b}$.

We put

$$P = \{j \,|\, (\bar{a}, a_j) \quad \text{is an arc}\},$$

$$Q = \{j \,|\, (a_j, \bar{b}) \quad \text{is an arc}\},$$

and

$$c(\bar{a}, a_p) = c_p \quad \text{for } p \in P$$

$$c(\bar{b}, a_q) = c'_q \quad \text{for } q \in Q.$$

Suppose that for every other arc $i \neq 1$, the capacity is $c_i = +\infty$.

Finally, to every arc $i \neq 1$ we assign a number l_i, which will be called its length. The transhipment problem, which has become classical in operational research, is the following:

Find a flow

$$\boldsymbol{\varphi} = (\varphi_1, \varphi_2, \ldots, \varphi_m)$$

such that

(1) $\varphi_i \geqslant 0$ *for* $i = 1, 2, \ldots, m$.

(2) $\varphi_p = c_p$ *for* $p \in P$, $\varphi_q = c'_q$ *for* $q \in Q$.

(3) *the total work* $\sum_{i \neq 1} l_i \varphi_i$ *is a minimum.*

It is obvious that this problem is a particular case of the transportation problem, but we will treat it separately because of its simplicity.

Notice that the required flow saturates all terminal arcs, and if the problem has a solution, we see from condition (2) that

$$\sum_{p \in P} c_p = \sum_{q \in Q} c'_q.$$

This condition is necessary but not sufficient; a necessary and sufficient condition for the solution of the problem is given by Gale's theorem (Section 9.7). This is that, for every set

$$A \subset \{a_1, a_2, \ldots, a_n\} \quad \text{such that } \omega^-(A) \subset \omega^+(a),$$

we have the relation

$$\sum_{\substack{p \in P \\ p \in \omega^-(A)}} c_p \geqslant \sum_{\substack{q \in Q \\ q \in \omega^+(A)}} c'_q.$$

The transhipment problem can also be expressed as follows.

Analytic form. *Given numbers* $d_1, d_2, \ldots, d_n$, *a set* $\mathscr{E}$ *of ordered pairs* (i, j) *with* $1 \leqslant i \leqslant n$, $1 \leqslant j \leqslant n$, *and numbers* l_j^i *for* $(i, j) \in \mathscr{E}$, *find numbers* x_j^i *such that:*

(1) $$x_j^i \geqslant 0 \quad ((i, j) \in \mathscr{E}),$$

(2) $$\sum_j x_j^i - \sum_h x_i^h = d_i \quad (i = 1, 2, \ldots, n),$$

(3) $$\sum_{(i, j) \in \mathscr{E}} l_j^i x_j^i \text{ is minimized.}$$

This analytic form is easily recognizable, for, each unknown x_j^i appears exactly twice in equations (2), and with different signs. Notice that if the problem has a solution $\mathbf{x}$, we get

$$\sum_{i=1}^{n} d_i = 0$$

by summing over all the equations in (2).

If $d_i > 0$, we put $i \in P$, $c_i = d_i$; if $d_i < 0$, we put $i \in Q$, $c'_i = -d_i$; then we have

$$\sum_{i \in P} c_i = \sum_{j \in Q} c'_j.$$

Construct a transportation network G whose vertices are $a_1, a_2, \ldots, a_n$, $\bar{a}$, $\bar{b}$, in which (a_i, a_j) is an arc if $(i,j) \in \mathscr{E}$, where $(\bar{a}, a_p)$ is an arc of capacity c_p if $p \in P$, and where $(a_q, \bar{b})$ is an arc of capacity c'_q if $q \in Q$. We want to solve the transhipment problem in the network G. x^i_j represents the flow directed along the arc (a_i, a_j).

NOTE. We say that the transportation network is *simple* if, except for the source and the sink, its vertices form two disjoint sets

$$A_P = \{a_p | p \in P\} \quad \text{and} \quad A_Q = \{a_q | q \in Q\}$$

and if

1. $(\bar{a}, a_p) \in U$, $c(a, a_p) = c_p > 0$ for $p \in P$,
2. $(a_q, \bar{b}) \in U$, $c(a_q, \bar{b}) = c'_q > 0$ for $q \in Q$,
3. In $A_P \bigcup A_Q$, there are only arcs directed from A_P to A_Q.

When the network G is of this particular form, the trans-shipment problem is sometimes called the transportation problem or Hitchcock problem.

If every Hitchcock problem is a transhipment problem, it is equally true that every trans-shipment problem can be formulated as a Hitchcock problem.

To see this, consider any network G with vertices $a_1, a_2, \ldots, a_n$, and two disjoint sets P and $Q \subset \{1, 2, \ldots, n\}$; associate with it, a simple network $\bar{G}$ with vertices

$$\bar{a}, \bar{b}, a'_1, a'_2, \ldots, a'_n, a''_1, \ldots, a''_n.$$

Take an arbitrary number

$$h > \max_{q \in Q} c'_q,$$

and join the following arcs:

$(\bar{a}, a'_p)$	with the capacity $h + c_p$	if $p \in P$,
$(\bar{a}, a'_q)$	with the capacity $h - c'_q$	if $q \in Q$,
$(\bar{a}, a'_j)$	with the capacity h	if $j \notin P \bigcup Q$,
(a'_j, a''_k)	with the capacity ∞ and the length $l(a_j, a_k)$	if (a_j, a_k) is an arc of G,
(a'_j, a''_j)	with the capacity ∞ and length 0	for $j = 1, 2, \ldots, n$.

To every flow φ in the network G, satisfying the proposed conditions, there corresponds a flow in $\bar{G}$, which saturates the terminal arcs, whose values are given in the following figure:

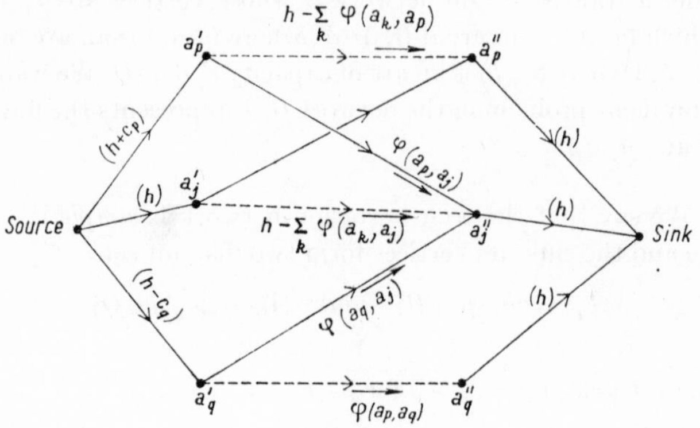

FIG. 9.15

The problem is thus reduced to finding the solution of a Hitchcock problem. Note, however, that this change of form doubles the number of vertices and this, generally speaking, is not desirable.

The more usual analytic form of the Hitchcock problem is as follows:

Analytic form. *Given the positive numbers* $c_1, c_2, \ldots, c_p, c'_1, c'_2, \ldots, c'_q$ *with*

$$\sum_{i=1}^{p} c_i = \sum_{j=1}^{q} c'_j,$$

a set $\mathscr{E}$ *of ordered pairs* (i, j) *with* $1 \leqslant i \leqslant p$, $1 \leqslant j \leqslant q$ *and the numbers* l^i_j *for* $(i, j) \in \mathscr{E}$, *find the numbers* x^i_j *such that*

(1) $$x^i_j \geqslant 0,$$

(2) $$\sum_{i=1}^{p} x^i_j = c'_j; \quad \sum_{j=1}^{q} x^i_j = c_i,$$

(3) $$\sum_{i,j} l^i_j x^i_j \textit{ is minimized.}$$

In one or other of its forms, the transhipment problem is often met in operational research, as in the following examples.

EXAMPLE 1. *Personnel assignment problem* (Votaw and Orden). Consider p operators $a_1, a_2, \ldots, a_p$ who operate q machines $a'_1, a'_2, \ldots, a'_q$. The output on machine a'_j by operator a_i is a number k^i_j, determined by tests. Let $x^i_j = 1$

if operator a_i is to work on a'_j and $x^i_j = 0$ if he is not. The problem consists in maximizing the total output

$$\sum_{i,j} k^i_j x^i_j$$

subject to the constraints

$$\sum_{j=1}^{q} x^i_j = 1, \quad \sum_{i=1}^{p} x^i_j = 1.$$

Hence it is a transhipment problem of the second analytic form.

EXAMPLE 2. *Empty merchant ships* (Koopmans). Consider the cargo traffic of 1913. Certain ports such as Lisbon, San Francisco, Athens, Yokohama export very little and import a great deal. Other ports such as New York, La Plata, Odessa, Rotterdam export a great deal and import little. It is therefore necessary to send empty cargo ships along the usual shipping routes, to provide the ships needed at New York, La Plata, etc. Given the distance l_i of the voyage on the ith shipping route one would also like to minimize the cost of these voyages. The problem may be reduced to the transhipment problem. First draw the graph $\bar{G}$ of the shipping lines. Join a source $\bar{a}$ to the ports which import a great deal with an arc of capacity equal to the monthly surplus of empty ships. Join a sink $\bar{b}$ to the ports which export a great deal with an arc of capacity equal to the monthly demand of empty ships. Then find a flow $\boldsymbol{\varphi}$ which saturates the terminal arcs and which minimizes the cost of transportation

$$\sum_i l_i \varphi_i.$$

EXAMPLE 3. *The soil removal problem* (Monge). Another example of the transhipment problem which has not been noticed by the theorists of operational research until recent years, was studied by Monge† in 1781. We have two surfaces S and S'. On the first surface S there are evenly distributed masses which are to be transported to the surface S' in such a way as to minimize the total labour involved.

Let $x^i_j = 1$, when a unit mass is transported from the point $a_i \in S$ to a point $a'_j \in S'$ and let l^i_j denote the distance (a_i, a'_j). As before we must minimize an expression of the form

$$\sum_{i,j} l^i_j x^i_j.$$

† That Monge's problem is a transportation problem was brought to our attention in 1956 by Professor Ulam. The problem has been studied also by Paul Appell who published a memoir on the subject [1].

(However, since the problem is continuous, summation should be replaced by integrals.)

By purely geometric arguments, we see that

1. The optimal path of a unit mass $a_i \in S$ to $a'_j \in S'$ is a segment of the straight line $a_i a'_j$, and no two of these segments should intersect except at their extremities.

2. The segments $a_i a'_j$ form an optimal system of routes if there is a convex surface R such that all segments $a_i a'_j$ are normal to R.

The problem is analogous to one in which a container holds a certain material which is to be transported piecemeal into another equivalent container.

A quick algorithm for solving these problems is developed in the following section in connexion with a completely different problem.

9.9. THE PROBLEM OF RESTRICTED POTENTIAL

Here we consider a particular case of the problem of potential, which may be solved easily because of its extreme simplicity.

Given a transportation network G, with vertices $a_1, a_2, \ldots, a_n, \bar{a}, \bar{b}$ and arcs $i = 1, 2, \ldots, m$, let us write

$$P = \{j \mid (\bar{a}, a_j) \text{ is an arc}\},$$

$$Q = \{j \mid (a_j, \bar{b}) \text{ is an arc}\}.$$

Suppose $P \cap Q = \emptyset$ and that p and q denote the indices of arcs $(\bar{a}, a_p)$ and $(a_q, \bar{b})$. For every $p \in P$, there is given a number $c_p \geqslant 0$; for every $q \in Q$, there is given a number $c_q \geqslant 0$; suppose

$$\sum_{p \in P} c_p = \sum_{q \in Q} c'_q = \gamma.$$

Finally, given the numbers l_i for $i \notin P \cup Q$. The restricted problem of potential is the following: *find in G a potential difference $\boldsymbol{\theta}$ such that*

(1) $$\theta_i \leqslant l_i \quad \textit{for } i \notin P \cup Q$$

(2) $$\sum_{p \in P} c_p \theta_p + \sum_{q \in Q} c'_q \theta_q + \gamma \theta_1 \textit{ is minimized.}$$

We can also give an analytic formulation of the problem:

Analytic form. *Given the numbers $d_1, d_2, \ldots, d_n$, a set $\mathscr{E}$ of ordered pairs (i, j) with $1 \leqslant i \leqslant n$, $1 \leqslant j \leqslant n$ and numbers l^i_j for $(i, j) \in \mathscr{E}$, find a vector*

$$\mathbf{t} = (t_1, t_2, \ldots, t_n),$$

such that

(1) $$t_j - t_i \leqslant l_j^i \quad ((i,j) \in \mathscr{E}),$$

(2) $$\sum_{j=1}^{n} d_j t_j = \langle \mathbf{d}, \mathbf{t} \rangle \textit{ is a minimum.}$$

Notice that for the problem to have meaning, it must be assumed, that

$$\sum_{j=1}^{n} d_j = 0;$$

for, otherwise, by adding the vector

$$\lambda \mathbf{u} = \lambda(1, 1, \ldots, 1)$$

to $\mathbf{t}$, the scalar product could have any value whatever:

$$\langle \mathbf{d}, \mathbf{t} + \lambda \mathbf{u} \rangle = \langle \mathbf{d}, \mathbf{t} \rangle + \lambda \sum_{j=1}^{n} d_j.$$

Returning to the original form, we can draw the transportation network G with vertices $a_1, a_2, \ldots, a_n, \bar{a}, \bar{b}$ in which (a_i, a_j) is an arc if $(i,j) \in \mathscr{E}$; for every a_p such that $d_p > 0$, draw an arc $(\bar{a}, a_p)$ of capacity $c_p = d_p$ and write $p \in P$; for every a_q such that $d_q < 0$, draw an arc $(a_q, \bar{b})$ of capacity $c_q = -d_p$ and write $q \in Q$.

We want to find a potential difference

$$\theta(a_i, a_j) = t_j - t_i$$

which will minimize the expression

$$\begin{aligned} \sum_{p \in P} c_p t_p - \sum_{q \in Q} c_q' t_q &= \sum_{p \in P} c_p \theta_p + t(\bar{a}) \sum_{p \in P} c_p + \sum_{q \in Q} c_q' \theta_q - t(\bar{b}) \sum_{q \in Q} c_q' \\ &= \sum_{p \in P} c_p \theta_p + \sum_{q \in Q} c_q' \theta_q + \gamma \theta_1. \end{aligned}$$

We see that the problem of restricted potential does not always have a solution. Consider the graph $\bar{G}$ obtained from G by suppressing $\bar{a}$ and $\bar{b}$. A necessary and sufficient condition for the problem to have a solution is that for every circuit μ of $\bar{G}$, we have

$$\sum_{i \in \mu} l_i \geqslant 0.$$

This is a corollary of the general existence theorem (Chapter 8, Section 8.3).

EXAMPLE (B. Roy). *Assignment of operations in an engineering workshop.* Machines $\alpha = 1, 2, \ldots,$ are at our disposal for certain jobs on the products $\beta = 1, 2, \ldots$. Machine α works on the product β and the work must be continuous. Write $(\alpha, \beta) = i$ and denote by k_i the time needed to finish this job i. Suppose finally that every product β has to go through the different machines in a certain order known in advance and that in each machine α, the different products must go through it in a certain order known in advance. The problem is to determine at what period t_i, job $i = (\alpha, \beta)$, should be done so as to finish as soon as possible and so as to minimize the storage cost of each product between its date of entry into the workshop and its date of departure. Draw the graph whose vertices are the jobs and where (i, j) is an arc in the following two cases:

$i = (\alpha, \beta)$, $j = (\alpha, \beta')$ and machine α works on product β' just after product β.

$i = (\alpha, \beta)$, $j = (\alpha', \beta)$ and the product β goes through machine α just before machine α'.

For every arc (i, j), the constraint is $t_j - t_i \geqslant k_i$, which by changing the sign is the same as condition (1) above. Minimizing the storage costs involves a constraint of the form (2).

Algorithm

To solve the problem of restricted potential, we follow the procedure described in [38].

Consider a vector

$$\mathbf{t} = (t_1, t_2, \ldots, t_n)$$

which satisfies

$$t_j - t_i \leqslant l^i_j \quad ((i, j) \in \mathscr{E});$$

we say that $\mathbf{t}$ is a *compatible* vector. We shall decrease it step by step until $\langle \mathbf{t}, \mathbf{d} \rangle$ reaches its minimum value.

Form the transportation network G as before, and denote by G_t the transportation network obtained from G by deleting the arcs (a_i, a_j) for which

$$t_t - t_i < l^i_j.$$

If $\boldsymbol{\varphi}$ is a flow in G, we write

$$x^i_j = \varphi(a_i, a_j); \quad \mathbf{x} = (x^i_j / (i, j) \in \mathscr{E})$$

$$\langle \mathbf{l}, \mathbf{x} \rangle = \sum_{(i,j) \in \mathscr{E}} l^i_j x^i_j.$$

This algorithm gives simultaneously the minimum value of $\langle \mathbf{l}, \mathbf{x} \rangle$ and of $\langle \mathbf{t}, \mathbf{d} \rangle$; it is described by the following two lemmas:

Lemma 1. *If, for a given* $\mathbf{t}$, *the maximum flow* $\mathbf{x}$ *of the transportation network* G_t *saturates the sink arcs, then* $\langle \mathbf{d}, \mathbf{t} \rangle$ *and* $\langle \mathbf{l}, \mathbf{x} \rangle$ *have their minimum values.*

Let $\bar{G}$ be the graph obtained from G by deleting the vertices $\bar{a}$, $\bar{b}$ and let S be its incidence matrix (Chapter 8, Section 8.2); by definition

$$s_j^i = \begin{cases} +1 & \text{if } i \text{ is an arc incident from } a_j, \\ -1 & \text{if } i \text{ is an arc incident to } a_j, \\ 0 & \text{if } i \text{ is an arc not incident with } a_j. \end{cases}$$

If $\mathbf{x}$ denotes the restriction to $\bar{G}$ of a flow $\boldsymbol{\varphi}$ saturating the sink arcs of G, we have

$$(S\mathbf{x})_j = \sum_i s_i^j \mathbf{x}_i = \begin{cases} 0 & \text{if } j \notin P \cup Q \\ c_j & \text{if } j \in P \\ -c_j & \text{if } j \in Q. \end{cases}$$

Hence

$$S\mathbf{x} = \mathbf{d} = (d_1, d_2, \ldots, d_n);$$

furthermore, the transpose S^* of S satisfies:

$$(S^* t)_i = t\,(\text{initial vertex of the arc } i) - t\,(\text{terminal vertex of the arc } i).$$

Therefore $-S^*\mathbf{t} \leqslant \mathbf{l}$ and consequently, for every compatible vector $\mathbf{t}$ and every saturating flow $\mathbf{x}$ in G, we can write

$$\langle \mathbf{t}, \mathbf{d} \rangle + \langle \mathbf{l}, \mathbf{x} \rangle \geqslant \langle \mathbf{t}, \mathbf{d} \rangle - \langle S^*\mathbf{t}, \mathbf{x} \rangle$$
$$= \langle \mathbf{t}, \mathbf{d} \rangle - \langle \mathbf{t}, S\mathbf{x} \rangle = \langle \mathbf{t}, \mathbf{d} \rangle - \langle \mathbf{t}, \mathbf{d} \rangle = 0. \quad (1)$$

Thus

$$\langle \mathbf{l}, \mathbf{x} \rangle + \langle \mathbf{t}, \mathbf{d} \rangle = 0$$

which shows that $\langle \mathbf{l}, \mathbf{x} \rangle$ and $\langle \mathbf{t}, \mathbf{d} \rangle$ are minimized.

Now let $\mathbf{x}$ be a flow saturating G_t;

$$x_j^i > 0 \Rightarrow t_j - t_i = l_j^i.$$

In relation (1) the equality holds; therefore $\langle \mathbf{t}, \mathbf{d} \rangle$ is minimized.

Lemma 2. *If, for a given* $\mathbf{t}$, *the maximum flow* $\boldsymbol{\varphi}$ *of* G_t *does not saturate the sink arcs, there exists by the Ford and Fulkerson theorem, Section* 9.6, *a cut* $\boldsymbol{\omega}^-(A)$ *of capacity*

$$c_A = \max \varphi_1 < \sum_{q \in Q} c_q'.$$

We write

$$\epsilon = \min \{ l_j^i - t_j + t_i / (a_i, a_j) \text{ is an arc of } G, \text{ but not an arc of } G_t \},$$

$$\epsilon_j(A) = \begin{cases} 0 & \text{if } a_j \notin A, \\ \epsilon & \text{if } a_j \in A. \end{cases}$$

The vector

$$\mathbf{t}' = \mathbf{t}+\boldsymbol{\epsilon}(A) = \mathbf{t}+(\epsilon_1(A), \epsilon_2(A), \ldots, \epsilon_n(A))$$

is then a compatible vector such that

$$\langle \mathbf{t}', \mathbf{d}\rangle < \langle \mathbf{t}, \mathbf{d}\rangle.$$

First we show that $\mathbf{t}'$ is a compatible vector.
If $a_i \in A$, $a_j \in A$, then

$$t'_j - t'_i = t_j - t_i \leqslant l^i_j.$$

If $a_i \notin A$, $a_j \notin A$, then

$$t'_j - t'_i = t_j - t_i \leqslant l^i_j.$$

If $a_i \in A$, $a_j \notin A$, then

$$t'_j - t'_i = t_j - t_i - \epsilon \leqslant t_j - t_i \leqslant l^i_j.$$

If $a_i \notin A$, $a_j \in A$ and if (a_i, a_j) is an arc of G not in G_t, then

$$t'_j - t'_i = t_j - t_i + \epsilon \leqslant l^i_j.$$

The case where $a_i \notin A$, $a_j \in A$ and (a_i, a_j) is an arc of G_t does not occur, for $\omega^-(A)$, a cut of capacity

$$c_A = \max \varphi_1 < +\infty,$$

cannot contain an arc of infinite capacity.

We now show that

$$\langle \mathbf{t}', \mathbf{d}\rangle < \langle \mathbf{t}, \mathbf{d}\rangle.$$

We have

$$\langle \mathbf{t}', \mathbf{d}\rangle - \langle \mathbf{t}, \mathbf{d}\rangle = \langle \boldsymbol{\epsilon}(A), \mathbf{d}\rangle = \epsilon \sum_{\substack{p\in P\\ p\in A}} c_p - \epsilon \sum_{\substack{q\in Q\\ q\in A}} c'_q$$

$$= \epsilon \left(\sum_{\substack{p\in P\\ p\in A}} c_p + \sum_{\substack{q\in Q\\ q\notin A}} c'_q \right) - \epsilon \sum_{q\in Q} c'_q$$

$$= \epsilon c_A - \epsilon \sum_{q\in Q} c'_q < 0.$$

The lemma is therefore proved, and the algorithm to be applied follows at once.

Notice that the method indicated gives at the same time a saturated flow $\mathbf{x}$ which minimizes $\langle \mathbf{l}, \mathbf{x}\rangle$ and which thus solves the problem of Section 9.8. The reader may find an illustration of this method in the exercise on page 243.

9.10. THE GENERAL TRANSPORTATION PROBLEM

Consider the transportation problem in the following general form: *Given a graph G, where to every arc i is assigned a convex function f_i defined in an interval $[b_i, c_i]$; minimize the quantity*

$$\sum_{i=1}^{m} f_i(\varphi_i) = F(\boldsymbol{\varphi}).$$

NOTE 1. It is always possible to replace the convex function f_i by a function which is *piecewise linear* in such a way as to obtain a sufficiently good approximation to the representing curve by a broken line. The error in the minimum of $F(\boldsymbol{\varphi})$ which this involves, can be made as small as we like.

NOTE 2. If there are a number of arcs joining two vertices in the same direction, we can always substitute a single arc. For, let 1, 2,..., h be such arcs, and $f_1, f_2, \ldots, f_h$ the corresponding convex functions with intervals $[b_1, c_1], [b_2, c_2], \ldots, [b_h, c_h]$. Consider a single arc $i = 0$ with the interval

$$[b_1+b_2+\ldots+b_h, \quad c_1+c_2+\ldots+c_h].$$

In a point φ_0 of this interval, define a function f_0 by

$$f_0(\varphi_0) = \min\left\{\sum_i f_i(\varphi_i) \,\middle|\, \sum_i \varphi_i = \varphi_0, \quad b_i \leqslant \varphi_i \leqslant c_i\right\}.$$

This function f_0 is convex, for if we consider two points φ_0 and φ_0' and two numbers p and $p' \geqslant 0$ with $p+p' = 1$, we can write

$$\begin{aligned} f_0(p\varphi_0+p'\varphi_0') &\leqslant \min\left\{\sum_i f_i(p\varphi_i+p'\varphi_i') \,\middle|\, \sum_i \varphi_i = \varphi_0, \quad \sum_i \varphi_i' = \varphi_0'\right\} \\ &\leqslant \min\{p\sum f_i(\varphi_i)+p'\sum f_i(\varphi_i')\} \\ &= pf_0(\varphi_0)+p'f_0(\varphi_0'). \end{aligned}$$

The arc 0, with the convex function f_0, meets the required conditions.

EXAMPLE 1. Consider localities where there is a demand for a given product, and others where there is a surplus of that product. There are several ways for the product to be carried between the two given localities and the costs of the different means of transport are $l_{i,0}, l_{i,1}, \ldots, l_{i,k}$ (per ton of product). The quantity of the product which may be carried by means of transport (i, k) is limited by the capacity $c_{i,k}$. The problem is to arrange the transport so as to satisfy the demand as cheaply as possible.

Here a transportation network is constructed and from the flows which saturate the terminal arcs we choose one which minimizes

$$\sum_{i=1}^{m} l_i \varphi_i.$$

There are several arcs joining the two localities, each arc corresponding to a method of transport, therefore we can replace them by a single arc as indicated above.

EXAMPLE 2. *The warehouse problem.* Consider the level of stock of certain merchandise stored in a warehouse at different instants of time $k = 1, 2, \ldots, n$ and assume that we know

c = total capacity of the warehouse;

s_0 = initial stock deposited in the warehouse;

p_k = selling price (per unit) at time k;

q_k = purchasing price (per unit) at time k;

r_k = storage price (per unit) at time k.

It is intended to buy and sell during a given length of time n, then to restore the stock in the warehouse to its original level, s_0. Therefore we require for all k

α_k = the amount sold at the start of the kth interval of time;

β_k = the amount bought in by the end of the kth interval of time;

γ_k = the amount in the warehouse during the kth interval of time;

δ_k = the amount in the warehouse after the purchase of the new stock at the end of the kth time interval.

The problem consists in maximizing the total gain

$$\sum_{k=1}^{n} (p_k \alpha_k - q_k \beta_k - r_k \gamma_k),$$

subject to the constraints:

$$\begin{cases} \delta_k - \alpha_{k+1} - \gamma_{k+1} = 0 & (k = 1, 2, \ldots, n-1); \\ -\alpha_1 - \gamma_1 = -s_0; & \\ \gamma_k + \beta_k - \delta_k = 0 & (k = 1, 2, \ldots, n-1); \\ \gamma_n + \beta_n = s_0; & \\ 0 \leqslant \alpha_k \leqslant \infty, & \\ 0 \leqslant \beta_k \leqslant \infty, & \\ 0 \leqslant \gamma_k \leqslant \infty, & \\ 0 \leqslant \delta_k \leqslant c. & \end{cases}$$

It is therefore a transportation problem with the transportation network indicated in the figure below:

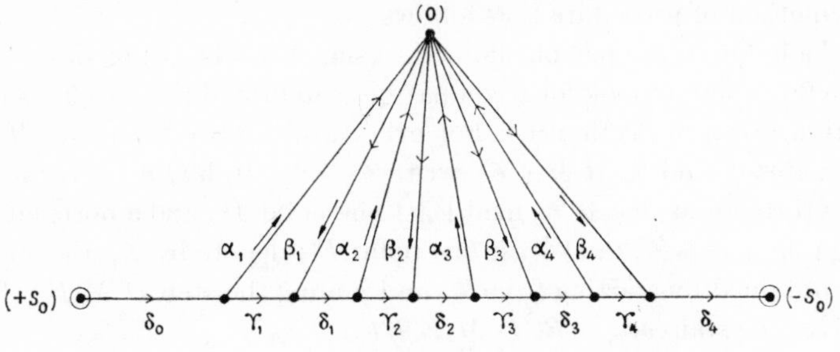

Fig. 9.16

General algorithm (Minty)

To solve this general transportation problem in its canonical form, duality theory (Chapter 8, Section 8.5) can clearly be used. To every function $f_i(x)$ there is assigned a convex conjugate $h_i(y)$ and by methods strictly analogous to those described in the preceding section we wish to minimize simultaneously

$$\sum_i f_i(\varphi_i)$$

and

$$\sum_i h_i(\theta_i).$$

This method has been described in detail by Charnes and Cooper [5] and Prager [35].

The algorithm (Minty) to be given now has the advantage of being easy to use on electronic computers. We start with a graph G with arcs $i = 1, 2, \ldots, m$, and in modifying the functions f_i we shall assume that there is not more than one arc connecting the same vertices in the same direction. Thus to every arc i is assigned a function f_i, which is piecewise linear, and the corresponding curve $\mathscr{C}_i$ is in the shape of a staircase rising to the right: *ABCDE*.

By Theorem 7 (Chapter 8) the problem reduces to one of looking for a flow $\boldsymbol{\varphi}$ and a potential difference $\boldsymbol{\theta}$ such that

(1) $\boldsymbol{\varphi}$ and $\boldsymbol{\theta}$ are *compatible*, that is to say

$$b_i \leqslant \varphi_i \leqslant c_i \quad (i = 1, 2, \ldots, m)$$

$$k_i \leqslant \theta_i \leqslant l_i \quad (i = 1, 2, \ldots, m).$$

(2) $\boldsymbol{\varphi}$ and $\boldsymbol{\theta}$ are *reciprocal images*, that is to say

$$(\varphi_i, \theta_i) \in \mathscr{C}_i \quad (i = 1, 2, \ldots, m).$$

The method of procedure is as follows.

We look for a compatible flow $\boldsymbol{\varphi}$, using the algorithm described in Section 9.7; then we look for a compatible potential difference $\boldsymbol{\theta}$, using the algorithm given in Section 9.4. For every arc i, draw the point M_i with co-ordinates φ_i and θ_i. If $M_i \in \mathscr{C}_i$, write $\mathscr{C}'_i = \mathscr{C}_i$. If $M_i \notin \mathscr{C}_i$, a vertical line passing through M_i meets $\mathscr{C}_i$ in at least one point D', and a horizontal line through M_i meets $\mathscr{C}_i$ in at least one point E'; denote by $\mathscr{C}'_i$, the staircase curve, obtained by starting from $\mathscr{C}_i$ and joining the step $D'M_iE'$. (Figure 9.17 gives the staircase: $ABCD'M_iE'EF$.)

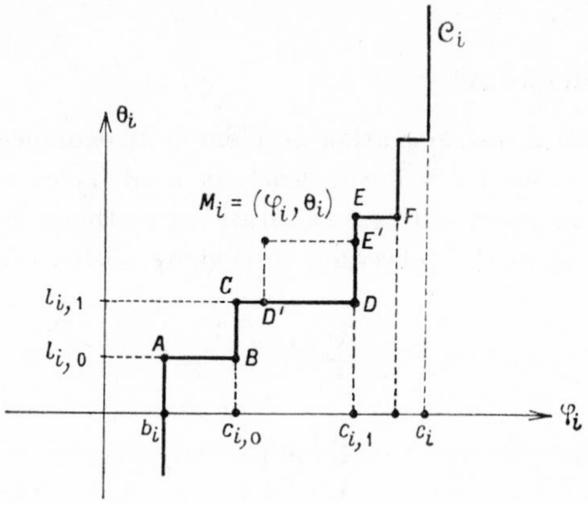

FIG. 9.17

Step by step, we reduce the number of arcs i for which $M_i \notin \mathscr{C}_i$. Assume, for example, that arc $i = 1$, then $M_1 \notin \mathscr{C}_1$. We will assume that M_1 is in the upper region bounded by the curve $\mathscr{C}_1$. Transform the flow $\boldsymbol{\varphi}$ and the potential difference $\boldsymbol{\theta}$ into a flow $\boldsymbol{\varphi}'$ and potential difference $\boldsymbol{\theta}'$ so that

$$M'_1 = (\varphi'_1, \theta'_1) \in \mathscr{C}_1,$$

and now we make transformations so that the points M_i with $i \neq 1$ are always on the curves $\mathscr{C}'_i$.

To define the transformation, colour the arcs of the graph in red, green and black.

The arc $i = 1$ is coloured black.

If M_i is at the extreme left of the horizontal segment of $\mathscr{C}'_i$ (for example, in the figure, if $M_i = A$) colour the arc i black; if M_i is at the extreme right (for example $M_i = B$), colour the arc i black and reverse the provisional orientation of the arc i (so that we are again at the extreme left of the segment).

If M_i is an interior point of the horizontal segment (such as AB), colour the arc i in red.

If M_i is an interior point of the vertical segment (such as BC) colour the arc i green.

By the Lemma on coloured arcs (Chapter 7), two cases arise.

FIRST CASE. There is a cycle $\boldsymbol{\mu}$ of red and black arcs containing the arc $i = 1$ with all the black arcs oriented in the same direction.

For every arc $i \in \boldsymbol{\mu}$, $i \neq 1$, write

$$p_i = \{\max x_i | (x_i, \theta_i) \in \mathscr{C}_i'\} - \varphi_i > 0;$$

and

$$p = \min_{\substack{i \neq 1 \\ i \in \mu}} p_i > 0.$$

The flow $\boldsymbol{\varphi}' = \boldsymbol{\varphi} + p\boldsymbol{\mu}$, and the potential difference $\boldsymbol{\theta}' = \boldsymbol{\theta}$ are still reciprocal images, but the value of the flow is increased, for

$$\varphi_1' = \varphi_1 + p > \varphi_1.$$

SECOND CASE. There is a coboundary $\boldsymbol{\omega}$ of green and black arcs, containing the arc $i = 1$, with all black arcs oriented in the same direction.

For every arc $i \in \boldsymbol{\omega}$, $i \neq 1$, write

$$q_i = \theta_i - \min\{y_i | (\varphi_i, y_i) \in \mathscr{C}_i'\} > 0;$$

and

$$q = \min_{\substack{i \neq 1 \\ i \in \omega}} q_i > 0.$$

The potential difference $\boldsymbol{\theta}' = \boldsymbol{\theta} - q\boldsymbol{\omega}$ and the flow $\boldsymbol{\varphi}' = \boldsymbol{\varphi}$ are still reciprocal images, but the value of the potential difference is decreased, for

$$\theta_1' = \theta_1 - q < \theta_1.$$

We then restore the original orientation of the arcs and repeat the same operation starting with the new flow $\boldsymbol{\varphi}'$ and the new potential difference $\boldsymbol{\theta}'$. In this way φ_1' is increased indefinitely and θ_1' is reduced indefinitely. Necessarily a time will come when the descending staircase, in going through the point $M_1' = (\varphi_1', \theta_1')$, will meet the increasing curve $\mathscr{C}_1$, and at this moment the number of arcs i, for which $M_i \notin \mathscr{C}_i$ will have been reduced by at least one unit.

Repeating this procedure with the arcs other than arc $i = 1$, we finally obtain a flow $\boldsymbol{\varphi}'$ and a potential difference $\boldsymbol{\theta}'$ which are reciprocal images.

Algorithm by simulation

Notice another procedure; considering the problem in its canonical form, we see that the model can always be represented by an electric circuit consisting of diodes, sources of current, and a source of voltage (potential difference), and we can measure the strength of the current in different leads with the usual instruments. In the arc i defined by the capacity c_i and the length l_i the increasing curve $\mathscr{C}_i$ could be obtained by a voltage source, l_i, a source of current c_i and two perfect diodes as in Figure 9.18.

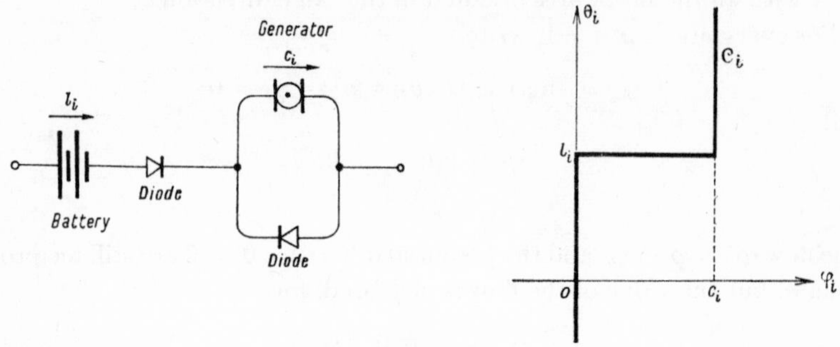

FIG. 9.18

This method is nevertheless not very precise, especially in connexion with present-day generators. Furthermore, it is unsuitable for flow problems with integers.

10. Problems related to the transportation problem

10.1. GENERAL STUDY OF A SYMMETRIC TRANSPORTATION NETWORK

Consider a symmetric graph whose vertices are $a_1, a_2, \ldots, a_n$; to every arc (a_p, a_q) we assign a number $c_{pq} \geqslant 0$, called its *capacity*, and to the arc (a_q, a_p) in the opposite direction, we assign the capacity $c_{qp} = c_{pq}$. Furthermore, if a given vertex a_i is the source and a vertex a_j the sink, we have a *transportation network* as defined earlier.

Let f_{ij} be the maximum amount of flow that it is possible to transport from vertex a_i to vertex a_j consistent with the capacities. The *matrix of maximum flows* $((f_{ij}))$ is often of interest in communication problems. The problem of determining this matrix as rapidly as possible has been studied by Mayeda, Chien, Gomory and Hu, and is called the *multi-terminal problem*. We give here Gomory and Hu's method [18], and we shall show that the determination of the matrix of maximum flows can be solved with only $n-1$ flow problems instead of $n(n-1)/2$.

Gomory–Hu theorem. *A matrix* $((f_{ij}))$ *of n rows and n columns is the matrix of maximum flows for a symmetric graph if and only if*

(1) $$f_{ij} = f_{ji} \quad \text{for every } i, j;$$

(2) $$f_{ii} = +\infty \quad \text{for every } i;$$

(3) $$f_{ik} \geqslant \min\{f_{ij}, f_{jk}\} \quad \text{for every } i, j, k.$$

By induction, it can be shown that condition (3) is equivalent to

(3′) $$f_{iq} \geqslant \min\{f_{ij}, f_{jk}, f_{kl}, \ldots, f_{pq}\}.$$

1. Let $((f_{ij}))$ be the matrix of maximum flows of a network G. (1) and (2) are obvious, and we have to show that (3) is true. From Ford and Fulkerson's theorem, the vertices a_i and a_k of the graph G are separated by a cut of capacity f_{ik}; this cut is of the form $\omega^-(A)$ with $a_i \notin A$, $a_k \in A$.

If $a_j \in A$, the vertices a_i and a_j are separated by a cut of capacity f_{ik}, thus

$$f_{ij} \leqslant f_{ik}.$$

If $a_j \notin A$, the vertices a_j and a_k are separated by a cut of capacity f_{ik}, thus

$$f_{jk} \leqslant f_{ik}.$$

In any case, we have

$$f_{ik} \geqslant \min\{f_{ij}, f_{jk}\}.$$

2. Let $((f_{ij}))$ be a matrix satisfying the conditions (1), (2) and (3). Now consider a symmetric network formed by the points $a_1, a_2, \ldots, a_n$, joined in all possible ways, the length of the edge $[a_i, a_j]$ is f_{ij}. Form the spanning tree of maximum length (cf. Chapter 9, Section 9.3).

If $[a_i, a_q]$ is not an edge of the tree H, the vertices a_i and a_q are joined by a chain of the tree, say, a_i, a_j, $a_k, \ldots, a_p$, a_q, and hence

$$f_{iq} \leqslant \min\{f_{ij}, f_{jk}, \ldots, f_{pq}\};$$

(for otherwise, a tree of greater length than that of H would be formed by joining the edge $[a_i, a_q]$ and suppressing the shortest of the edges $[a_i, a_j]$, $[a_j, a_k]$; etc.). From (3′) the other inequality still holds. Thus, finally

$$f_{iq} = \min\{f_{ij}, f_{jk}, \ldots, f_{pq}\}. \tag{4}$$

This represents precisely the value of the maximum flow in the network H, obtained by taking the capacity $c_{ij} = f_{ij}$ if the edge $[a_i, a_j]$ belongs to the tree, and $c_{ij} = 0$ otherwise. The matrix $((f_{ij}))$ is therefore a matrix of maximum flows.

NOTE. To see if a given matrix $((f_{ij}))$ is a matrix of maximum flows, the inequality (3) should always be satisfied. However, it is much more economical to construct a tree of maximum length and to verify the inequality (4) for pairs of vertices (a_i, a_q) which are not edges of the tree. In this way we need consider only

$$\frac{n(n-1)}{2} - (n-1) = \frac{(n-1)(n-2)}{2}$$

equations. Since (4) implies that $((f_{ij}))$ is a matrix of maximum flows it follows that (4) implies (3).

Let a symmetric graph G be given with capacities c_{ij}. If we say that we 'condense' (or 'shrink') a set of vertices A, we mean that the whole set A is assimilated into a single vertex and is joined to the other vertices in the same way as the set A. A graph H obtained in the following way is called *the contracted tree* associated with G.

Consider two vertices a_1 and b_1 of a graph G, determine the maximum flow ν_1 between these two vertices, as well as the corresponding cut, of capacity ν_1. This cut is defined by two classes A_1 and B_1. The first operation is depicted by the following figure H_1:

H_1:

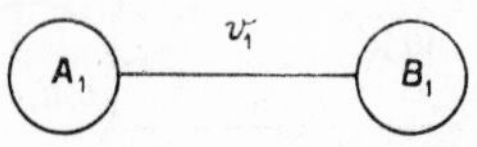

If one of the two classes of H_1, for example B_1, contains at least two distinct vertices, we look for the value of the maximum flow between these two vertices in the graph G_2 obtained from G by condensing the set A_1. Let (A_2, B_2) be the corresponding cut of capacity ν_2. The second operation, represented by figure H_2, is obtained from H_1 by replacing B_1 by the two classes A_2 and B_2 joined by an edge of value ν_2. The class A_1 is itself attached to one of the two classes A_2 or B_2 on the same side of the cut; for example:

H_2:

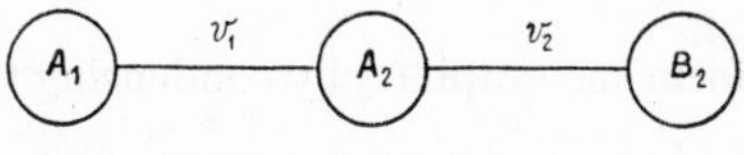

Repeat this process choosing one of the three classes A_1, A_2 or B_2 which contains more than one vertex by considering the graph G_3 obtained from G by condensing each of the other classes attached to the chosen class, etc.

After $n-1$ operations, every class of the figure contains only a single element and every edge of the figure has a unique value ν_i; H_{n-1} is called the *contracted tree* of the graph G. As an example, consider the following graph:

G:

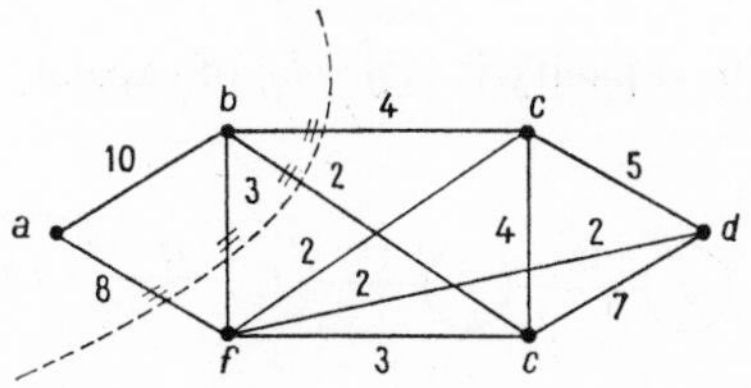

Select two vertices b and f arbitrarily, and we find that the cut of minimum capacity is $(ab; cdef)$ with capacity $\nu_1 = 17$ (as indicated in the figure). The figure H_1 is therefore:

H_1:

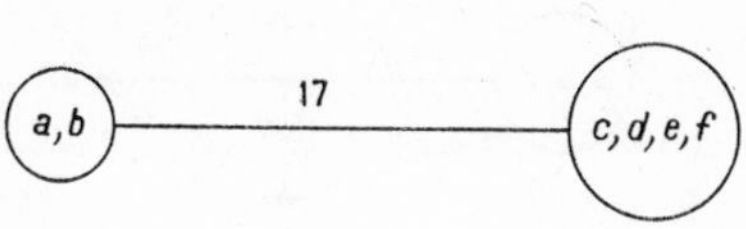

Next consider two vertices a and b and form the graph G_2 by condensing the set $\{c,d,e,f\}$ in G:

G_2:

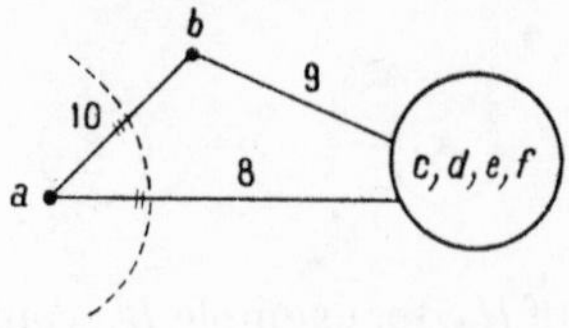

In this graph, the cut of minimum capacity is $(a;bcdef)$; with capacity 18. Then obtain figure H_2 from H_1 as follows:

H_2:

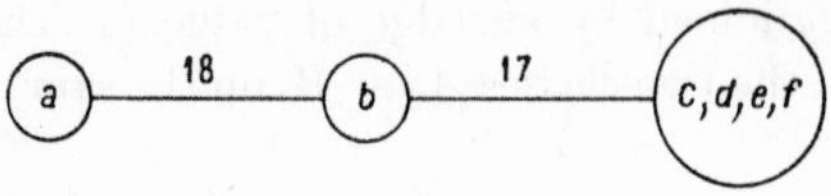

Choose c and f and form the graph G_3 by condensing the branch $\{a,b\}$ in G.

G_3:

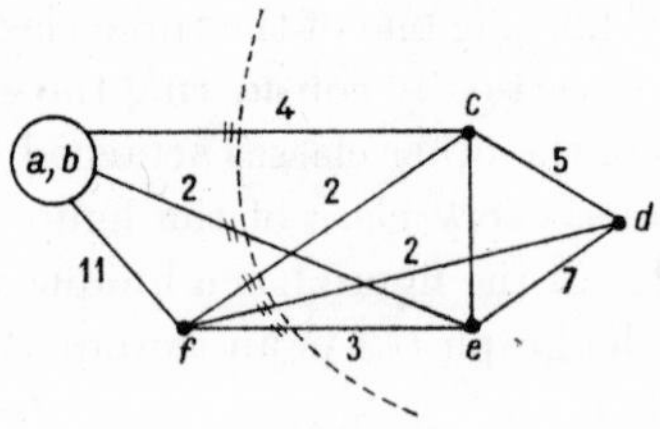

The cut of minimum capacity is $(abf;cde)$ of capacity 13. The figure H_3 is:

H_3:

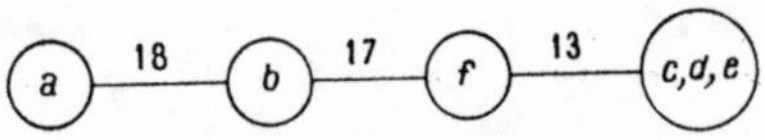

Choose the vertices c and e:

G_4:

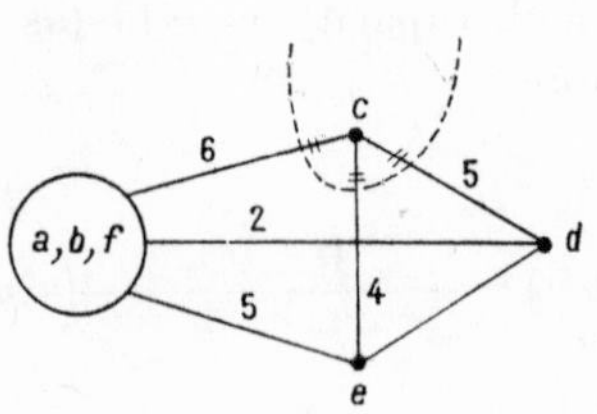

The cut of minimum capacity is $(c; abdef)$ of capacity 15; hence

H_4:

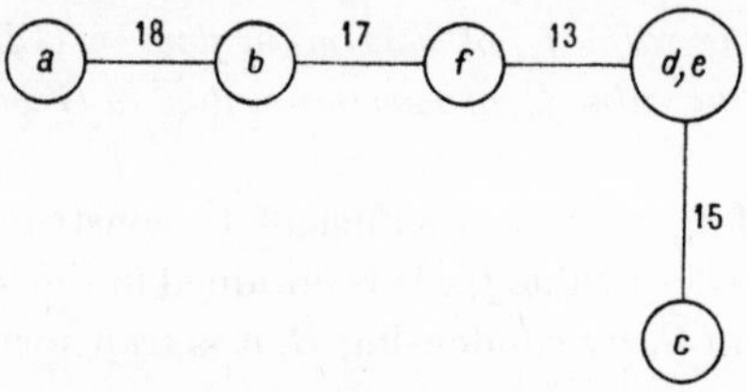

Take the vertices d and e and condense separately the sets $\{a,b,f\}$ and $\{c\}$ in G.

G_5:

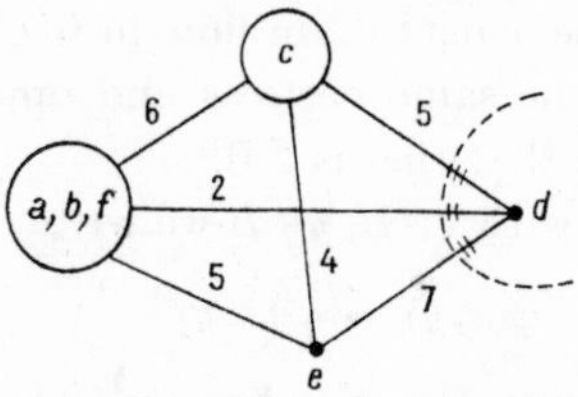

We find the cut $(d; abcef)$ of minimum capacity 14, hence the final figure is:

H_5:

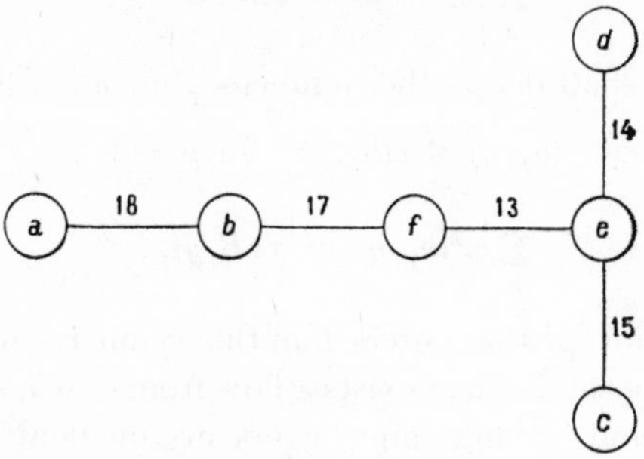

This is the required contracted tree.

The justification for this algorithm is given by the following:

Theorem. *In the transportation network G, let a_i and a_j be two arbitrary vertices and let*

$$\nu_{k_1}, \nu_{k_2}, \ldots, \nu_{k_p}$$

be the values associated with the different edges of the chain which join a_i and a_j in the contraction of G; then

$$f_{ij} = \min\{\nu_{k_1}, \nu_{k_2}, \ldots, \nu_{k_p}\}.$$

First we prove two lemmas.

Lemma 1. *Let G be a symmetric network, (A, B) a cut of minimum capacity between two vertices $\bar{a} \in A$ and $\bar{b} \in B$, G' the network obtained from G by condensing the set B; the value f_{ij} of maximum flow in G between two vertices a_i, $a_j \notin B$ is equal to the value f'_{ij} of maximum flow in G' between the same two vertices.*

(1) To show that $f'_{ij} \geqslant f_{ij}$, it is sufficient to construct a flow $\boldsymbol{\varphi}'$ in the condensed network G', of value f_{ij}. It is obtained in the following way: If $\boldsymbol{\varphi}$ is a maximum flow of G, by condensing B, it is transformed to a flow $\boldsymbol{\varphi}'$ of value f_{ij}.

(2) To show that $f_{ij} \geqslant f'_{ij}$, it is sufficient to construct in the original transportation network G, a flow $\boldsymbol{\varphi}$ with the value f'_{ij}. It is obtained in the following way: Let $\boldsymbol{\varphi}'$ be a maximum flow in G'. We can always assume that for two arcs with the same vertices and opposite direction, one of the two flows is zero and the other is $\geqslant 0$.

If (x, y) is an arc of G' with $x \notin B$, $y \notin B$ we write

$$\varphi(x, y) = \varphi'(x, y).$$

If $\varphi'(x, B) \geqslant 0$, then define the numbers $\varphi^1(x, b_1)$, $\varphi^1(x, b_2), \ldots$, so that

$$0 \leqslant \varphi^1(x, b_p) \leqslant c(x, b_p) \quad \text{for } p = 1, 2, \ldots,$$

$$\sum_p \varphi^1(x, b_p) = \varphi'(x, B).$$

If $\varphi'(y, B) < 0$, we shall define the numbers $\varphi^2(b_1, y)$, $\varphi^2(b_2, y), \ldots$ so that

$$0 \leqslant \varphi^2 \quad (b_p, y) \leqslant c(b_p, y) \quad \text{for } p = 1, 2, \ldots$$

and

$$\sum_p \varphi^2(b_p, y) = \varphi'(B, y).$$

The amount of flow $\boldsymbol{\varphi}^1$ that enters B in this manner, can be transported into $\bar{b}$, since by hypothesis there exists a flow from $\bar{a}$ to $\bar{b}$, saturating every arc incident to B and leaving empty every arc incident from B. For the same reason, there exists a flow $\boldsymbol{\varphi}^2$ from $\bar{b}$ to A and whose flow in the sink arc (b_p, y) is precisely $\varphi^2(b_p, y)$. In general, the first flow $\boldsymbol{\varphi}^1$ from A to $\bar{b}$ and the second flow $\boldsymbol{\varphi}^2$ from $\bar{b}$ to A cannot be combined without violating the capacity constraints. For, incident to B there are arcs which are oriented in the same direction for $\boldsymbol{\varphi}^1$ and $\boldsymbol{\varphi}^2$. Let us call such an arc a 'bad' arc. The number of bad arcs can easily be decreased in the following way without augmenting the flow $\boldsymbol{\varphi}^1$ or $\boldsymbol{\varphi}^2$: if k is a bad arc, we need not direct the flow, $\min\{\varphi^1_k, \varphi^2_k\}$, from the initial vertex of the arc k into the sink $\bar{b}$. This amount of flow is derouted to A by following the return arcs taken by the flow $\boldsymbol{\varphi}^2$; by repeating this procedure as often as necessary, the flow $\boldsymbol{\varphi}^1 + \boldsymbol{\varphi}^2$ will become compatible with the capacities and will define the required flow $\boldsymbol{\varphi}$.

Lemma 2. *If, on the contracted tree, two vertices a and b are joined by an edge of value ν, denote by S_a and S_b the two sets of vertices separated by this edge; in the network G, (S_a, S_b) is a cut of minimum capacity between a and b, and this cut is of capacity ν.*

More precisely, we shall show that whatever the condensed network H_k forming the contracted tree, the edge of value ν that joins the two classes A_i and A_j has the following property:

If $x \in A_i$ and $y \in A_j$, let S_x^k and S_y^k denote the sets of vertices separated by the edge considered in the condensed network H_k: there exists an $x \in A_i$ and a $y \in A_j$ such that (S_x^k, S_y^k) is a cut of minimum capacity between x and y in the network G, and the capacity of this cut is equal to ν.

This is obvious for the condensed network H_1. Suppose it is true for figure H_{k-1} and we shall prove it to be true for figure H_k obtained from H_{k-1} by dividing class A_i into two sub-classes A'_i and B'_i.

1. *The property holds for the edge of value ν′ which joins the classes A'_i and B'_i.*

Consider the graph G_{k-1} obtained from G by separately condensing the branches incident from A_i in figure H_{k-1}. Following the method previously indicated, figure H_k is first defined by a cut of minimum capacity ν' between two vertices a and $b \in A_i$ in the condensed network G_{k-1}. From Lemma 1, this cut determines a cut of minimum capacity between a and b on the initial graph G.

2. *The property is true for the edge of value ν which joins the two classes A_j and A'_i.*

According to the induction hypothesis, in the graph G there exists a vertex $a_i \in A_i$ and a vertex $a_j \in A_j$ such that $(S_{a_i}^{k-1}, S_{a_j}^{k-1})$ is a cut of minimum capacity ν.

If $a_i \in A'_i$, the property holds for the vertices $a_i \in A'_i$ and $a_j \in A_j$.

If $a_i \in B'_i$, consider the two vertices $a \in A'_i$ and $b \in B'_i$ defined in 1, and prove the property for the vertices $a \in A'_i$ and $a_j \in A_j$.

According to 1, the value $f(a,b)$ of the maximum flow between a and b, satisfies

$$(1) \qquad f(a,b) = \nu'.$$

As the cut (S_a^k, S_b^k), of capacity ν', also separates a_i and a_j, we have

$$(2) \qquad \nu = f(a_i, a_j) \leqslant \nu'.$$

Consider now the network G' obtained from G by condensing the set S_b^k; that is, replace the set A by a single vertex $\bar{b}$. Denote by $f'(x,y)$ the value of the maximum flow between x and y in the network G'. According to condition (3) of the Gomory–Hu theorem, we have

$$(3) \qquad f'(a, a_j) \geqslant \min\{f'(a,\bar{b}), f'(\bar{b}, a_j)\}.$$

Now

$$f'(a, a_j) = f(a, a_j) \qquad \text{(by Lemma 1)}$$

$$f'(a, \bar{b}) \geqslant f(a, b) = \nu' \geqslant \nu \qquad \text{(from (1) and (2))}$$

$$f'(\bar{b}, a_j) \geqslant f(a_i, a_j) = \nu.$$

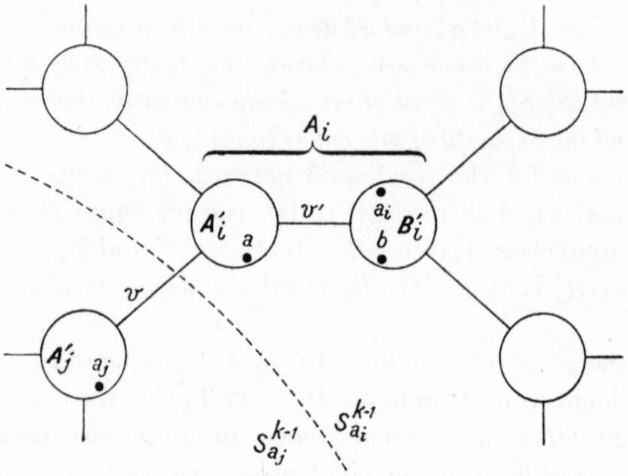

Fig. 10.1

Hence inequality (3) gives

(4) $$f(a, a_j) > \nu.$$

Furthermore, the cut $(S^{k-1}_{a_i}, S^{k-1}_{a_j})$ of capacity ν also separates the vertices a and a_j and, from (4), it is a cut of minimum capacity between a and a_j. Hence the property is proved with $a \in A'_i$ and $a_j \in A_j$.

Proof of the theorem

It is required to prove the formula

$$f_{ij} = \min\{\nu_{k_1}, \nu_{k_2}, \ldots, \nu_{k_p}\}.$$

If on the contracted tree, the vertices a_i and a_j are joined by an edge of value ν, then Lemma 2 shows that $f_{ij} = \nu$, therefore, the formula is proved for this case.

Consider now two vertices a_i and a_j joined by a chain

$$[a_i, a_{i_1}, a_{i_2}, \ldots, a_{i_{p-1}}, a_j]$$

of the contracted tree, with edges of value

$$\nu_{k_1}, \nu_{k_2}, \ldots, \nu_{k_p}.$$

From (3′) in the Gomory–Hu theorem

$$\begin{aligned} f_{ij} &\geqslant \min\{f_{ii_1}, f_{i_1 i_2}, \ldots, f_{i_{p-1} j}\} \\ &= \min\{\nu_{k_1}, \nu_{k_2}, \ldots, \nu_{k_p}\}. \end{aligned}$$

The reverse inequality also holds, since to every edge $(a_{i_{t-1}}, a_{i_t})$ of this chain, there corresponds a cut separating the vertices a_i and a_j of capacity ν_k. Hence,

$$f_{ij} = \min\{\nu_{k_1}, \nu_{k_2}, \ldots, \nu_{k_p}\}.$$

The reader may verify that the Gomory–Hu algorithm gives, for the above example, the following matrix of maximum flows:

	a	b	c	d	e	f
a	$+\infty$	18	13	13	13	17
b	18	$+\infty$	13	13	13	17
c	13	13	$+\infty$	14	15	13
d	13	13	14	$+\infty$	14	13
e	13	13	15	14	$+\infty$	13
f	17	17	13	13	13	$+\infty$

10.2. THE TRANSPORTATION NETWORK WITH MULTIPLIERS

Consider a graph G with vertices $a_1, a_2, \ldots, a_n, \bar{a}, \bar{b}$ and arcs $i = 1, 2, \ldots, m$.

G is said to be a *network with multipliers* if:

1. The vertex $\bar{a}$, the *source* of the network, satisfies $\omega^-(\bar{a}) = \varnothing$; the arcs $\omega^+(\bar{a})$ are the *source arcs* of the network.

2. The vertex $\bar{b}$, the *sink* of the network, satisfies $\omega^+(\bar{b}) = \varnothing$; the arcs $\omega^-(\bar{b})$ are the *sink arcs* of the network.

3. To every arc $i = 1, 2, \ldots, m$, there corresponds an interval $[b_i, c_i]$ and a convex function $f_i(x)$, defined in that interval.

4. To every vertex a_j, which is neither the source nor the sink, there is assigned a number $h(a_j) > 0$, called its *multiplier*.

The *problem of generalized optimal flow* consists in finding a vector

$$\boldsymbol{\varphi} = (\varphi_1, \varphi_2, \ldots, \varphi_m)$$

such that

(1) $\quad b_i \leqslant \varphi_i \leqslant c_i \qquad$ for $i = 1, 2, \ldots, m$;

(2) $\quad \sum_{i \in \omega^+(a)} \varphi_i = h(a) \sum_{i \in \omega^-(a)} \varphi_i \qquad$ for every vertex $a \neq \bar{a}, \bar{b}$;

(3) $\quad \sum_{i=1}^{m} f_i(\varphi_i) \qquad$ is minimized.

For a vertex a_j with $h(a_j) > 1$, the flow which passes through it is amplified (amplifying vertex), while if $h(a_j) < 1$, the flow is diminished (diminishing vertex); however, in practice, the majority of vertices have multipliers equal to 1 (conserving vertices) and in these vertices the flow is neither generated nor destroyed.

The classical transportation problem corresponds to a network with all conserving vertices (except the source and the sink which must be situated so that they do not play any role at all).

One sometimes speaks of a *multiplier associated with an arc* whenever the flow directed through the arc is multiplied by a constant between its start and finish; this is what happens in particular in electric networks (circuits) with transformers. Whenever this case arises, put a vertex with a multiplier in the middle of the arc, to obtain our formulation of the problem.

A particular case of the preceding problem is the *generalized problem of maximum flow*: there is only one source arc denoted by $i = 1$; find a vector

$$\boldsymbol{\varphi} = (\varphi_1, \varphi_2, \ldots, \varphi_m)$$

such that:

$$0 \leqslant \varphi_i \leqslant c_i \qquad \text{for } i = 2, \ldots, m;$$

$$\sum_{i \in \omega^+(a)} \varphi_i = h(a) \sum_{i \in \omega^-(a)} \varphi_i \qquad \text{for every vertex } a \neq \bar{a}, \bar{b};$$

φ_1 is maximized.

These problems are met with particularly in operational research.

EXAMPLE 1. *Total operation time of several machines.* (Iri, Amari, Takata.) It is proposed to process six kinds of products denoted by $i = 1, 2, \ldots, 6$ with three machines $j = 1, 2, 3$ each being able to carry out the process. Each machine can process any one of the products, but the time which machine j takes to process one unit of product i is a known quantity h_{ij}, depending on i and j.

Furthermore, we know

the quantity s_i of the product i which has to be processed;
the period of time c_j during which machine j is available.

The problem is to distribute units of the different products so that the total machine time will be minimized.

This problem has been investigated and solved by M. Iri, S. Amari and M. Takata (*R.A.A.G. Research Notes, 3rd Series, No.* 47, *Tokyo, April* 1961). It involves finding an optimal flow in the transportation network with multipliers, as in Figure 10.2; the flow is given by x_{ij}, subject to

$$0 \leqslant x_{ij} \leqslant 1 \qquad \text{for every } i \text{ and every } j;$$

$$\sum_{=1}^{3} x_{ij} = s_i \qquad \text{for } i = 1, 2, \ldots, 6;$$

$$\sum_{i=1}^{6} h_{ij} x_{ij} \leqslant c \qquad \text{for } j = 1, 2, 3;$$

$$\sum_{i=1}^{6} \sum_{j=1}^{3} h_{ij} x_{ij} \qquad \text{is minimized.}$$

The s_i represent the capacities of the source arcs, the c_j the capacities of the sink arcs and the h_{ij} represent the multipliers of the intermediate vertices. The vertices not marked are all conserving vertices.

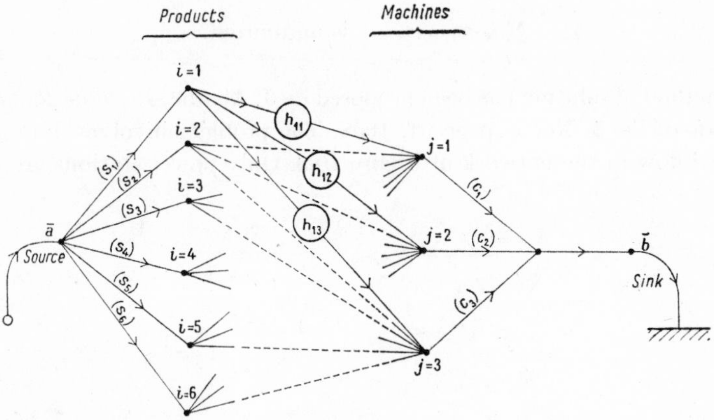

FIG. 10.2

If, instead of finding the minimum total time, we only want to know if the problem has a solution, we would have had to solve a problem of maximum flow in a network with multipliers.

EXAMPLE 2. *Problem of fuel supply to power stations.* (Abadie.) There are power stations, $i = 1, 2, \ldots, p$, which run on fuels found in places $j = 1, 2, \ldots, q$; we know whether the station i is or is not able to use the fuel j, and we want to satisfy a total demand d_0 of electricity.

We know the following:

the quantity s_j of fuel available at place j;
the maximum production c_i of electricity which station i must not exceed;
the cost l_{ij} of transport of one unit of fuel from j to station i;
the quantity h_i of fuel necessary to produce one unit of energy at station i.

It is required to satisfy the total demand of electricity, if possible, while minimizing the total fuel cost. In this case, the unknown quantities x_{ij} of fuel j to be brought to station i satisfy

$$x_{ij} \geqslant 0 \qquad \text{for every } i, j;$$

$$\frac{1}{h_i}\sum_{j=1}^{q} x_{ij} \leqslant c_i \qquad \text{for every } i;$$

$$\sum_{i=1}^{p} x_{ij} \leqslant s_j \qquad \text{for every } j;$$

$$\sum_{i,j} \frac{1}{h_i} x_{ij} = d_0$$

$$\sum_{i,j} l_{ij} x_{ij} \qquad \text{is minimized.}$$

A method of solution has been proposed by J. Abadie, *Revue de Recherche Opérationnelle*, **2**, No. 7, page 94, 1958. The problem involves finding an optimal flow in the network of Figure 10.3. Only power stations are non-

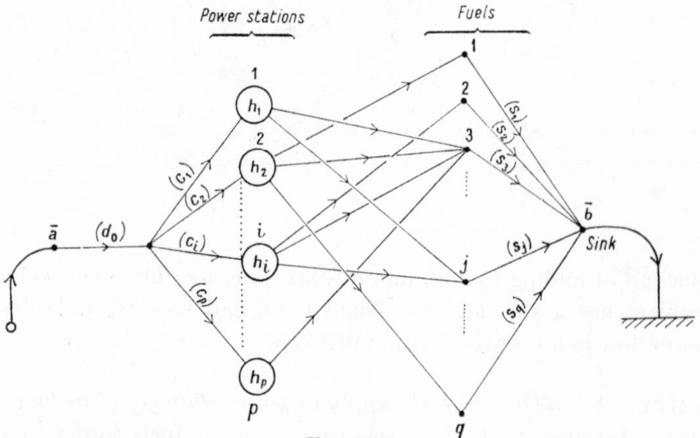

FIG. 10.3

conserving vertices, and the intermediate arc (i, j) exists only if station i is able to use the fuel coming from j. If we only want to satisfy the total demand of electricity regardless of cost, it becomes a problem of generalized maximum flow.

The theory of transportation networks with multipliers is developed along the lines of the theory of ordinary transportation networks.

We call the vector

$$\boldsymbol{\varphi} = (\varphi_1, \varphi_2, \ldots, \varphi_m)$$

a *generalized flow* if

$$\sum_{i \in \omega^+(a)} \varphi = h(a) \sum_{i \in \omega^-(a)} \varphi_i \quad \text{for every vertex } a \neq \bar{a}, \bar{b}.$$

Their space is denoted by Φ^*. This is a vector subspace of $\mathbf{R}^m$, since

$$\boldsymbol{\varphi} \in \Phi^*, s \in \mathbf{R} \Rightarrow s\boldsymbol{\varphi} \in \Phi^*$$

$$\boldsymbol{\varphi}^1, \boldsymbol{\varphi}^2 \in \Phi^* \quad \Rightarrow \boldsymbol{\varphi}^1 + \boldsymbol{\varphi}^2 \in \Phi^*.$$

Let $\boldsymbol{\omega}^*(a) = (\omega_1, \omega_2, \ldots, \omega_m)$ be a vector defined by:

$$\omega_i = \begin{cases} +1 & \text{if } i \in \omega^+(a) \\ -h(a) & \text{if } i \in \omega^-(a) \\ 0 & \text{if } i \notin \omega^-(a) \text{ and } i \notin \omega^+(a). \end{cases}$$

Every linear combination

$$\boldsymbol{\theta} = \sum_{j=1}^{n} s_j \, \boldsymbol{\omega}^*(a_j)$$

is by definition a *generalized potential difference*. The space of generalized potential differences, which is clearly a vector subspace of $\mathbf{R}^m$, will be denoted by Θ^*.

The results related to generalized flows are analogous to those related to ordinary flows, and we shall not repeat proofs which are exactly the same as before.

Theorem 1. *A vector* $\boldsymbol{\varphi} \in \mathbf{R}^m$ *is a generalized flow if and only if*

$$\langle \boldsymbol{\varphi}, \boldsymbol{\theta} \rangle = 0 \textit{ for every } \boldsymbol{\theta} \in \Theta^*.$$

If we consider the set of real numbers, Φ^* *and* Θ^* *are two complementary orthogonal vector subspaces of* $\mathbf{R}^m$.

Theorem 2. *A vector* $\boldsymbol{\theta} \in \mathbf{R}^m$ *is a generalized potential difference if, and only if, there exists a function t defined on the set of vertices, such that for every arc* $i = (a, b)$

$$\theta_i = h(b)\, t(b) - t(a).$$

Let

$$\boldsymbol{\theta} = \sum_{j=1}^{n} s_j \, \boldsymbol{\omega}^*(a_j)$$

be a generalized potential difference.

To the vertex a_j, let there correspond a function $t_j(a)$ defined by

$$t_j(a) = \begin{cases} 0 & \text{if } a \neq a_j, \\ -1 & \text{if } a = a_j. \end{cases}$$

For the arc $i = (a,b)$, we have

$$h(b)\,t_j(b) - t_j(a) = \begin{cases} +1 & \text{if } a = a_j, \\ -h(a_j) & \text{if } b = a_j, \\ 0 & \text{if } a \neq a_j,\ b \neq a_j. \end{cases}$$

Therefore,

(1) $$\omega_i^*(a_j) = h(b)\,t_j(b) - t_j(a);$$

if we write

$$t(a) = \sum_{j=1}^{n} s_j t_j(a),$$

then

$$\theta_i = \sum_{j=1}^{n} s_j \omega_i^*(a_j) = \sum_{j=1}^{n} s_j h(b)\,t_j(b) - \sum_{j=1}^{n} s_j t_j(a)$$
$$= h(b)\,t(b) - t(a).$$

Conversely, let t be a function defined on the set of vertices of the network, and for the arc $i = (a,b)$, write

$$\theta_i = h(b)\,t(b) - t(a).$$

The function $t_j(a)$ is defined as -1 if $a = a_j$, and 0 if $a \neq a_j$; put $t(a_j) = -s_j$. We can then write

$$t(a) = \sum_{j=1}^{n} s_j t_j(a).$$

Thus from equation (1),

$$\theta_i = \sum_{j=1}^{n} s_j h(b)\,t_j(b) - \sum_{j=1}^{n} s_j t_j(a) = \sum_{j=1}^{n} s_j \omega_i^*(a_j).$$

$\boldsymbol{\theta}$ is therefore a generalized potential difference.

Theorem 3. *Consider the transportation problem with multipliers. The increasing curves $\mathscr{C}_i$ correspond to the related convex functions $f_i(x)$ (as on page 161). The generalized flow $\boldsymbol{\varphi}$ is a solution if, and only if, there is a generalized potential difference $\boldsymbol{\theta}$ with*

$$(\varphi_i, \theta_i) \in \mathscr{C}_i \quad \text{for } i = 1, 2, \ldots, m.$$

(For the proof, cf. Theorem 7, Chapter 8, Section 8.4.)

Theorem 4. *Consider the transportation problem with multipliers. With the convex functions $f_i(x)$, associate their Legendre transforms $g_i(y)$; if*

$$F(\boldsymbol{\varphi}) = \sum_{i=1}^{m} f_i(\varphi_i) \quad \text{for } \boldsymbol{\varphi} = (\varphi_1, \varphi_2, \ldots, \varphi_m) \in \boldsymbol{\Phi}^*$$

$$(\text{with } b_i \leqslant \varphi_i \leqslant c_i \text{ for every } i),$$

and

$$G(\boldsymbol{\theta}) = \sum_{i=1}^{m} g_i(\theta_i) \quad \text{for } \boldsymbol{\theta} = (\theta_1, \theta_2, \ldots, \theta_m) \in \boldsymbol{\Theta}^*,$$

then

$$\min_{\varphi} F(\boldsymbol{\varphi}) + \min_{\theta} G(\boldsymbol{\theta}) = 0.$$

(For the proof, cf. the Duality theorem, Chapter 8, Section 8.5.)

Theorem 5. *If a generalized flow*

$$\boldsymbol{\varphi} = (\varphi_1, \varphi_2, \ldots, \varphi_m)$$

exists such that $b_i \leqslant \varphi_i \leqslant c_i$ (for $i = 1, 2, \ldots, m$) then

$$\sum_{i \in \omega^+(a)} c_i \geqslant h(a) \sum_{i \in \omega^-(a)} b_i \quad \text{for every vertex } a \neq \bar{a}, \bar{b},$$

and

$$\sum_{i \in \omega^+(a)} b_i \leqslant h(a) \sum_{i \in \omega^-(a)} c_i \quad \text{for every vertex } a \neq \bar{a}, \bar{b}.$$

(For the proof, cf. the Existence theorem for a flow, Chapter 8, Section 8.3.)

Using these theorems, algorithms for networks with multipliers can be developed in the same way as those for ordinary networks. W. Jewell [24] first noticed that Ford and Fulkerson's labelling procedure could be applied to the generalized maximum flow problem. The generalized optimal flow problem can be solved along lines similar to the method given in Chapter 9, Section 9.10.†

10.3. SPECIAL PROBLEMS OF MAXIMUM FLOW

Let G be a transportation network whose arcs are 1, 2,…, m; several classical problems in operational research can be reduced to the determination of an optimal flow $\boldsymbol{\varphi}$, by imposing constraints on the network G different from those already studied. In particular, we mention the following.

† Notice however that a great deal of theoretical complication is introduced when there are circuits which generate or destroy flows. For this the reader is referred to [24].

Firstly, *networks with pairs of homologous arcs*: given, in a graph G, pairs of homologous arcs: (i,i'), (j,j'), ..., it is required to find a flow $\boldsymbol{\varphi}$ such that

$$\varphi_i = \varphi'_i, \; \varphi_j = \varphi'_j, \ldots.$$

Secondly, *networks with bundles*: in a graph G, let $I_1, I_2, \ldots, I_l$ be sets of arcs; a set I_k is called a *bundle* and we associate with it a number $c_k > 0$, which is its *capacity*. The problem is to find a flow $\boldsymbol{\varphi}$ such that

$$\sum_{i \in I_k} \varphi_i \leqslant c_k \quad (k = 1, 2, \ldots, l).$$

EXAMPLE 1. *Problem of triads.* Consider the individuals a, b, c, d, e, ...; we wish to find the maximum number of triads that can be formed with these individuals so that no two individuals are together in more than p distinct triads. This type of problem has been introduced in biology (under the name of 'balanced incomplete block design') for experiments with treatments on different varieties of wheat; some problems in statistics are of this type.

To reduce it to a transportation network with homologous pairs, indicate the triads abc, abd, ..., by vertices and every pair ab, bc, ac, ad, ..., by a vertex. Join every triad to the three pairs contained in it. Then find the maximum flow in the network given below (Figure 10.4), where capacities are indicated in parentheses and where two homologous arcs are indicated by the same Greek letter:

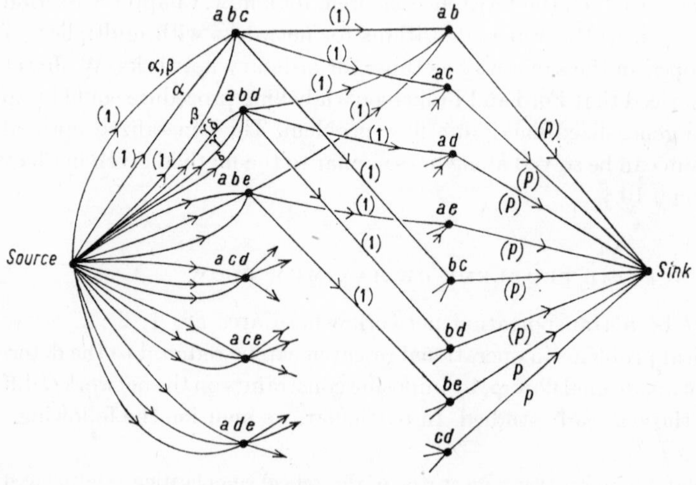

FIG. 10.4

EXAMPLE 2. *Determining the factors of a graph.* In a graph (X, U), a family of pairwise disjoint (with respect to the vertices) circuits is called a *factor*. In mathematical analysis, we sometimes wish to simplify a function of n complex variables by isolating its invariant terms. This can be reduced to the following problem: *Find in a graph a factor which uses the maximum number of vertices* (cf. [2]).

The problem can be solved by drawing a transportation network G, with the vertices $\bar{a}$, $\bar{b}$, a', b', c', d',..., a'', b'', c'', d'',... where a', b',... represent different vertices of X and similarly a'', b'',.... In G, draw the arc (a', d''), for example, if and only if (a, d) is an arc of the original graph. Finally determine a maximum flow in the following transportation network (where the homologous arcs are labelled with the same Greek letter):

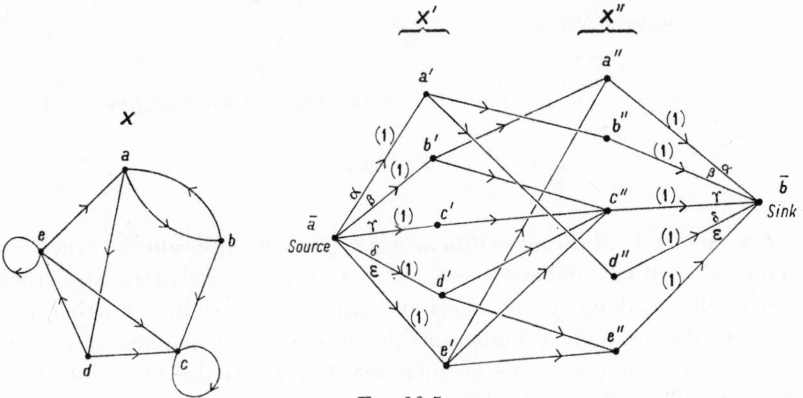

FIG. 10.5

EXAMPLE 3. *Determining the maximum stable set in a graph.* In a graph (X, U) a *stable set* is a set S of vertices such that there are no arcs joining two vertices of S. In many combinatorial problems, we want to find a stable set with the maximum number of vertices. For example, in the *problem of queens* (Gauss), we want to know the maximum number of queens that can be placed on a chess-board so that none of the queens can be taken by another.

In Shannon's problem, in information theory, it is required to define a code, but among the signals available at the source, there are some that can be confused on being received; what is the maximum number of signals to be chosen so that no two signals may be confused at the receiving end?

Determining a maximum stable set can be reduced to looking for the maximum flow in a network with bundle capacities. The arcs $(a, \bar{b})$ and $(d, \bar{b})$ form a *bundle* ϵ of capacity 1 if, and only if, in the original graph the vertices a and d are joined (cf. Figure 10.6).

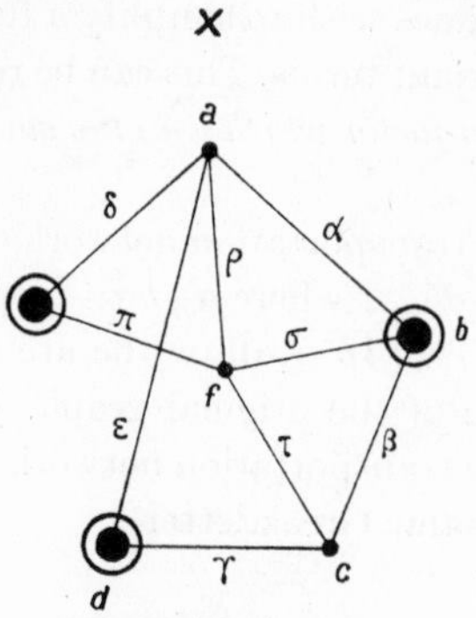

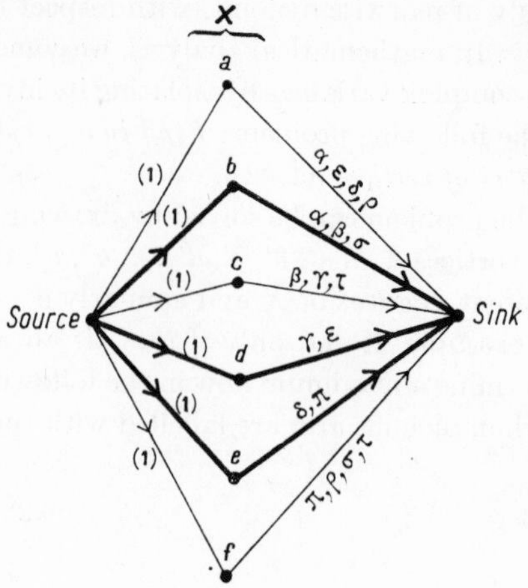

FIG. 10.6

EXAMPLE 4. *Multicommodity networks.* In a given locality a_0, there are n products with available stocks $s_1, s_2, \ldots, s_n$. It is required to transport them to a locality b_0 along a graph whose arcs have given capacities. Furthermore, some of the products are inflammable, others are perishables, etc.... and on some arcs there must not be inflammable or perishable products, etc.... Is it possible to transport all the stocks subject to these conditions?

Let n copies of the graph, $G^1, G^2, \ldots, G^n$, correspond respectively to the transportation of the n products. Let $a_0^1, a_0^2, \ldots, a_0^n$ be their sources, and $b_0^1, b_0^2, \ldots, b_0^n$ their sinks. Join a source $\bar{a}$ and a sink $\bar{b}$ and draw the arc $(\bar{a}, a_0^i)$ with capacity s_i, and the arc $(b_0^i, \bar{b})$ with capacity $+\infty$.

If, in the initial graph, the arc (a_i, a_j) of total capacity c_{ij} is not allowed to take products 1, 2 but is allowed to take products 3, 4 and 5, then delete the arcs (a_i^1, a_j^1), (a_i^2, a_j^2), and form a bundle of capacity c_{ij} with the arcs (a_i^3, a_j^3), (a_i^4, a_j^4), (a_i^5, a_j^5). If the maximum flow in this network with bundles, saturates the source arcs, then the problem has a solution.

Notice that the three types of problems just described are linear programmes in whole numbers, and can be theoretically solved by analytic methods (Gomory).

The problem with bundle capacities has been solved graphically by Matthys and Ricard for certain planar graphs; other more general methods of solution have been proposed by Kalaba and Juncosa and by Matthys [30] but it was found necessary to combine graphical methods and algebraic calculations. The problem of networks with homologous pairs was studied using graphical methods in different particular cases.

An important case solved by Ghouila-Houri [17] is that in which every source arc has a unique homologous sink arc and vice versa (as in Example 2: Determining the factors of a graph). If we join every sink arc to the source arc which is homologous to it, we find, in effect, that it is reduced to the following problem:

Given a transportation network and a subset I of arcs, find a flow $\boldsymbol{\varphi}$ such that

$$\sum_{i \in I} \varphi_i$$

is maximized.

Another important case of a network with homologous pairs has recently been studied by A. J. Hoffman: Consider a *simple* transportation network, formed by the source $\bar{a}$, the sink $\bar{b}$, and two sets

$$A = \{a_1, a_2, \ldots, a_i, \ldots, a_p\} \quad \text{and} \quad A' = \{a'_1, \ldots, a'_j, \ldots, a'_q\}.$$

The arcs of the graph are only those from $\bar{a}$ to A, from A to A' and from A' to $\bar{b}$. For every $i \leqslant p$, two numbers c_i and d_i are given, and for every $j \leqslant q$, two numbers c'_j and d'_j. We want to find a flow $\boldsymbol{\varphi}$ such that

(1) $$c_i \leqslant \varphi(\bar{a}, a_i) \leqslant d_i \quad (\text{for } i = 1, 2, \ldots, p)$$

(2) $$c'_j \leqslant \varphi(a'_j, \bar{b}) \leqslant d'_j \quad (\text{for } j = 1, 2, \ldots, q)$$

(3) $$\left.\begin{matrix} (a_i, a'_j) \in U \\ (a_i, a'_k) \in U \end{matrix}\right\} \text{implies } \varphi(a_i, a'_j) = \varphi(a_i, a'_k).$$

In the present case, any two arcs of $\boldsymbol{\omega}^+(a_i)$ are homologous.

Denote by $m_i = |\boldsymbol{\omega}^+(a_i)|$ the number of arcs from vertex a_i (necessarily directed towards A'). If A'_P and A'_Q are two given subsets of A', denote by I_0 the set of indices i such that

$$|\omega^+(a_i) \cap \omega^-(A'_p)| = |\omega^+(a_i) \cap \omega^-(A'_Q)|;$$

by I_{+1} the set of indices i such that

$$|\omega^+(a_i) \cap \omega^-(A'_p)| = |\omega^+(a_i) \cap \omega^-(A'_Q)| + 1;$$

by I_{-1} the set of indices i such that

$$|\omega^+(a_i) \cap \omega^-(A'_p)| = |\omega^+(a_i) \cap \omega^-(A'_Q)| - 1.$$

Then we have:

Hoffman's theorem. *A necessary condition for the above problem to have a solution is that*

$$\left.\begin{aligned} &P, Q \subset \{1, 2, \ldots, q\} \\ &P \cap Q = \varnothing \\ &I_0 \cup I_{+1} \cup I_{-1} = \{1, 2, \ldots, p\} \end{aligned}\right\} \text{implies}$$

$$\sum_{i \in I_{+1}} \frac{c_i}{m_i} - \sum_{i \in I_{-1}} \frac{d_i}{m_i} \leqslant \sum_{j \in P} d'_j - \sum_{j \in Q} c'_j.$$

Furthermore, if the incidence matrix of vertices a_i compared with the vertices a'_j is totally unimodular,† *this condition is also sufficient.*

Here we prove only that the condition is necessary.

$$\sum_{i \in I_{+1}} \frac{1}{m_i} \varphi(\bar{a}, a_i) - \sum_{i \in I_{-1}} \frac{1}{m_i} \varphi(\bar{a}, a_i) \geqslant \sum_{i \in I_{+1}} \frac{1}{m_i} c_i - \sum_{i \in I_{-1}} \frac{1}{m_i} d_i.$$

Furthermore, if all indices i belong to I_0, or to I_{+1} or to I_{-1}, then

$$\sum_{i \in I_{+1}} \frac{1}{m_i} \varphi(\bar{a}, a_i) - \sum_{i \in I_{-1}} \frac{1}{m_i} \varphi(\bar{a}, a_i) = \sum_{j \in P} \varphi(a'_j, \bar{b}) - \sum_{j \in Q} \varphi(a'_j, \bar{b})$$

$$\leqslant \sum_{j \in P} d'_j - \sum_{j \in Q} c'_j.$$

Comparing the two relations, we get the required condition.

10.4. SPECIAL PROBLEMS OF FLOW AND POTENTIAL DIFFERENCE

Here we indicate some important problems whose formulation can be simplified by the associated ideas of flows and potential differences.

EXAMPLE 1. *The travelling salesman problem.* A travelling salesman with headquarters at $\bar{a}$ proposes to visit n towns: $b, c, d, \ldots$, once and once only, and then return to town $\bar{a}$. During his trips, he must return to his point of

† Cf. Berge [2], Chapter 17. The coefficient in the ith row and jth column of the incidence matrix is, by definition, equal to $+1$ if $(a_i, a'_j) \in U$ and equal to 0 if $(a_i, a'_j) \notin U$; the matrix is said to be totally unimodular if all its minors have a determinant equal to $+1$ or -1 or 0. This may be seen in the following two cases:

(1) if all the cycles formed with the vertices of A and A' are a multiple of 4 in length;

(2) if, for all indices i:

$$\left.\begin{aligned} &(a_i, a'_j) \in U \\ &(a_i, a'_k) \in U \\ &j \leqslant l \leqslant k \end{aligned}\right\} \text{implies } (a_i, a'_l) \in U$$

departure $\bar{a}$ exactly k times and he must not visit more than p towns in each trip.

Furthermore, the roads he uses form a graph G whose vertices are $\bar{a}$, b, $c, \ldots$, we assume that he always travels along the arcs of the graph G which are numbered $i = 1, 2, \ldots, m$.†

His route, if it exists, determines a flow $\boldsymbol{\varphi}$ where $\varphi_i = 1$ if the salesman uses the arc i in the course of his travels and $\varphi_i = 0$ if he does not. The flow, $\boldsymbol{\varphi}$, we are looking for, satisfies the following conditions:

$$\text{(1)} \qquad \varphi_i \text{ is an integer for } i = 1, 2, \ldots, m,$$

$$\text{(2)} \qquad 0 \leqslant \varphi_i \leqslant 1 \quad \text{for } i = 1, 2, \ldots, m,$$

$$\text{(3)} \qquad \sum_{i \in \omega^+(x)} \varphi_i = 1 \quad \text{for every vertex, } x \neq \bar{a},$$

$$\text{(4)} \qquad \sum_{i \in \omega^-(x)} \varphi_i = 1 \quad \text{for every vertex } x \neq \bar{a},$$

$$\text{(5)} \qquad \sum_{i \in \omega^-(a)} \varphi_i = k.$$

On the other hand, there exists a vector $(\theta_1, \theta_2, \ldots, \theta_m)$ satisfying the following conditions:

$$\text{(6)} \qquad \theta_i \text{ is an integer,}$$

$$\text{(7)} \qquad \theta_i + p\varphi_i \leqslant p-1 \quad \text{for } i \notin \boldsymbol{\omega}^-(\bar{a}),$$

$$\text{(8)} \qquad \theta_i \leqslant p \quad \text{for } i \in \boldsymbol{\omega}^-(\bar{a}),$$

$$\text{(9)} \qquad \boldsymbol{\theta} = (\theta_1, \theta_2, \ldots, \theta_m) \text{ is a potential difference.}$$

If a_i denotes the initial vertex of the arc i, and b_i its terminal vertex, the inequality (7) can be written

$$\text{(7}'\text{)} \qquad \begin{cases} t(a_i) - t(b_i) \leqslant -1 & \text{if } \varphi_i = 1 \\ t(a_i) - t(b_i) \leqslant p-1 & \text{if } \varphi_i = 0. \end{cases}$$

Here the potential $t(x)$ is equal to 0 if $x = \bar{a}$, and equal to r if $x \neq \bar{a}$, and if the town x is the rth town visited in the course of his travels.

It is noteworthy that every flow $\boldsymbol{\varphi}$, satisfying the conditions (1)...(9) represents a family of admissible circuits for the travelling salesman problem. For, the first inequalities show that every town $x \neq \bar{a}$ will be on one, and only one circuit and that the town $\bar{a}$ will be on exactly k circuits. It

† This is, in fact, a generalization of the well-known classical problem due to H. Whitney; the generalization is due to C. E. Miller, A. W. Tucker and R. A. Zemlin (*J. Association for Computing Machinery*, **7**, 326, 1960). Here the treatment has been slightly modified.

remains to be shown that every circuit passes through $\bar{a}$, and that every circuit has a length $\leqslant p+1$.

Let μ be the circuit obtained of length q; if the circuit does not pass through $\bar{a}$, then

$$\theta_i \leqslant (p-1)-p\varphi_i = -1 \quad \text{for every } i \in \mu.$$

Thus

$$0 = \sum_{i \in \mu} \theta_i \leqslant -q,$$

which is impossible; therefore every circuit passes through $\bar{a}$.

Furthermore, if the circuit

$$\mu = (i_1, i_2, \ldots, i_q)$$

begins and ends at the vertex $\bar{a}$, then

$$\theta_{i_q} \leqslant p;$$

hence,

$$0 = \sum_{i \in \mu} \theta_i \leqslant -(q-1)+p;$$

therefore the length of the circuit μ is certainly $q \leqslant p+1$.

Notice that the classical problem of the travelling salesman, where $k = 1$, and where the total distance travelled is to be minimized, is reduced by this formulation, to a linear programming problem in integers.

The problem described here can be reduced to finding the associated potential difference and flow. For, we can modify the graph G by replacing

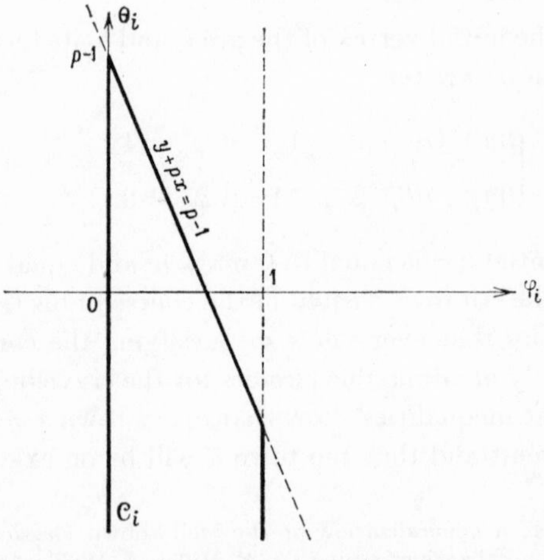

Curve C_i associated with an arc $i \notin \omega^-(a)$

FIG. 10.7

every vertex x by two vertices x' and x'', by making all arcs of $\boldsymbol{\omega}^-(x)$ lead to x', and all arcs of $\boldsymbol{\omega}^+(x)$ come from x''; also by drawing the arc (x',x'') and writing

$$\varphi(x',x'') = \begin{cases} 1 & \text{if } x \neq \bar{a} \\ k & \text{if } x = \bar{a} \end{cases}$$

$$\theta(x',x'') = 0.$$

If, for example, i is an arc of G which does not belong to $\omega^-(\bar{a})$, the pair (φ_i, θ_i) will be on the curve $\mathscr{C}_i$ defined by

$$0 \leqslant \varphi_i \leqslant 1,$$

$$\theta_i + p\varphi_i \leqslant p-1.$$

This curve, represented in Figure 10.7, is not monotonic; so Minty's algorithm (Chapter 9, Section 9.10) cannot be applied here.

EXAMPLE 2. *Problem of complementary industries.* A fundamental problem in economics can be summarized in the following way:

Consider a certain group of commodities $a_1, a_2, \ldots, a_p$ with initial stocks $s_1, s_2, \ldots, s_p$. Final stocks $s_1', s_2', \ldots, s_p'$ are required. Suppose that the intrinsic value of the total stock does not change, that is

$$\sum_{i=1}^{p} s_i = \sum_{i=1}^{p} s_i'.$$

To carry out this transaction, there are q factories, $b_1, b_2, \ldots, b_q$, each one of these uses some of the commodities and produces others, but without changing the total intrinsic value of the stock. Factory b_1, for example, working at one unit of intensity, uses d_i^1 units of commodity a_i, d_k^1 units of the commodity $a_k \ldots$, and produces l_j^1 units of the commodity $a_j, \ldots$; then

$$d_i^1 + d_k^1 + \ldots = l_j^1 + \ldots.$$

We want to determine how much each factory must work. The solution is given by a flow on the network of Figure 10.8; the potential at $\bar{a}$, at $\bar{b}$ and at a_i ($i = 1,2,\ldots,p$) and at a_j' ($j = 1,2,\ldots,p$) is zero and the potential at b_1 is the intensity function $t(b_1)$ for the factory b_1.

We look for a flow saturating the terminal arcs with which is associated a potential difference (following the characteristic curves $\mathscr{C}$, which are straight lines, but not necessarily increasing).

Notice that the problem of triads (Example 1, Section 10.2) can also be reduced to this form.

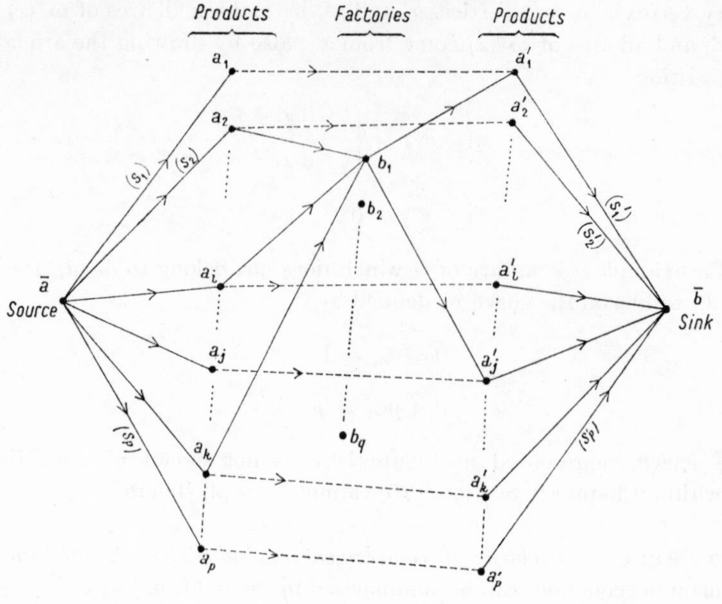

FIG. 10.8

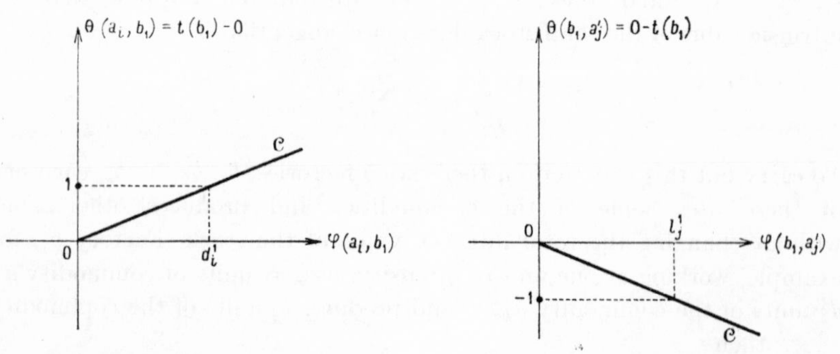

Factory b_1 produces commodity a_j: *characteristic curve of the arc* (a_j, b_1)

Factory b_1 uses commodity a_i: *characteristic curve of the arc* $(a\ , b_1)$

FIG. 10.9

EXAMPLE 3. *Dissection of a rectangle into squares*. Given a rectangle we want to dissect it into n squares so that no two squares of the dissection are of the same size. If a rectangle can be dissected in this way, it is said to be a *perfect rectangle of order* n. For a long time it was thought that there was no perfect rectangle. The first example was given in 1925 by Moron, another was given by Sprague and the general theory by Brooks,

Smith, Stone and Tutte [41]. All perfect rectangles up to order 15 are now known and recently tables have been published.†

If $n < 9$, there are no perfect rectangles of order n; if $n = 9$, there are exactly two perfect rectangles given by the following figures:

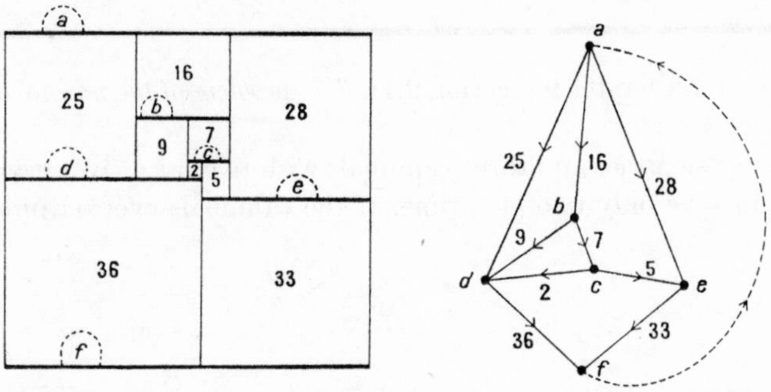

Fig. 10.10

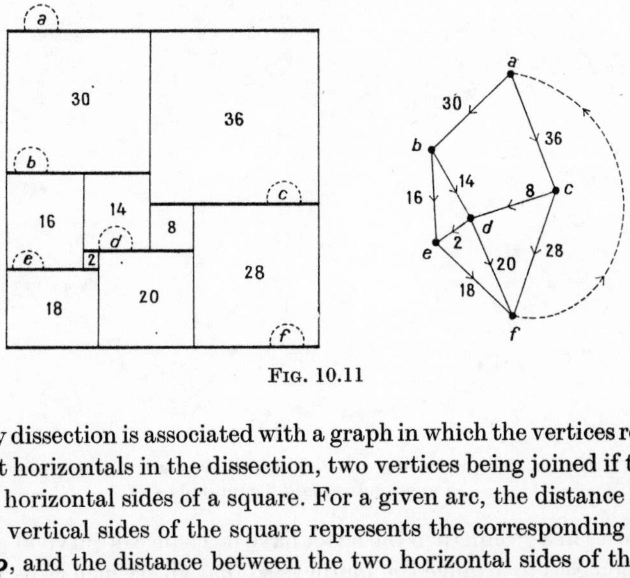

Fig. 10.11

Every dissection is associated with a graph in which the vertices represent different horizontals in the dissection, two vertices being joined if these are the two horizontal sides of a square. For a given arc, the distance between the two vertical sides of the square represents the corresponding value of a flow $\boldsymbol{\varphi}$, and the distance between the two horizontal sides of the square represents the corresponding value of a potential difference. Thus $\varphi_i = \theta_i$, for every arc i; the characteristic curve is therefore the bisection of the two axes.

† C. J. Bouwkamp, A. J. W. Duijvestijn and P. Medema, 'Tables relating to simple squared rectangles of order 9 through 15', *Dep. Math. Technisch. School,* Eindhoven, Holland, 1960.

Exercises

Exercise 1 (on Chapter 9, Section 9.1). *The problem of the missionaries and the cannibals.*

Three missionaries and three cannibals wish to cross a river using a boat which can take only two at a time. If the cannibals ever outnumber the

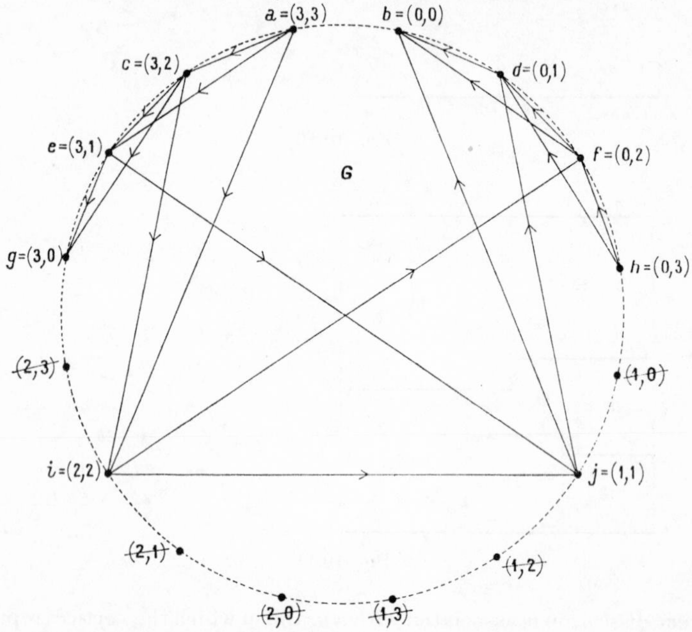

FIG. 1. Graph G representing the different situations in the problem of 3 missionaries and 3 cannibals

missionaries in a group, then the latter have no chance of survival. How are the missionaries to arrange the journeys so that all six men cross the river safely?

This problem can be reduced to the path problem: denote by (m,c) the situation where m missionaries and c cannibals are together on the first bank of the river. All possible pairs (m,c) can be arranged on a circle, except the pairs of (m,c) which correspond to the assassinations of missionaries on the original bank of the river ($m < c$ and $m \neq 0$) or on the opposite bank ($m > c$ and $m \neq 3$). Then draw an arc from (m,c) to (m',c') if

$$m' \leqslant m, \quad c' \leqslant c, \quad (m+c)-(m'+c') \leqslant 2.$$

We obtain the graph G of Figure 1 and the problem is to finding a chain starting from the point $a = (3,3)$, arriving at the point $b = (0,0)$ and such that every two successive edges are of opposite orientation.

We can associate a graph G' with G (Figure 2) in which the vertices represent all the ordered pairs of adjacent vertices of G; it reduces then to finding a path from $\bar{a}$ to $\bar{b}$.

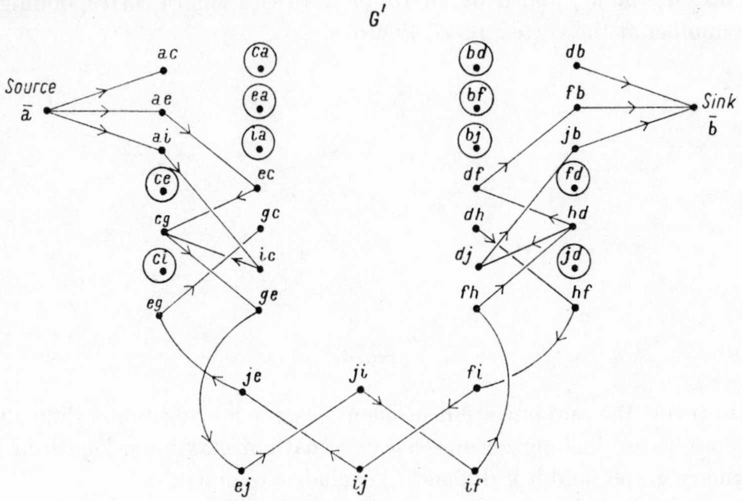

FIG. 2. Graph G' obtained from graph G

Exercise 2 (on Chapter 9, Sections 9.2 and 9.4). *A maximization (or minimization) puzzle.*

Consider the following graph (Figure 3):

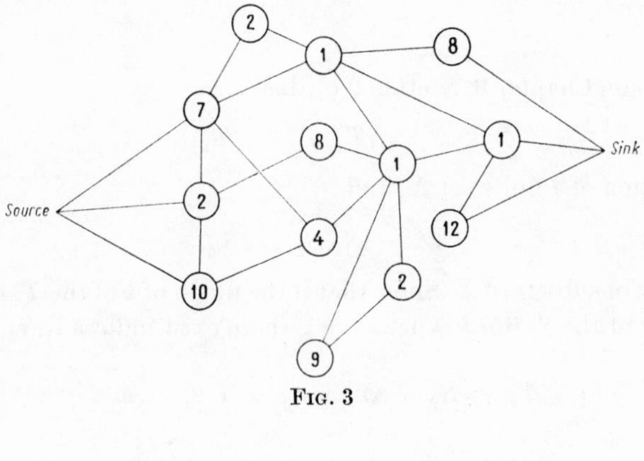

FIG. 3

The problem consists in finding a path going from the source to the sink with the following properties:

(1) it does not pass twice through the same vertex;
(2) it maximizes (or minimizes) the sum of the numbers it meets at the vertices.

The minimization problem is reduced to the problem of the shortest path in the auxiliary graph obtained by replacing every edge by two arcs of opposite orientations (and of length 0), every vertex a by two distinct vertices a' and a'', joined by an arc (a', a'') (with length corresponding to the number at the vertex a): cf. Figure 4.

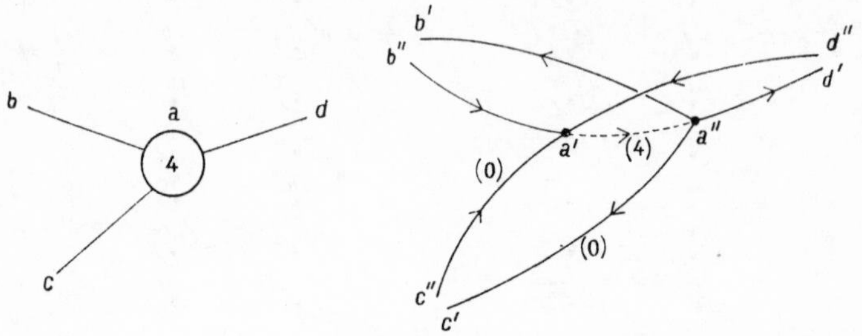

FIG. 4

However, the maximization problem poses some additional difficulties because we are looking for an *elementary* path of maximum length in the auxiliary graph (and it is difficult to exclude circuits).

Exercise 3 (on Chapter 9, Section 9.6). During a dance where there are n boys and n girls, each girl is to dance with a boy she knows. Prove that the problem always has a solution if every set of k girls collectively knows at least k boys (for $k = 1, 2, \ldots, n$). Deduce from this that the problem has a solution if every girl knows exactly m boys and every boy knows exactly m girls.

Exercise 4 (on Chapter 9, Section 9.6). Let

$$\mathscr{T} = (T_1, T_2, \ldots, T_n)$$

be a partition of a finite set X, and

$$\mathscr{S} = (S_1, S_2, \ldots, S_m)$$

be a family of subsets of X. Show that if the union of k of the T_i contains at the most k of the S_j (for $k = 1, 2, \ldots, n$), there exist indices $i_1, i_2, \ldots, i_m \leqslant n$ such that

$$T_{i_p} \cap S_p \neq \varnothing \quad \text{for } p = 1, 2, \ldots, m.$$

Exercise 5 (on Chapter 9, Section 9.6). Let

$$\mathscr{T} = (T_1, T_2, \ldots, T_n)$$

be a partition of a finite set X and

$$\mathscr{S} = (S_1, S_2, \ldots, S_m)$$

be a family of subsets and $c_1, c_2, \ldots, c_n$ be positive integers. It is required to find a set of representatives

$$A = \{a_1, a_2, \ldots, a_m\},$$

with $a_1 \in S_1$, $a_2 \in S_2, \ldots$, such that

$$|A \cap T_j| \leqslant c_j \quad \text{for } j = 1, 2, \ldots, n.$$

By reducing this to a maximum flow problem in a suitably chosen transportation network, show that the problem has a solution if

$$|\bigcup_{i \in I} S_i \cup \bigcup_{j \in J} T_j| \geqslant |\dot{I}| + \sum_{j \in \dot{J}} |T_j| - \sum_{j \in J} c_j$$

for every $I \subset \{1, 2, \ldots, m\}$ and for every $\dot{J} \subset \{1, 2, \ldots, n\}$.

Exercise 6 (on Chapter 9, Section 9.6). Let

$$\mathscr{T} = (T_1, T_2, \ldots, T_n)$$

be a partition of a finite set X,

$$\mathscr{S} = (S_1, S_2, \ldots, S_m)$$

be a family of subsets, and $b_1, b_2, \ldots, b_n$ be positive integers. It is required to find a set of representatives

$$A = \{a_1, a_2, \ldots, a_m\},$$

with $a_1 \in S_1$, $a_2 \in S_2, \ldots$, such that

$$|A \cap T_j| \geqslant b_j \quad \text{for } j = 1, 2, \ldots, n.$$

Show that the problem has a solution if

$$|\bigcup_{i \in I} S_i \cap \bigcup_{j \in J} T_j| \geqslant |\dot{I}| - m + \sum_{j \in J} c_j$$

for every $\dot{I} \subset \{1, 2, \ldots, m\}$ and every $\dot{J} \subset \{1, 2, \ldots, n\}$.

Exercise 7. Let $A = (a_j^i)$ be a square matrix of order n; using Gale's theorem (Chapter 9, Section 9.6) prove that every term in the expansion of its determinant is zero if and only if there exists a submatrix of zeros of p rows and $n - p + 1$ columns (for a certain value of $p \leqslant n$).

COROLLARY 1. If the matrix A is doubly stochastic, that is, if

$$a_j^i \geqslant 0, \quad \sum_j a_j^i = 1, \quad \sum_i a_j^i = 1,$$

then at least one term in the expansion of the determinant is not zero.

COROLLARY 2. The set of doubly stochastic matrices is the convex hull of the set of permutation matrices (G. Birkhoff, *Rev. Univ. Nac. Tucuman, series* A, **5**, 147, 1946).

Exercise 8. Let an infinite graph be composed of two disjoint sets of vertices X and Y and let its arcs be defined by a mapping Γ of X into Y such that $|\Gamma x| < +\infty$ for every x. With the help of Gale's theorem (page 192), it can be shown that X can be matched into Y if and only if

$$|\Gamma A| \geqslant |A| \text{ for every } A \subset X \text{ with } |A| < +\infty.$$

This result has a number of applications in algebra, in particular:

1. Bernstein's theorems on transfinite numbers (cf. König, *Fund. Math.*, **8**, 129, 1926).
2. Dilworth's theorem on ordinal sets (cf. G. Dantzig and A. J. Hoffman, *Annals of Math. Studies*, no. 38, page 207).
3. 'If H is a subgroup of a finite group H, there exist elements which represent the right cosets and the left cosets of H simultaneously.' (cf. M. Hall, *Some aspects of analysis and probability*, Wiley, 1958.)
4. 'In a vector space X, two bases are of the same power.' (cf. M. Hall, *ibid.*)

Exercise 9. Using Gale's theorem (Chapter 9, Section 9.6), prove the following result. Given the integers $r_1, r_2, \ldots, r_m, s_1, s_2, \ldots, s_n$, with

$$r_1 \geqslant r_2 \geqslant \ldots \geqslant r_n$$

$$s_1 \geqslant s_2 \geqslant \ldots \geqslant s_n,$$

form the sequence $(r_1^*, r_2^*, \ldots, r_m^*)$, where r_k^* denotes the number of r_i which are $\geqslant k$. A necessary and sufficient condition for the existence of a graph with the vertices $a_1, a_2, \ldots, a_n$ satisfying

$$|\omega^+(a_i)| = r_i; \quad |\omega^-(a_i)| = s_i \quad \text{for } i = 1, 2, \ldots, n,$$

is that

$$r_1^* + r_2^* + \ldots + r_k^* \geqslant s_1 + s_2 + \ldots + s_k \quad \text{for every } k$$

$$r_1^* + r_2^* + \ldots + r_m^* = s_1 + s_2 + \ldots + s_n.$$

(This result was found independently by D. Gale and H. J. Ryser.)

Exercise 10. Using the Ford and Fulkerson theorem (Chapter 9, Section 9.6) prove the following result, called Menger's theorem: if G is a non-oriented connected graph, and if the deletion of only one vertex cannot disconnect the graph, then every pair of vertices a and b can be joined by two distinct chains and without common vertices other than a and b.

Exercise 11. Using A. J. Hoffman's Existence theorem for a flow (Chapter 8, Section 8.3), prove the following result:

Let G be a transportation network with source $\bar{a}$ and sink $\bar{b}$. With every source arc $i \in \omega^+(\bar{a})$, associate two numbers b_i and c_i with $0 \leqslant b_i \leqslant c_i$; with every sink arc $j \in \omega^-(\bar{b})$, associate two numbers b'_j and c'_j with $0 \leqslant b'_j \leqslant c'_j$. A necessary and sufficient condition for the existence of a flow $\boldsymbol{\varphi}$ satisfying

$$b_i \leqslant \varphi_i \leqslant c_i \quad \text{for } i \in \omega^+(\bar{a}),$$

$$b'_j \leqslant \varphi_i \leqslant c'_j \quad \text{for } j \in \omega^-(\bar{b}),$$

is that the following two conditions are satisfied simultaneously:

(1) there exists a flow $\boldsymbol{\varphi}^1$ with

$$\varphi^1_i \geqslant b_i \quad \text{for } i \in \omega^+(\bar{a})$$

$$\varphi^1_j \leqslant c'_j \quad \text{for } j \in \omega^-(\bar{b}),$$

(2) there exists a flow $\boldsymbol{\varphi}^2$ with

$$\varphi^2_i \leqslant c_i \quad \text{for } i \in \omega^+(\bar{a})$$

$$\varphi^2_j \geqslant b'_j \quad \text{for } j \in \omega^-(\bar{b}).$$

(D. R. Fulkerson, *Canad. J. of Math.*, **3**, 440, 1959.)

Exercise 12 (on Chapter 9, Section 9.9). Solve the problem of optimal journeys for empty merchant ships (Example 2, page 201) with the data given by Koopmans and Reiter for the year 1913 on the map of Figure 5.

The length l_i of the route, measured in tenths of months, is given along the dotted lines.

For example:

$$l(\text{Durban, Sydney}) = 124,$$

means that an empty cargo-ship took a year and 12 days to go from Durban to Sydney.

At every port, the average monthly surplus of empty cargo-ships in thousands of tons, denoted by d_j, is given in brackets.

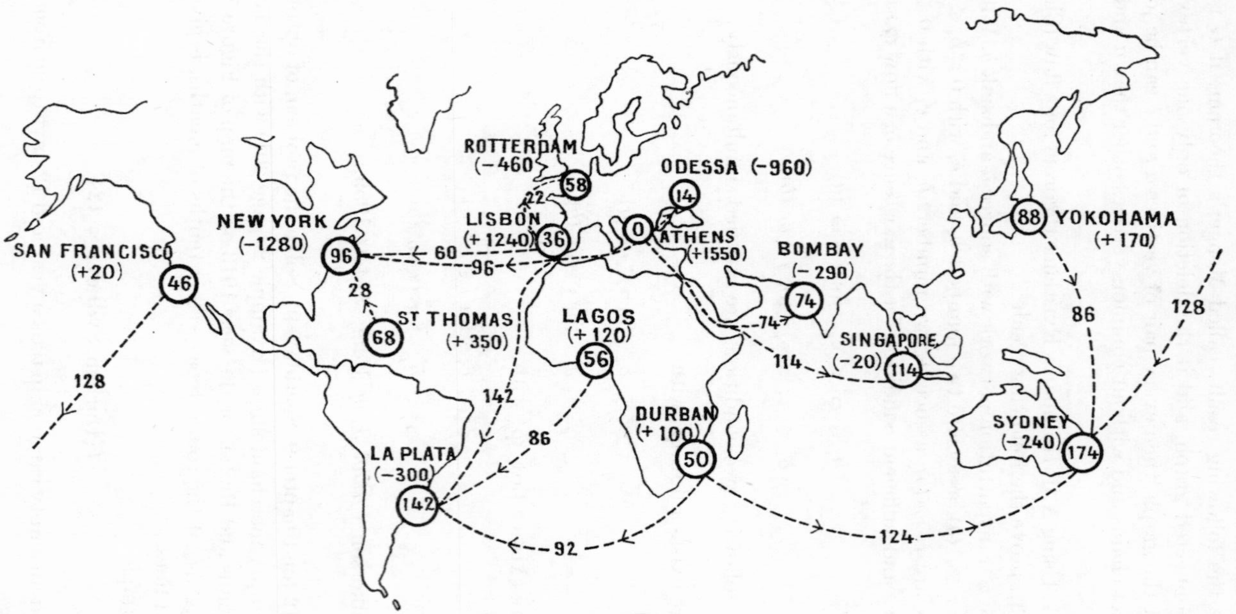
SAN FRANCISCO
(+20)
46
128
NEW YORK
(-1280)
96
60
96
28
ST THOMAS
(+ 350)
68
ROTTERDAM
(-460)
58
22
LISBON
(+ 1240)
36
142
LA PLATA
(-300)
142
LAGOS
(+ 120)
56
86
92
ODESSA (-960)
14
0
ATHENS
(+1550)
BOMBAY
(- 290)
74
SINGAPORE
(-20)
114
DURBAN
(+ 100)
50
124
YOKOHAMA
(+ 170)
88
86
SYDNEY
(-240)
174

FIG. 5

For example:

$$d\,(\text{Durban}) = +100$$

$$d\,(\text{Sydney}) = -240,$$

means that at Durban there is a surplus of empty cargo-ships equal to $c\,(\text{Durban}) = 100$ thousand tons and that at Sydney there is a deficiency of empty cargo-ships equal to $c'\,(\text{Sydney}) = 240$.

If we do not take into account ocean currents, the graph $\bar{G}$ is symmetric. In the transportation network G, obtained from $\bar{G}$, find a flow $\boldsymbol{\varphi}$ saturating the terminal arcs, which minimizes the total cost of the movement of the ships, that is, except for a constant factor:

$$\sum_{i=1}^{m} l_i \varphi_i = \langle \mathbf{l}, \boldsymbol{\varphi} \rangle.$$

To solve this problem, it is be necessary to find a vector

$$\mathbf{t} = (t_1, t_2, \ldots, t_n)$$

such that $t_j - t_i \leqslant l_j^i$ and which minimizes $\langle \mathbf{t}, \mathbf{d} \rangle$. One can also find a compatible vector $\mathbf{t}$ such that the graph G_t, generated by the arcs (i, j) so that $t_j - t_i = l_j^i$, has a flow saturating the terminal arcs.

This graph $\bar{G}_t$ is quickly found, and is drawn on the Figure in dotted lines. The value of $t(x)$ at the port x is written inside a circle: for example, we verify that

$$t\,(\text{Sydney}) - t\,(\text{Durban}) = 174 - 50 = 124 = l\,(\text{Durban, Sydney}).$$

The graph $\bar{G}_t$ is here a tree, and consequently contains a 'pendant' vertex a_i (Chapter 7, Theorem 5). The flow in the pendant arc is uniquely determined by the value of $d(a_i)$, we can then eliminate this pendant vertex a_i and begin again with the new tree thus obtained. We eventually obtain

$\varphi\,(\text{Yokohama, Sydney}) = 170$	$d\,(\text{Sydney}) = -240+170 = -70$
$\varphi\,(\text{San Francisco, Sydney}) = 20$	$d\,(\text{Sydney}) = -70+20 = -50$
$\varphi\,(\text{Durban, Sydney}) = 50$	$d\,(\text{Durban}) = 100-50 = +50$
$\varphi\,(\text{Durban, La Plata}) = 50$	$d\,(\text{La Plata}) = -300+50 = -250$
$\varphi\,(\text{Lagos, La Plata}) = 120$	$d\,(\text{La Plata}) = -250+120 = -130$
$\varphi\,(\text{Athens, La Plata}) = 130$	$d\,(\text{Athens}) = 1{,}550-130 = 1{,}420$
$\varphi\,(\text{Athens, Odessa}) = 960$	$d\,(\text{Athens}) = 460-290 = 170$
$\varphi\,(\text{Athens, Bombay}) = 290$	$d\,(\text{Athens}) = 170-20 = 150$
$\varphi\,(\text{Athens, Singapore}) = 20$	$d\,(\text{New York}) = -1{,}280+150 = -1{,}130$
$\varphi\,(\text{Athens, New York}) = 150$	
$\varphi\,(\text{Saint-Thomas, New York}) = 350$	$d\,(\text{New York}) = 1{,}130-350 = 780$
$\varphi\,(\text{Lisbon, New York}) = 780$	$d\,(\text{Lisbon}) = 1{,}240-780 = 460$
$\varphi\,(\text{Lisbon, Rotterdam}) = 460$	$d\,(\text{Rotterdam}) = 0$

The flow so obtained minimizes the cost of transport of empty cargo-ships, it is assumed that all ships have the same tonnage.

Exercise 13 (on Chapter 7). Use the Lemma on coloured arcs to prove:

1. If every cycle has as many components, $+1$, as there are components, -1, the arcs of the graph can be partitioned into disjoint elementary cocircuits.

2. If every coboundary has as many components, $+1$, as there are components, -1, the arcs of the graph can be partitioned into disjoint elementary circuits. (P. Camion's result.)

Exercise 14 (on Chapter 8). Show that a flow $\boldsymbol{\varphi}$ composed only of 0, $+1$ or -1 is necessarily a sum of disjoint cycles, show that a potential difference $\boldsymbol{\theta}$ which has only the components 0, $+1$ or -1 is necessarily a sum of disjoint coboundaries. (P. Camion's result.)

Bibliography to Part II

[1] APPELL, P., 'Le problème géométrique des déblais et remblais', *Mém. des Sciences math.*, **27**, Paris, 1928.

[2] BERGE, C., *The theory of graphs*, Methuen, 1962.

[3] BERGE, C., 'Sur l'équivalence du problème du transport généralisé et du problème des réseaux', *C. R. Acad. Sci., Paris*, **251**, 324, 1960. 'Les problèmes de flot et de tension', *Cahiers du Centre d'Etudes de Rech. Opérat., Brussels*, **3**, 69, 1961.

[4] CAMION, P., 'Quelques propriétés des chemins et des circuits hamiltoniens dans la théorie des graphes', *Cahiers du Centre d'Etudes de Rech. Opérat., Brussels*, **2**, 10, 1960.

[5] CHARNES, A., COOPER, W. W., 'Non linear network flows and convex program ming over incidence matrices', *Nav. Res. Logist. Q.*, **5**, 231, 1958.

[6] DANTZIG, G. B., 'On the shortest route through a network', *Mgmt Sci.*, **6**, 187, 1960.

[7] DENNIS, J. B., *Mathematical programming and electrical networks*, Wiley, 1959.

[8] DIKSTRA, E. W., 'A note on two problems in connexion with graphs', *Num. Math.*, **1**, 269, 1959.

[9] DUFFIN, R. J., 'Non linear networks', *Bull. Amer. math. Soc.*, **53**, 963, 1957; **52**, 833, 1946.

[10] FLAMENT, C., 'Analyse des structures préférentielles intransitives', *Proceedings of the 2nd Int. Conf. on Oper. Res., London*, 1960, p. 150.

[11] FLOOD, M. M., 'On the Hitchcock distribution problem', *Pacif. J. Math.*, **3**, 369, 1953.

[12] FORD, L. R., FULKERSON, D. R., 'Maximal flow through a network', *Can. J. Math.*, **8**, 399, 1956. 'A primal dual algorithm for the capacited Hitchcock problem', Rand P-827, Santa Monica, 1956.

[13] FORD, L. R., FULKERSON, D. R., 'A network flow feasibility theorem and combinatorial applications', *Canad. J. Math.*, **11**, 440, 1959.

[14] GALE, D. 'A theorem on flows in networks', *Pacif. J. Math.*, **7**, 1073, 1957.

[15] GHELLINCK, G. DE, 'Aspects de la notion de dualité en théorie des graphes' *Cahiers du Centre d'Etudes de Rech. Opérat., Brussels*, **3**, 94, 1961.

[16] GHOUILA-HOURI, A., 'Sur l'existence d'un flot ou d'une tension prenant ses valeurs dans un groupe abélien', *C. R. Acad. Sci., Paris*, **250**, 3931, 1960.

[17] GHOUILA-HOURI, A., 'Recherche du flot maximum dans certains réseaux lorsqu'on impose une condition de bouclage', *Proceedings of the 2nd Int. Conf. on Oper. Res., London*, 1960, p. 156. 'Une généralisation de l'algorithme de Ford-Fulkerson', *C. R. Acad. Sci., Paris,* **250**, 457, 1960.

[18] GOMORY, R. E., HU, T. C., 'Multi-terminal network flows', *I.B.M. Report* RC-318, Yorktown Heights, Sept. 1960.

[19] HARARY, F., 'Graph theory and electric networks', *I.R.E. Trans. Circuit Theory*, C.T. **6**, 95, 1959.

[20] HITCHCOCK, F. L., 'The distribution of a product from several sources to numerous localities', *J. Math. Phys.*, **20**, 224, 1941.

[21] HOFFMAN, A. J., quoted in BERGE [2], p. 81.

[22] IRI, M., 'Cone construction on a network and its application to the theory of multi-trees', *Raag Mem.*, Vol. **3**, 1959.

[23] IRI, M., SUNAGA, T., 'Raag memoirs of the unifying study of basic problems in engineering and physical sciences by means of geometry', Vol. 2, p. **444**, Tokyo, 1958.

[24] JEWELL, W. S., 'Optimal flows through networks with gains', *Inter. Rep. M.I.T.*, **8**, 1958; *Mim. of the 2nd Int. Conf. on Oper. Res., Aix-en-Provence*, 1960.

[25] KANTOROVITCH, L., 'On the translocation of masses', *Dokl. Akad. Nauk., U.R.S.S.*, **37**, 199, 1942.

[26] KOOPMANS, T. C., REITER, S., 'A model of transportation', *Cowles Commission monograph*, No. 13, 222, Wiley, 1951.

[27] KUHN, H. W., 'The Hungarian method for the assignment problem', *Nav. Res. Logist. Q.*, **2**, 83, 1955.

[28] KRUSKAL, J. B., 'On the shortest spanning subtree of a graph', *Proc. Amer. math. Soc.*, **7**, 48, 1956.

[29] MACLANE, S., 'A structural characterisation of planar combinatorial graphs', *Duke math. J.*, **3**, 466, 1937.

[30] MATTHYS, G., 'Flot optimum dans un réseau à capacités de faisceaux', *Proceedings of the 2nd Int. Conf. on Oper. Res., London*, 1960, p. 164.

[31] MINTY, G. J., 'Monotone networks', *Proc. roy. Soc.*, A, **257**, 194, 1960. 'Solving steady-state non linear networks of monotone elements', *I.R.E. Trans. Circuit Theory*, **8**, 99, 1961.

[32] MONGE, 'Déblai et remblai', *Mém. Acad. Sci.* 1781.

[33] ORDEN, A., 'The trans-shipment problem', *Mgmt Sci.*, **2**, 1956.

[34] POLLACK, M., WIEBENSON, W., 'Solutions of the shortest route problem (A review)', *Operations Research*, **8**, 224, 1960.

[35] PRAGER, W., 'A generalisation of Hitchcock's transportation problem', *J. Math. Phys.*, **36**, 99, 1957. 'Numerical solution of the generalized transportation problem', *Mimeogr. Brown Univ.*, 1956.

[36] RIGUET, J., 'A quick method to find the matrix of conductances of a given switching network', *Z. für Math. logik und grundlagen d. Math.*, **6**, 134, 1960.

[37] ROY, B., 'Contribution de la théorie des graphes à l'étude de certains problèmes linéaires', *C. R. Acad. Sci., Paris*, **248**, 2437, 1959.

[38] ROY, B., 'Cheminement et connexité dans les graphes, application aux problèmes d'ordonnancement' (Paris, 1962).

[39] SOLLIN, M., 'Le tracé des canalisations' (unpublished).

[40] SCHUTZENBERGER, M. P. (unpublished).

[41] BROOKS, R. L., SMITH, C. A. B., STONE, A. H. and TUTTE, W. T. 'The dissection of rectangles into squares', *Duke Math. J.*, **7**, 312, 1940.

Note: L. R. FORD and D. R. FULKERSON's: *Flows in networks*, Princeton University Press, 1962.

Index

Index

Index of notation